Adventures of the Mind

Adventures

OF THE

MIND

BY

ARTURO CASTIGLIONI, M.D.

Translated from the Italian by V. GIANTURCO

NEW YORK : ALFRED A. KNOPF

1946

THIS IS A BORZOI BOOK
PUBLISHED BY ALFRED A. KNOPF, INC.

Copyright 1946 by Alfred A. Knopf, Inc.

Published simultaneously in Canada by the Ryerson Press

Published April 11, 1946
Second Printing, July, 1946

TO MY GRANDCHILDREN

Fabrizio, Florence, Doris, and Gerardo

MY LOVE AND MY HOPE

❄ PREFACE ❄

IN THESE PAGES *I have gathered the results of my experience and observations during fifty years devoted to studies in medicine and its history, to voyages in different countries of the world, and to teaching students of different nations.*

In reviewing the history of the sufferings of mankind and of the attempts to restore sound conditions I was particularly impressed by certain facts. First, the continuous evidence among all peoples of a firm belief in and a constant appeal to mysterious, supernatural, magic forces, the power of which is attested not only by unshakable faith, but also by allegedly unbiased witnesses. The need for a miracle, the anticipation of and firm belief in wonder-healing, recurs at all times, although in different forms. It is dictated by the desire for escape, and directly or indirectly originates all magic practices. Such practices were generally connected, especially in times of epidemics, wars, famines, or other social catastrophes, with powerful individual or collective suggestions, and often with individual or collective mental disturbances.

All myths, from the sun myth of the primitives to the political myth of the super-race, have played a decisive role in the history of humanity. These mass-suggestions sometimes assumed the aspect of mass-psychoses, and in all of them shamans, magicians, priests of different religions, or leaders having a transcendent influence on the mind had an important part.

An analogy between these troubles of the collective mind

and certain characteristic features of the course of epidemic diseases appears no less remarkable to the physician and historian. There is an undeniable analogy between some of the conditions accompanying the origin (miasma, mal-aria; i.e., polluted air of the ancients, abnormal unfavourable social and economic surroundings in the modern conception), the mode of contagion (through direct infection or through carriers), and the consequences of both forms of social disturbances: epidemics and collective tragic adventures of the mind. Revival of ancient superstitions and magic practices, rebellion against moral laws, and violent hatred and persecution of minorities are constant phenomena.

Contemporary with or following these manifestations, the feeling of frustration and the desire to escape turn, sometimes, toward self-destruction and annihilation under the operation of incidental facts difficult to identify. There occurs a longing for destruction that may culminate in epidemics of suicides and that reminds one of analogous developments in the course of individual psychoses. The expectation of a catastrophic end is evident, for instance, in the collective psychoses of the year 1000, when the end of the world had been predicted; after the plague of 1300 in the episodes of the Flagellants; in the mass suicides in Magdeburg in 1520, when astrologers had predicted an imminent deluge; in the so-called revolution of the "backlanders" in Brazil; and more commonly in the yearning of the Hindu fakirs for self-inflicted tortures. It is the manic-depressive fear of mysterious powers that leads to the longing for destruction and death as a way of escape. The "honourable death" of the Japanese belongs to this chapter.

One of the most significant developments in the conception of disease and its causes took place in recent times and is closely related to these facts. Up to fifty years ago it was generally accepted that the laboratory was or might be able to give a correct answer to all problems concerning the origin and course of diseases. Although microbiological and biochemical evidence still is and will always be a prominent factor in explaining these problems, it does not give a satisfactory solution of them. This conviction has brought about a new evaluation of some factors that were formerly neglected. The constitutional disposition of individuals and groups, the importance of which was first stressed by Hippocrates, plays an important role.

The role that psychic factors and suggestion may play has come again to the fore in recent times. This current of thought, on which the doctrine of Freud and his school had an undeniable impact, has emphasized the importance of extensive studies in the psychology of primitive or non-literate people. Comprehension of the mind of past generations appears to be as important for understanding the mind of the individual and the collectivity of today, as a knowledge of the ideation of the child for understanding the mind of the adult. Just as the history of the life of the child has clarified many problems concerning the origin of the mental disorders of the adult, a study of the evolution of the mind in the past may throw light on the tragic adventures of our time.

It is evident that the events which have endangered our civilization must be considered from a psychological viewpoint. Should not the prevention and treatment of collective mental disorders be directed according to the same principles that have brought about such significant success in the conquest of epidemic diseases? Soil sanitation and nutrition, education of children in sanitary practices, isolation of carriers, strict

*control over foci of infection, protection of less resistant in-
dividuals, improvement of general conditions, chiefly and
above all sanitation, not so much through fighting germs,
which cannot be definitely suppressed, as through increasing
the power of resistance of the individual and group, and their
adjustment to surroundings—all these are measures that have
succeeded in diminishing the frequency of diseases and increasing the span of human life. They have obtained a success
that all the energetic legislative measures of former times were
unable to achieve.*

*If there is an analogy between the tragic social events that
brought about a mortal danger to humanity and the great epidemic diseases of the past as regards their origins, some of their
causes, and especially their psychological factors; if it is true
that they differ in extension and intensity more than in their
essential character; is it not obvious that the psychologist, the
educator, the "hygienist of the soul" may obtain the same result as was so brilliantly achieved by public health organizations? Are we not justified in believing that if immunization
through increased resistance of the healthy, strong control
over the carriers of infection, and creation of a rational sanitary
defence have succeeded in conquering epidemics, the same
means must be the principal factors in avoiding or at least
limiting the extension of the epidemic diseases of the mind?
Does the pollution of the public mind not play the same role
in the tragic adventures of the mind that the pollution of food
or of drinking water plays in the diffusion of typhoid and
dysentery?*

*It is not in the program of this book to present a chrono-
logical history of events that may be explained in connection
with psychological causes; that would mean rewriting the*

*history of humanity. This book—a part of which was pub-
lished in Milan (Mondadori, 1934) under the title* Incantes-
imo e Magia—*is an attempt to present some historical facts
that appear to have a common character in their origin, development, and consequences, without claiming that the
psychological causes were the most important and, still less,
the only ones determining them.*

*I want to express my warm thanks to my old friend Dr.
Paul Federn for his invaluable help and for his kind suggestions
and criticism.*

*I am aware that I am able to make but a small contribution
to the discussion of the problem. By choosing some of the most
important adventures of the mind among different peoples and
at various times I have tried to prove the permanent actions of
some of their factors, the analogy between seemingly different
phenomena, their origins, development, and consequences, and
the necessity for an analogous defence against their menaces.*

Yale University   Arturo Castiglioni
January 1946

❀ CONTENTS ❀

❧ ILLUSTRATIONS ❧

Adventures of the Mind

PART ONE

THE MAGIC WORLD

I

The Human Mind Is Adventurous

THE human mind is, as Santayana says, curious, adventurous, and redundant. It seeks to lift the veil of mystery, to find protection and defence, to flee from threats and dangers, and to achieve happiness or well-being in the form that appears the most desirable at the moment. The child is animated above all by curiosity, by the desire to understand the hidden or unknown, strange or inexplicable things that are beyond its range and easy comprehension. The young man, through the appetites of his senses, is spurred on to sensual and sometimes heroic sentimental and romantic adventures. The physically and intellectually mature adult, who has reached the age when life appears to have a firm foundation, lives or attempts to live reasonably, because this is necessary for his own personal security and for that of his dear ones and for the preservation of his possessions. But he retains, nevertheless, a need for adventure, which may take different forms of escape: of a political or erotic adventure, or of a hobby. Perhaps interest in and capacity for adventure are the most characteristic indications of a permanent vitality or agility of the mind. The child's adventure in seeking new, strange, or dangerous things is limited by the danger that he perceives or by the will of parents or teachers: the adventure in search of pleasure or power, this or that form of escape or of aggression, is held in check by moral or social laws, by public opinion, and by fear of punishment. The external factors that determine great social and collective adventures are the ones that exert their influence simultaneously on the mass of the individuals who form an organized or non-organized society.

First heredity and surroundings play a role in forming the

physical condition and consequently the disposition of the mind. Other factors weighing upon or threatening the conditions of life suggest the necessity for escape and make every suggestion of the best way appear easy or acceptable. Meteorological phenomena, earthquakes and floods, epidemics and wars are among these factors. Magicians and miraculous healers, dreamers and visionaries, leaders or persons supposed to possess supernatural powers become the leaders of these adventures and determine their direction. All persons who are capable of giving hope or faith in a success which otherwise would appear impossible to individuals or crowds play a decisive part.

Adventures may be within the limits of ethical, moral, or social laws and give a collective impulse to new economic structures, to the attempt to form a new, greater, and more just social structure in which power and well-being, rights and duties are equally distributed. They may develop into political and social revolutions and change the order of things. Finally, for different motives and under different influences, they may lead to collective aggressive attempts to overthrow an established order that is believed to be harmful or fatal.

In periods of economic depression, after grave sufferings, when the critical faculty appears diminished, the emotional necessity for new trends of ideas comes to the surface. It is then that as a collective, ethical, and constructive influence the religious idea points to all the miraculous physical and spiritual paths of salvation and of healing and prompts attempts to concentrate the emotional faculties on the single aspiration for a better life on earth. When that does not appear possible, it leads to aspiration for a future life, the beyond, which offers a just recompense with rewards for those who have suffered and eternal punishment for sinners. On the other hand, other antiethical and antisocial attempts at revolutionary adventures occur: the rise of the Antichrist against the Messiah, an alliance with evil forces when the help received from religious faith or from moral and social laws appears insufficient. Diabolical magic, the covenant with the Devil, assume an infinite number of names and guises. It is an attempt to overthrow all moral laws, to attack all constituted orders, and to destroy individuals or groups of individuals, families, clans, or ethnic groups, or races or social classes that seem to hinder this new program. It results finally in the rise of the idea of the super-race and in racial persecutions: that is, an attempt to superimpose a new law created by egoistical or egocentric and antisocial motives on the already firmly constituted one. The sometimes tragic and violent battle against the stable and progressive order of things which constitutes our civilization develops in this way.

The history of the various adventures of the mind may be compared with the life of a river, which under normal conditions flows along, bathing and fertilizing the banks which it has created through the centuries and which have been strengthened by man in defence of the earth he cultivates. The river may suddenly overflow its banks for various reasons, but even this flood can be a source of fecundity if it is checked in time and wisely directed. If in its overflow, however, it breaks its barriers and dikes, it destroys in a few short moments the work of long and patient effort, and those same forces which have been creative and fecundating bring about a tragic, destructive, and violent development.

2. THE MIND OF PRIMITIVE MEN

It has to be stressed here that, according to the different conditions of life, of surroundings, of education, of extraneous influences, the evolution of the mind of primitive people cannot be considered as following one line. Many fundamental differences exist between the ways of thinking and acting of the various primitive tribes of the American Indians and again between these and those of Polynesia or of other regions. I think, however, that a certain current of thoughts may be identified that has common characteristics, especially in the appreciation of the most decisive facts of birth and life, of disease and death. I have tried to choose and to quote some among the many examples that show these general characteristics in the evolution of the personality and in the social behaviour of the groups. In face of the problem of life and death and in the attempts to create a defence or an escape there is a correlation and often an analogy between the ideation of the primitive and that of the modern man. Pain, fear, hope have always determined the same reaction from the sufferers at all times and they were and are the primary cause of the expectancy of the miracle and of the orientation toward magic.

Witchcraft and *magic* are terms used in the widest and most varied sense to indicate ideas and practices, impressions and rituals, events invoked and desired or feared and abhorred, marvellous and inexplicable occurrences, which extend from the symbolical rites of the ancients to the sorcery of fortune-tellers, from the impression on our souls of an orchestral symphony to the therapeutic virtues of suggestion, from the fascination exerted by pure feminine beauty to the sleight-of-hand of a prestidigitator. Upon close consideration we realize that probably nothing takes place in the life of nature and in the history of mankind that does not have a touch of enchantment, is not infiltrated by subtle magic. One of the most difficult of problems is to define these concepts exactly and to discover their origins and significance.

Since the earliest times scholars, inquirers, believers, and sceptics have faced this problem and attempted to solve it from various viewpoints: emotional or religious, artistic or literary, analytical or analogical, by examining its external manifestations and seeking their significance. Judgments have been most varied, and often in complete opposition: some admit all facts without criticism, others deny them without discernment. Some proclaim magic to be omnipotent in all its forms, others judge it to be simply a collection of impostures or morbid facts. All the individual aspects, all the manifestations of magic have been scrutinized, interpreted, and judged a thousand times and almost always differently according to the opinion of the author and, above all, according to the tendency of thought and the scientific knowledge of the given epoch.

Today we believe that, in order to understand the significance or the scope of an idea or group of ideas, we must seek the origins of certain orientations of thought in the gestures, sounds, shapes, or other expressions by which primitive man reacted to impressions or perceptions. These reactions occurred at a time when man had barely appeared on the stage of history and his physical, psychic, and social individuality was slowly assuming a definite form.

We know barely, disjointedly, the most important events of eight or ten millenniums of the history of man. He has lived for hundreds of thousands of years on this planet, and from the few traces that we possess of the events of ancient times we can reconstruct but a few scraps of history. However, from the judgments we can form concerning the thought-processes of primitive man, we can assume the existence of ideas and conceptions that, in spite of certain changes, are present in the mind of modern man.

The most ancient inscriptions, traced on the walls of the caves that sheltered the first inhabitants of the earth seeking refuge from inclement weather and from wild beasts, express an association of ideas that is complete, although simple, and show a certain skill in translating it into graphic form. Yet, it is evident, therefore, that those which we have been accustomed to consider the initial traces of civilization are the result of a period of gestation that spanned many thousand years. Likewise, drawings, primitive tools, weapons, domestic utensils, graves, and rough stone monuments attributed to prehistoric epochs represent the outcome of an already advanced process, the result of an extremely slow evolution.

These drawings and objects, and the traces of events and attitudes of the life and death of primitive man, are precious documents and enable us to follow, at least to a certain extent, the orientation of thought in its first organized manifestations in the most remote epochs and at times to point out its origins. But for our purposes a much greater value must be attributed to the ineffaceable vestiges that the events of human history, from the most ancient times, and the multiple phenomena determining, accelerating, or arresting the evolution of humanity have left in the mind of the man of today.

We may be able to discover the psychic individuality of primitive man by interpreting these residues, not always easy to recognize, which appear, as we shall see, only or particularly under determined circumstances, just as prehistoric fragments come to the surface only when the earth undergoes a profound upheaval.

Since the exhaustive and documented studies of Freud and his school, there can be no doubt that emotional events with their accompanying impressions leave deep and lasting traces in the individual, even when they reach him as a child incapable of reasoning, and remain even when he has lost all memory of the events themselves. A number of facts may suggest that the identical phenomenon holds good for the collectivity, which necessarily obeys the same laws governing the life of its components. The most recent historical and palæontological research has irrefutably demonstrated that ancient tales of strange events and beings, whose traces are to be found in the earliest myths, can no longer be considered fantastic legends, as they were up to a short time ago.

Some conceptions to be found in all primitive peoples point to the existence of a biological human type quite different from those whose vestiges have been preserved. Thus we find everywhere the traditional belief in a bisexual being, the hermaphrodite. All ancient peoples imagined the hermaphrodite as a supreme deity who ruled over life and death. In the Hebrew tradition, a trace of which is to be found in the book of Zohar, it is said that according to ancient belief the first human being was bisexual: this desire dream in the tradition of magic, mystic and supernatural bisexuality, is preserved throughout the centuries, and probably originates in the physiological and psychological bisexuality of the human race.[1]

The tales of the flood, of Atlantis, of the presence on the earth of enormous, monstrous reptiles and quadrupeds, of gigantic birds, the stories of titanic battles between grotesque animals and of strange metamorphoses, represent recollections, condensed by time, of facts that occurred in prehistoric times. Since these facts have their place in history, since we know of the existence of a flood, of Atlantis, of gigantic animals, and of biological metamorphoses, naturally the men who witnessed these things and transmitted the memory of them also have their place in history.

Myths are a necessary product of infant minds and of the minds of primitive peoples. They originate as an escape into

[1] Windhuis has made an interesting contribution to this subject in his *Das Zweigeschlechter-Wesen.*

the field of magic, as an apparently acceptable explanation and a hope of salvation. This explains the existence of such well-known and universal myths as that of the serpent, which because of its sudden appearance and strange way of life, the cool viscidity of its skin, and the mortal poison of its fangs, has been an object of terror and adoration since prehistoric times. The serpent was perhaps the first creature to be considered a miraculous healer, worshipped in the temples of Greece and in those of Nineveh, in Africa and Polynesia, India and Egypt: adored out of fear and with the hope of rendering it benevolent. The same is true of the myths of astrology, alchemy, and so on, down to the current myths of the superman and the super-race.

3. THE CHILD AND PRIMITIVE MAN

Recollections of events and beings of primordial days in certain epochs and under determinate circumstances, or in contact with certain reagents, rise again to the surface from depths in which they had seemingly disappeared. Just as the impressions and sensations of early infancy, or the recollections of them, unexpectedly, and often without any apparent reason, re-enter the consciousness of mature man, so, for motives not always discernible, memories or ideas from the primordial life of humanity reappear in the collective mind.

The explanation can be made simpler and clearer perhaps by an example from the biological life of the individual. We know for certain that an infinitesimal amount of toxic substance introduced into the blood-stream of a child while it is in the uterus is sufficient not only to modify strongly throughout its life the quality of its blood, but also to determine changes in its organs or tissues, and to create a predisposition to certain illnesses and an immunity to others. Syphilis infection in the uterus determines for the entire life of the individual a condition in which it is possible that the disease may become manifest many decades after the infection, and at the same time immunity against a new infection of the disease may occur. Many similar examples might be quoted.

We also know that an impressive event which took place during early infancy and brought about an often unperceived emotional shock (psychic trauma) is sufficient to modify the mind of the individual, and to cause pathological manifestations many years later. It is in this way that Freud explains the origins of some elements in the symptoms of psychoses.

It is now an established fact that analogous biological phenomena exert their influence through many generations in respect to both physical and mental evolution. It would be a mistake to limit this hereditary transmission to facts that we consider pathological; evidently constitutional dispositions are also transmitted from generation to generation as a result of largely unknown laws.

The history of the collectivity reflects the history of the individual, just as the history of the individual repeats in an abbreviated cycle the history of the race. The great events that affected humanity in early times, the ferocious battles against bad weather, against animals stronger than man, against adverse fortune, have moulded the human body and therefore the mind in a certain manner, rendering it sensitive to certain influences, resistant to others, ready to contract certain disturbances of the mental functions, certain contagions of ideas, and immunizing it to others. The history of mental epidemics bears a close resemblance to the history of epidemics of contagious diseases. Contagious diseases, in fact, undergo through the centuries certain transformations in their manifestations, through the modifications of the physical characteristics of man and the changes in his surroundings. Through the generations man becomes immunized. It is evident that the man of our age is less susceptible to leprosy than was the man of ancient times, and it is well known that certain diseases have completely lost their virulence.

Another fact leads us to the same conclusions. Just as in the infancy of the individual we find certain expressions, gestures, and concepts which appear also in adults whose development was retarded or arrested (either through accidental external events or because of hereditary or constitutional defects), so we still find in savage and primitive peoples who have had no contact with civilization forms, manifestations, and concepts that are probably identical with those of our most remote ancestors, the same causes having brought about the same reactions. We say "probably" through prudence, because it is certain that this identity cannot be materially and objectively proved, and because uncontrollable facts have slowly and sometimes profoundly affected the surrounding atmosphere, however apparently closed and impenetrable.

This accounts for the fact that in legends, tales, beliefs, and popular superstitions of all the human races, living in various climates and under the most varied conditions, common conceptions that connect them with their remote common source have been preserved. Those origins have often been irretrievably lost, as occurs with certain ideas, gestures, and languages (like Basque or Etruscan), the origins of which it is impossible to discover because certain links in the chain are missing.

Fantasy offers us the first and easiest escape from the reality of life. Each one of us comforts himself by imagining satisfactions and joys or possible acts of revenge. Children imagine revenge against their teachers, men revenge against a judge or policeman; whoever is irritated or saddened by bad news has the immediate wish to revenge himself on the man who brought him the news, and instinctively reacts against the object itself, the letter or telegram, before revenging himself on the cause of the occurrence; aggression arises from frustration (pain, injustice). This explains the ease with which suggestions against persons or groups, like the Jews, or against democracy, capitalism, bolshevism, and so forth, have found acceptance at all times.

4. THE RECOLLECTION OF THE PAST

Certain conceptions and acts of the adult which seem strange, unreasonable, and sometimes monstrous to us can be explained by comparing them with acts of individuals affected with mental diseases, which are almost always deviations in development, or by closely scrutinizing the mind of a child and its manifestations and discovering the germ of the ideas to which these acts are related. Thus the origins of ideas, gestures, and actions of a man belonging to a civilization many thousand years old which seem in absolute contrast to this civilization appear clear to observers of the mental development of primitive peoples. The explanation lies in the conditions that have determined the physical and mental trauma that peoples have undergone. Thus it seems easy, with a knowledge of totemism, to account for the persistence of the heraldic animal, the wolf, the eagle, the bull, the lion, and so on, which appear on coats of arms and seem to represent the traditions and the ideals of a people in an epoch when the most violently fought struggles occurred. Numberless examples could be given of antithetical cases which appear such only because of the fact that two or more phases in the history of the race have been loosely placed side by side without the historical thread uniting them being visible.

The earth—mother of mankind and womb of life, cradle of all living species—jealously preserves all that has been entrusted to her and that can be developed, transformed, or preserved in accordance with the conditions of the earth itself, climate, or surroundings. A certain kind of earth, sand, clay, etc., preserves intact bones, weapons, and structures, while others macerate and transform them into new forms of life so that they are no longer recognizable if they survive this metamorphosis. The human mind preserves, changed or unchanged but always alive, the traces of everything that has been entrusted to it. Primitive mind, exposed to few external influences, preserves ancient impressions almost on the surface, just as in lands removed from civilization the traces of primeval life lie under a light layer of sand and are easily disclosed to the observer's eye. In some regions a ferocious and glorious history of war and civilization, of destruction and reconstruction, has occurred; the earth and the climate have favoured tremendous, luxuriant vegetation. In these cases it is only with long and arduous research, by destroying superstructures and vegetation, often by sacrificing later architectural remains, that one can bring to light the history that has been buried in the depths of the earth. Other land, finally, has absorbed and destroyed the ancient forms, transmuting them into substantial nourishment for seeds that the wind deposited, and the life of the past is resurrected in the new vital form to which it has given precious nourishment. I am thinking of the civilizations superimposed on Rome and of those that sprang out of the desert sands of Egypt.

Thus, I think, one may connect monuments of ancient civilizations with creations of the most modern art and find contacts that otherwise would be sought in vain. It is thus possible to explain certain manifestations of our minds that are apparently irreconcilable with the present degree of evolution. Thus the conviction is borne in upon us that those manifestations are related to ideas which, although seemingly buried, still live in us. These ideas come to the surface for reasons akin to those which caused the reappearance of the buried monuments of ancient civilizations. These phenomena are upheavals that destroy the superstructures for a certain time or for ever, as occurs in psychic diseases which bring about a dissociation of personality. Other facts, like volcanic earthquakes, great wars, or other events affecting the collectivity, overthrow the superstructure, reducing the body politic to conditions of life analogous to those of primitive groups. The patient work of the searchers who probe into the profound strata of the subconscious may reveal their presence.

Under the action of kindred facts or similar surroundings, ancestral or archaic ideas spring up again. This accounts for the phenomenon, well known to colonials, that is designated under the name of nativism. Civilized men living among primitive peoples, after having lost contact with civilization for many years, show analogies and sometimes identity with the mentality of the natives. Return to ancestral ideas derives from the repetition of those aspects or conditions of life, climate, and surroundings which determined the primeval formation. The same explanation can be given for the regression of entire civilized groups to manifestations similar to those of prehistoric or primitive man, which history records in the course, or as a consequence, of great catastrophes like epidemics, famines, wars, or telluric upheavals that overtook the collectivity, and which is analogous to the regression of the individual—that is, the return to an early state of evolution—which takes place after a trauma or a violent shock. The superstructures of civilization were then destroyed and man, weakened and defenceless, was thrown back to the conditions of a primitive age, struck with terror ready to overestimate the dangers menacing him and the needs for defence, to resort to casts of thought or action that apparently had been for a long time forgotten.

5. THE VITAL PRINCIPLE

The characteristic conditions of the primitive mind are determined by the external conditions of the life and surroundings of the individual, and by his degree of adjustment. It is undoubtedly not easy, and it is perhaps even impossible, to conceive in what way men whose perceptions and reactions differed so widely from ours imagined the essence of life. What we call "soul" was to primitive man the vital principle, material and immaterial at the same time, visible and recognizable and identifiable sometimes in the humblest or remotest objects, sometimes fleeting, hidden, and invisible. The most interesting and easily verifiable fact is that according to primitive man the soul could be present in two or many places at once. The soul, force, or vital principle could exist at the same time in the body of an individual and of a plant or an animal. Numerous examples may be cited of this way of thinking, common to all the races that have been observed and studied. The soul lives, or may live, simultaneously or successively in all these relations. It is therefore logical that bi-presence or multipresence and all-presence should argue the possibility and even the certainty of survival. This constitutes the continuity of life under another form (and in another seat) — that is, in the adjuncts of the individual (shadow, image, etc.) or in living things that were in contact with him and that had an influence on his life (plants, animals, etc.).

The vital principle (the *mana* of certain savage peoples) might be external to and higher than the individual. In the most important facts of existence — birth, sickness, death — it intervened. It acted in pregnancy, which, according to the concept of primitive man, could not occur without the active participation of one or another object (a plant, a fruit, an animal, or a star) to which his soul was attached. It determined all the events of his life up to the moment when the vital force left the body to find another abode, and subsequently lived in a figure which remained close by the deceased, the "ka" of the ancient Egyptians, the "dschinn" of

Serpent dance of the Hopi Indians. Painting by Fred Kabotie (Museum of the American Indian, New York)

Image of a child for the incineration ceremony of the Diegueño Indians (Museum of the American Indian, New York)

the Arabs, the "fravashi" of the Avesta, and similar symbols of other peoples.

All magical or mystical practices seek the presence of the soul, or the vital principle, hence these are almost always identified with certain organs or materials. Frequently among primitive peoples the soul is considered to reside in the fat of the kidneys. The vital principle is necessarily and essentially sacred and intangible, "taboo," encompassing within itself the two contrary characteristics of fear and horror, respect and desire, which, as we shall have occasion to see, are united in a series of ambivalent concepts.

Primitive man, because of the mutable seat of his soul—that is, of his vital principle—had a profound feeling that his surroundings were a part of himself. He clung to his group, from which he barely managed to detach himself at a much later moment, just as in early times he detached his personality from his mother and became aware of himself as an individual. The killing of the totem animal, which was eaten by the whole tribe, is probably the symbol of the detachment of the individual from the tribal tradition. A like conflict is expressed in the mythology of a later period—the Œdipus legend—when the clinging to the mother is combined with the rebellion of the individual against paternal authority (Œdipus complex). In primitive society the individual exists permanently as an element of the group, from which he is not yet able to detach himself. He feels the need of defending himself against his group, also, single elements of which attract or repulse him, there apparently being a constant law of simultaneous attraction and repulsion, adjustment and rebellion, in all organic aggregates as well as in the original cell.

6. BONDS AND BELONGINGS

In the first period of primitive social life even the simplest and most elementary functions of life (sex, food, etc.) can be carried on only in the heart of the family or the tribe. Without the help of other men belonging to the same group, man is unable to kill game and draw sustenance from it, or to pick fruit from trees; without their help he is unable to live or to bring up his children. The ego, therefore, is not a limit, bounding his body and his scanty and infirm self-awareness, but it embraces all things surrounding him and participating in his life, even those which, after a brief contact with him, detach themselves from his body; such as nails, teeth, hair, secretions, excrements, footprints, images, names, garments, weapons, or such objects as are a contingent and permanent part of his personality.

A few words about the significance attached to hair are apposite here. It is a very old notion that the vital force of an individual is located in his hair, and that, by having his hair cut, he grows weak and feckless. Antiquity supplies us with much evidence in regard to this magic conception; it is sufficient to mention the legend of Samson. He grew weak when Delilah sheared off his hair. *Vir pilosus seu fortis seu libidinosus* ("A hairy man is either strong or libidinous") says the Latin proverb; and in the folklore of all peoples indubitable traces of the magical power of hair persist. Nessos, King of Megara, had a gold hair in which his strength resided; when Megara was besieged by the Cretans and Scylla, Nessos' daughter, who had fallen in love with Minosses, King of the Cretans, pulled the fatal hair from Nessos' head, and he fell dead. Much evidence concerning this tradition is quoted by Frazer, who states that the natives of Amboine Island still believe that strength resides exclusively in the hair. The annals of the Inquisition inform us that Sprenger, the famous inquisitor, was in the habit of ordering that individuals suspected of witchcraft should have their hair shorn off; and his colleague Cumanus caused forty witches to be totally shorn before torturing them.

More particularly typical of the mentality of primitive man is the fact that any picture of him is considered to be a part of him even when it is separated from him: it continues to live his life, to suffer his sorrows, and may act as his substitute, inasmuch as everything that strikes the image has its repercussions on the life of the prototype. This accounts for the many severe prohibitions which, among ancient peoples, forbid the use of portraits in all their forms and order that images should be concealed; the same explanation holds good for practices still existing among savage populations which aim at preventing explorers from taking photographs of them. An enormous structure of superstitions is built around mirror-images; even today among civilized nations traces of such superstitions are to be found in the belief that the breaking of a mirror portends misfortune; such a breaking, it was imagined, worked grievous harm on the person whose image had been reflected in the mirror. Perhaps the concept of the important role played by the image accounts for the origin of certain distorted images that are frequently to be found in the iconologies of remote civilizations—for instance, in those of pre-Columbian America. Perchance it also accounts for the grotesque figures of Oriental deities, which evidence a tendency to depart from human shape, and owe their origin to the prohibition of images that faithfully render reality. I refer to the interesting study of Roheim on *"Spiegel-zauber"* (mirror-magic).

According to this concept, all things that belong or belonged to an individual continue to be himself. The same bond ties the individual to the group to which he belongs, and in which he may, in turn, replace someone else or be replaced. This is confirmed by many a blood-rite asserting the strict character of such a bond. The exchange of blood between the various individuals of the same group or the simultaneous sacrifice of human victims, for which, probably, in later epochs rites like that of circumcision were substituted, constitute demonstrations of that conception and are the symbols of that belonging. This primitive idea contains the intuitive perception of a fundamental truth, as shown by the results of the recent studies on blood-groups, which give evidence as to the real existence of an objectively ascertainable biological kinship between the blood of individuals of the same family and group, and which prove that biological examination of the blood may indicate or exclude kinship between certain individuals. The voice of the blood, which was believed to exist only in the conventional phraseology of the romanticists, must at present be considered as really existing. In the primeval epoch all these blood-rites tended to create, according to the primitive conception, a closer and more indissoluble tie between various individuals, a tie that was rendered more

sacred and awesome by other practices such as those center-
ing in the taboo which enclosed certain individuals or classes
of individuals within an impenetrable circle, riveting the tribal bonds still more tightly.

Let us then mark some of the most important and characteristic features of primitive mentality: numerous appurtenances embracing all things which were in contact with the
individual, and close bonds linking him to the group and linking the group to the individual from the moment when he
begins to be, and down to the moment when he ceases to be,
a valid participant in the group's activities. Hence no limits
are set to the shackling of the individual by the group, nor are
limits set to the shackling of things by the individual. Limits
on the individual begin to be experienced whenever one group
comes into contact with another.

From these premises derives the explanation of the origin
of the kind of religion that is presumed to be mankind's earliest faith: i.e., totemism. The group, marking its own individuality off from that of other groups, is inwardly compelled
to choose, among living beings, the one with which it feels
the closest kinship. This choice is the *totem*, the animal that
constitutes the group's possession *par excellence*, the being
from which the group claims to derive, to which it feels
closely bound, by which it is represented or replaced, and
which the group in turn replaces or represents. It is probably
the animal which is most feared and from which the collectivity eagerly desires protection; or whose help is most
needed, to which therefore are assigned the particular virtues
of strength, courage, and astuteness essential to the life of the
group. There takes place, so to speak, a violent annexation,
the capturing of a being held to be superior because it is
stronger and possibly more dangerous. The totem is sacred,
may not be eaten, can have no use made of it, and cannot even
be mentioned. Among some primitive tribes only once, at a
common banquet at which all the members of the group must
be present, was the totem animal killed and eaten in common.
This was the immediate and direct manner in which, it was
imagined, the totem and its virtues were transmitted to all the
members of the group; a conception which, as we know, is

to be found repeated in all later religions under the more or less mystic form of the communion of flesh and blood, and in which, as I said, we may, at the same time, see disclosed the principle of a collective revolt against authority, of the struggle of the group's individuality against its ancestral traditions. This primitive cult, which I shall discuss at length, is characterized by other very important laws, the most remarkable and least easily explainable of which is that prohibiting sexual relations among members of the same totemic group. Totemism, a remotely old primitive religion, marks an indestructible stage of history; the clan of the owl, that of the she-wolf, of the bear, are, ideologically, the primordial ancestors of Athens, Rome, Berlin, and so on.

7. THE MAGIC WORLD

If we try to form an approximate idea of the mind of primitive man in his most salient and typical traits, we perceive that these traits stem, as is natural, from the environment and the conditions in which his life and that of his predecessors have developed. Primitive man is closely bound to the earth, from which he has, materially, hardly detached himself, but to which he is firmly fixed by the taproots of his race, the customs and habits of his daily living, the needs created by his existence. He tends to establish a profound and real union, which later becomes mystical between his own being and all things that surround him and from which he feels himself to be inseparable, as a necessary participant in all forms of life and death. For the same reasons, deriving from historical evolution, in his conception of life he is unaware of the limits of time and space. The vital principle of the individual is identified with, and multiplied in, that of the animals, trees, and stars, to which he bears a continuous and reciprocal relation. The life that he feels in his own ego lives also, simultaneously or successively, in other beings and forms, in an uninterrupted interaction, because of which his own existence may, according to the circumstances, dominate other lives or be dominated by them. A consequence of this fundamental conception is the affirmation that every element in this life composed of complex, infinite interrelations can entirely or partially replace, in one or in all its functions, another element. Such a replacement occurs primarily within the boundaries of the group representing the closest and most immediate circle of interest, and later beyond the limits of that circle. This accounts for the idea of metamorphosis, which is perhaps a mystical remembrance of some remote primeval facts of evolution, and for the idea of metempsychosis, deriving—at a much later date—from it.[1]

Primitive man, then, lives his life within the group to which he is bound, close to the earth from which he has barely become detached by his erect posture, in the midst of animals, trees, sounds, fragrances, sunshine, and rain, which he daily observes, which belong to him, and to which he belongs, just as the cell of an organ belongs to a complex organism. His individuality is not limited or definite because he is not aware of it;[2] his life has no well-ascertained beginning or well-marked end, because he does not conceive of the life of the ego as possible outside its endless attachments. In this magical world the whole cosmos, all that surrounds man, appears, like himself, animated and alive; ideas are real things. An objective evaluation of the reality of things does not exist. Concept and reality are still identical; life and death are but a transition to new forms. This is why, in the earliest age of mankind, the mentality of man appears to be both childish and universal. The boundary between reality and unreality is non-existent; everything seems equally possible, fearful, and adorable. This is a world peopled by continuous anguish, unbounded desire, and limitless fantasies, in which every day may bring to every individual a change in the law dictated by fear and the need for defence. Directly and immediately man feels the fascination and enchantments of the earth, of the antithetical laws of preservation and destruction, of life and death. In this world of magic his simple mind soars above the spaces of the irrational world.

[1] Primitive man's identification with animals or with objects may be considered as a consequence of the fact that in him there are no limits of personality. The magic world exists when the critical activity of the ego, which examines the reality of facts, is missing.

[2] P. Federn has made an exhaustive contribution to the study of the limits of the ego.

The conflict, in which the existence of the opposite tendencies is manifested, gives rise to a thirst for liberation from slavery, to a need for escape, to a search for another ego which may dwell in the individual or outside of him. The need for the father or leader, the admiration or worship of the man promising protection, or defence, or freedom from the rule exerted by a good or evil demon, enter the stage. Man, struck or menaced by earthquake, thunderbolt, pestilence, or enemy invasion, is forced to seek protection; and when the created and accepted law is not sufficient, he seeks protection outside the law. If the law is too hard or too exacting, man revolts against it. Thus two fundamental tendencies of magic stand out: one consisting in the search for supernatural help for creating protection, a social and constructive magic; the other representing an escape from the law that prevents all freedom of action or that prohibits manifestations of instinct, an antisocial or antitribal form of escape and aggression. A whole system of escape from and aggression against unpleasant reality is thus formed.

II

The Spell of Life and Death

N O fact in the individual or collective life is of greater importance, from the psychological viewpoint, than the behaviour of man, in the various stages of his intellectual evolution, in the face of suffering and death. Nothing is more impressive than the eternal drama of the battle fought by the individual for his life and for the defence of his existence against constantly threatening dangers. Spurred on by the instinct for self-preservation, overcome with terror of the unknown and inexplicable, which all living beings share, by the passionate desire to live and to know, man seeks, in all the open and secret ways of earth and sky, to learn the causes of death. Death is apparently avoidable because not all beings appear destined to die. Man seeks the origin of life, the causes of the change which may be its end. He wishes to defend life by any means, to protect his existence by the most effective remedies and fend off death. Watching the facts accompanying fecundation and the inception of life in plants, animals, and human beings, he seeks to secure the protection of the stars, which he imagines to have power over his life and well-being. He tries by every means to discover the causes of the interruption of life, and he thinks that the prime cause may be the arbitrary act of an external agent. He sees the causes of life and death in all the close and remote beings not subject to his will and by whose influence he fancies himself to be affected. Animals, plants, and stars, to him, appear to be aware of, or accomplices or participants in, the events of life, and likely, therefore, to exercise a beneficial or harmful influence: hence his belief that it is necessary to surround them constantly with a whole system of defence, encouraging and invoking benevolent and favourable manifestations and fending off or changing the direction of injurious influences. Nothing seems irreparable

to those who firmly believe that they can drive away or conquer causes. Nor is life's end final, inasmuch as the beings
that appear to be dead revive under another form, like the
butterfly issuing from the cocoon, like the plants that seem
dead and yet put forth leaves and flowers in spring, like earth,
which seems dead in the frozen winter and later blossoms forth
into all its glory.

It seems evident, therefore, that for primitive man death
meant only a mutation, due to the fact that the body is abandoned by something which, under certain circumstances and
after some time, may return to reanimate it, resuming its old
place, or assuming a new one, in the body of an animal, a plant,
or any other form of nature. Such an explanation seemed to
the primitive mind the simplest and at the same time the one
capable of overcoming the fear of the unknown and of removing all tragic character from the dreaded event of death. Since
survival appeared to him certain, primitive man was led to believe that death was simply a transformation from one stage
of life to another and that all the mutations and transitions
depended on other individuals or the objects in their service,
or, perhaps, on other animate or inanimate beings which
govern man's fate. It is obvious that our primeval ancestor attempted to discover the causes of illness, which threaten
death, and the causes which can hinder or influence the development of natural processes, such as the fecundation of the
earth, the ripening of fruits, pregnancy, etc. Logically these
causes were assigned to adverse vital principles residing in
other creatures, other close or remote beings, and their appurtenances. The idea that life is a constant struggle in which
victory belongs to the strongest of the combatants, a perfectly exact biological concept, undoubtedly predominates
in the mind of the primitive who must defend himself daily
against the dangers that surround and threaten him, against
climate, meteorological phenomena, animals, and so forth.

The world, as is shown by multiple but fundamentally identical primitive figures and designs common to all peoples, is
recognized as being the scene of adverse forces continuously
fighting one another: light and darkness, heat and cold, spring
and winter, good and evil being ceaselessly at war. A mystic

continuity obtains in the facts of life, and is symbolically expressed by the magic circle. Sleep is a temporary suspension of active life, a foreshadowing of death. Dreams thus appear to be the continuation of life under another form, on a plane that makes possible communications and contacts with distant invisible beings, with those beings, that is, who pursue their life in a changed form or in other abodes. Thus the concept of the continuation of life beyond physical death is consolidated and the idea of the coexistence of two souls in one body or in different places, although both souls belong to the same individual, is formed. Primitive man was undoubtedly familiar with the doubling of personality in the insane, or as a result of the action of poisonous substances. Two personalities —that is, two souls—can live near one another in a permanent or casual conflict.

2. THREAT AND DEFENCE

Fear of distant yet always menacing danger, the more threatening because unknown, dominates in this magic world. It is the essential aim of every human act to hinder or drive away harmful elements through the establishment of firm contacts with those which are beneficial. The means for this act of defence, which is inspired by fear, are indicated primarily by experience. Pliny observes that magical conception derives from the empirical knowledge of medicine. The cause of the evil is quickly identifiable in many cases, and especially in those in which primitive man most quickly and easily perceives dangerous symptoms. Thus in the case of wounds primitive man knows that by removing a thorn, extracting an arrow, untying a cord, and so forth, the cause of the injury can be removed and healing facilitated. He also knows that many illnesses are in a causal relation with parasites or dangerous animals, and that therefore it is necessary to keep away from them, protect oneself against contact with them, or kill them. He knows the dangers that may derive from atmospheric conditions, rain, storms, lightning; he has learned to take shelter in caves, under the leaves of trees, or in enclosures. It is therefore logical that vital, volitional, and conscious forces should be attributed to all the beings and things that may harm him: thorns, stones, parasites, serpents, the rain, light-ning, all of which, therefore, appear to be animated by the will to harm him or to be destined to injure him by superior forces. Likewise, beings or substances that are beneficial to man appear to him animated: the sun, the stars, domestic ani-mals, plants, the garments that protect him, his forebears who defend or guide him. This animistic conception is one of the paths leading to magic.

From this, by means of simple analogy, derives the convic-tion that all maladies and misfortunes, like all propitious facts in life, in the same way depend directly or indirectly on analo-gous causes even when these causes are neither visible nor identifiable. For example, since it is known that parasites are the cause of certain intestinal ailments, it is believed that all intestinal ailments are caused by parasites, even when these are not visible. Since it is known that hæmorrhages are often the consequence of wounds, the conclusion is that all hæmor-rhages derive from lesions inflicted by weapons that are pre-sumed to be hidden in the body. In cases of insanity it is obvi-ously supposed that an extraneous and hostile being has pene-trated the body of the individual and acts and talks with him, for him, or against him. Finally, since the relations that exist between celestial bodies, meteorological phenomena, and the life of man, on which these phenomena exert manifest influ-ences (facts of female life, inflammations caused by sunstroke, illnesses dependent on cold and humidity, etc.), are known, an active part in all the facts of life, of illnesses, and of death is attributed to these remote and unreachable beings. The re-lations between meteorological phenomena and the facts of the normal and pathological life of all beings living on the earth appear ever clearer, and the primitive magic conception has the support of experience. Not only are the fertility of the earth, the sprouting of crops, the ripening of fruit, in relation to these factors, but also the repetition of physiological facts in fixed terms marked by the course of the stars (menstrua-tion) and pathological facts (critical days, cycle of intermit-tent fevers) naturally lead to seeking the cause of the series of the facts of life and of death in the sun, the moon, the stars, and the rain and in sudden atmospheric changes.

Thus the heavenly bodies, whose mutations visibly rule the
life of the cosmos, and which profoundly impressed the imagination of primitive man, became, in his conception, fundamentally correct, the rulers over all the manifestations of life;
this explains the importance that the solar myths, founded on
observations of celestial revolutions, had as the fundamental
basis of all the most ancient religions. They are, as I have already said, the fundamental structures of human mentality,
which stand firm even when the subsequent superstructures,
erected on the basis of critical reasoning, conceal their origin.
They have, to a certain extent, a positive foundation.

There is thus formed, through an evolution the steps of
which are not ascertainable, a whole complex, sometimes systematic hierarchy of powerful beings, who are all the stronger
and more to be feared as they are difficult to reach and to
subdue to the will of man and his needs. It is a hierarchy in
which the celestial bodies, and first among them the sun, occupy the most important place. But every being, whether animated or not (that is to say, everything surrounding man
which is perceptible to his senses or accessible to his imagination) finds a place there. The majestic trees which rise in their
magnificent vegetation, the high peaks of the inaccessible
mountains which cast their vast shadows and cut off the horizon, appear to him as stupendous and inexplicable examples
of a superhuman, unreachable grandeur. The impetuous and
terrible rivers seem to carry in their flow infinite promises and
unknown threats. Man is also filled with awe by the large
flowers, with their vivid colours and intoxicating perfumes,
by the mortal poisons hidden in plants, by the animals, which
in so many aspects of their physical life—such as in the
marvellous metamorphoses of insects, in the perfect associations of bees and ants, in the birds' power to rise in the air in
flight and other animals' to disappear in the deepest recesses
of the earth—appear to be and are superior to man. Finally,
among men themselves there is manifested very early a differentiation between the individuals of a group in which a
certain person excels because he is endowed with qualities
possessed by few. Men with very robust or deformed bodies,
or with hair or eyes of a rare colour, who, in short, have

physical qualities that are different from those of the majority, are considered marked for good or evil and thus capable of exerting a beneficial or malignant influence.

From this idea may derive a tribal mysticism which gives rise to racial superstitions and hatred and considers as dangerous or harmful the men of other races who appear different because of the colour of their hair or their skin, or because of other exterior marks that are recognizable as different from the majority. This is the cause of the enmity for, and the persecution of, men of other races, and it is in this primitive concept that one must look for the origin of racial hatred, which under certain circumstances and at certain moments manifests itself in the most decided manner and the most ferocious forms.

Lévy-Bruhl, who has keenly studied the mentality of primitive man, has collected some valuable observations. Those made by Rasmussen, a Dane, are particularly noteworthy. Rasmussen was bound by ties of kinship to some Eskimos, and was able to obtain from them, and in particular from an Eskimo shaman, a physician and magician by the name of Aous, a series of valuable statements on the mind of this ethnic group which lives so far from the centres of civilization, under peculiar climatic conditions. "We," said this intelligent magician, "are not worshippers, but we are afraid. All our customs derive from life and are directed toward life. We fear the god of the moon, Sila, and Takanakapsaluk, the great woman who lives at the bottom of the sea and reigns over marine creatures. We fear the souls of the dead and those of the animals we have killed; and putting to use the experience of our fathers, we protect ourselves against misfortune."

No different is the concept of magic that, according to travellers and missionaries, is to be found among the natives of Polynesia, whose affection, devotion, and attachment to their masters and their gods is inspired primarily by fear.

From this motive of fear derive alliances between man and supernatural forces, with a view to a tacit but sure conclusion of a pact with the invisible powers, a pact that must be strictly complied with and upon which secret laws are founded, as we shall see. This pact determines the value of amulets and talismans and the intervention of the magician, who is the agent and intermediary of the pact.

Fear is the dominant factor and the primary cause in the history of the adventures of the mind, or at least creates the environment in which they develop most easily. There is the fear of death, of sickness, of poverty, and, on the other hand, of the punishments hanging over those who do not comply with the laws established by the group or by its leader (frustration). The secret of the success of great magicians lies in the fear that pre-exists in the environment and is determined by exterior facts, and in that fear which they create artificially to defeat or dominate the group.

As soon as man is convinced that infinite external forces exercise a determining action, either favourable or harmful, on his life, that no fact of his life can be removed from the action of these forces, he seeks every means to become stronger than they and make himself their master. He has conquered animals because he has known how to make weapons; he has conquered men weaker than himself and the enemies who have threatened him, and he has subjugated them. He has overcome the adversities of nature, creating protection for himself. It therefore appears evident that it is possible and necessary to find a means of conquering the invisible enemies, which cannot be subdued by physical force or attacked with weapons, and of defending the life of the individual and the group against these harmful elements, which in many respects bring about damages analogous to those caused by forces already known to primitive man and already conquered by him, and which these elements help or protect. The defence and the aggression are organized in this way and on the foundation of this idea.

Thus it was necessary to protect all the facts accompanying fecundation, pregnancy, and birth, essential facts on which are founded the existence and the strength of the group. The structures of phallic rites, the prehistoric monuments that symbolize the genital organs in gigantic forms, prove to us that the facts concerning generation constituted the fulcrum of the social conception in the most ancient times; and this is because protective and prophylactic powers are attributed to these symbols. Magic makes use of all these weapons to identify and constrain both visible and invisible external forces and to turn them to the advantage of the individual or the group.

The religious idea differs from magic essentially in the means. Religion does not tend toward a constraint of supernatural beings: the favour of the beings may be invoked and obtained through prayer, invocations, pious acts, and numerous other means, but the will or the decision of the conscious and willing divinity cannot be constrained in any way.

Magic, Hegel affirmed, belongs to all times and all peoples. Though it is difficult to define exactly and within limits the meaning of the word, it may be affirmed that it represents the efforts made during a certain permanent or transitory state of mind to achieve the realization of a wish in a world in which there exist no boundaries between the real and the unreal. Magic means not only a complex of actions, but also a nexus of ideas and representations with multiple and vast interrelations which are understandable when one thinks that in successive times and under changed conditions, and even today, doctors and warriors, mystics and charlatans, musicians and poets, scientists and philosophers, great thinkers and outstanding men of action have been considered magicians. In reality it is evident to the careful observer that in all these cases, which are so diverse, this attribution appeared to be, and was, to a certain extent, right. Clearly, each of these men possessed, in various forms and for different reasons, the qualities essential for creating the necessary state of mind, the power of suggestion, the capacity to sweep other individuals or groups along with his word or with his action, with the will expressed in gesture, speech, rhythm, or example.

There is, therefore, magic in the facts determining fascination (a word that because of its significance is closely related to sexual images), charm (which derives directly from *carmen*, meaning poem, from verse, from rhythm), enchantment (which etimologically derives from *chant*), or witchcraft. There is magic in the fascination of ideas that permit or accompany this state of mind, in the facts which develop in it and which in their turn bewitch those who determined them, active magic which derives from natural facts or from an exceptional mood, but above all from faith in success and from the will of the enchanter, who imposes faith and will on his listeners. This state of mind is the ground on which all beliefs and all faiths are born—the condition in which critical judgment is suppressed or silenced. This is why, as we shall see, in a broad sense the history of outstanding men, warriors and poets, founders of religions and explorers, adventurers and healers, is closely bound with that of hallucinations, visions, collective obsessions and mass suggestions, and belongs to the history of magic.

Environment and the mental state of the individual determine the psychological moment most favourable to the acceptance of suggestion. In organized or unorganized groups, it is the milieu and a state of physical or psychic depression such as occurs after a war, famine, or epidemic, that create a collective state of mind in which currents of morbid thought exercise a vast and profound influence. The masses, when under the dominance of demoniacal or destructive spell, may be likened to persons attacked by a sickness epidemically spread by an infected person among healthy individuals, or rather among individuals predisposed to contagion, as in the case of communicable diseases.

Frazer claims that wizards are the most ancient organized social class in history; beliefs of a magic character such as totem and taboo are the earliest religious systems of mankind. According to Combarieux, the origin of music must be sought in magic. In Huvelin's opinion, the plastic arts, and doubtless the theatre and the dance as well, derive from magic. It is evident that if one admits that primitive man—as has been shown by recent explorers and missionaries—lived and still lives in a magic world, one must infer that all emotional manifestations are bound to primeval magic concepts.

Magic considered as a complex of ideas originating acts various in form, but unified by a single tendency, characterizes the first development of early historical periods. The evolution of magic is parallel to that of thought and gives rise to facts that have by now sometimes completely lost their connection with the causes that determined them. Who would think, observing a ring or a necklace of pearls, watching a picturesque dance or uttering a vow, that these objects and facts stem directly from remote magic concepts?

The magic act probably has its origin, like words and language, in a series of gestures or acts tending to a definite aim, which slowly grew into a complex set of practices, formulas, and rhythms. But the most important characteristic of magic from the psychological viewpoint, that which must be emphasized if we want to understand its evolution, is the preexistence, the premise of a special state of mind which originates it, and upon which it is founded. It is a psychological state in which the critical faculties either are not yet born or have been abolished or greatly impaired (owing to reasons that I propose to examine later), while emotional and imaginative powers are, for the same or different causes, excited to the maximum degree of intensity. It is a state of mind that is aptly termed "incantation," undoubtedly because rhythm, song, and music were probably the first and simplest means by which the magic spell was brought about.

Magic postulates as necessary, on one side, a magic factor and, on the other, the abolition or absence of criticism—that is, an utter lack of causal criticism or correction (Schopenhauer). This latter condition may exist in the child or the primitive man, in whom critical powers, present only at an advanced stage of psychic evolution, are absent or weak. It may be caused by mental illnesses of a dissociative type or by poisons such as certain chemical substances and bacteria that circulate in the blood during or after an infection, or by states of depression or, on the other hand, of psychic overexcitement. It may be determined, finally, by a suggestion which in its turn may be self-suggestion, created by the individual himself, or heterosuggestion—that is, exercised by others. This psychic factor of the "incantational spell"—a term that perhaps states its character more clearly and immediately—constitutes the fundamental, essential feature of magic.

3. THE MAGIC SPELL OF NATURE

The earliest form of magic spell is to be found in nature. In nature light, music, colours, and fragrances play a notable role as means of exerting a definite action on the senses of living beings and arouse or sharpen sensations or desires. In fact, the first spell of life stems from nature itself, and aims at exciting or directing the sexual instincts of living beings and thus at ensuring the preservation of the species. The melodious songs of birds, the colours of their plumage, the smells of flowers, the secretion of odorous substances in certain animals, and other facts of this kind are surely to be classified among the innumerable means, not all identifiable, by which nature exercises her spell and creates a special and thousand-fold state of incantation. For this reason the remotest attempts made by men at casting a magic spell by these means were imitations of the aspect, the colours, the smells of animals, the songs of birds. It was probably later that men attempted to take the place of the animal by donning its skin, adopting its cry and attitudes, and assuming its name.

The music of the universe, in its thousands of manifestations, thus is the most ancient form of the spell of life.

Contemporary with the incantatory and determining force of this great harmony, man undoubtedly noticed with deep terror the antithetical phenomena of nature. He felt intense sensations of fear when the sky thundered or lightened, he was cowed by the violent beating of rain, awed by the cruel destruction of life under the furious torrents of fire pouring forth from volcanoes; he was overwhelmed by the floods which he saw wipe out the fruits of his labours in a few hours. He perceived the spell of dark, starless nights, of illimitable silences, the appeal of the dark profundities of skies and seas, the enchantment of death. Little by little, slowly through the centuries, unconsciously listening to the voices of nature, man realized the dominant accents of the great universal laws, of the supreme antagonistic tendencies.

Seeking for protection or escape, he drew an example and a warning from the spells of life and death in nature. He protected his life, making use of loud unpleasant noises, fire, and blinding colours to keep his enemies at a distance, by arousing in them a fantastic feeling of terror. He attempted to propitiate adverse forces—as one placates animals and as he would have liked to be placated himself—by offering them

food and sacrifices, either real or fictive. Doubtless this concept gave rise to numberless sanguinary rites, from human
sacrifice to the sacrifice of animals. Man strove to attract the
benevolent forces with music, by an imitation of the songs of
birds. The earliest musical instruments, carved from a rein-
deer bone, belong to the palæolithic age, and were used to
call animals. Magic practices were accompanied by the clap-
ping of hands or by beating pieces of wood together. The
sound of the drum, in which, it was believed, the demon of
war was hidden, accompanied battles. Without magic songs
no battle could begin. The sorcerer begins the song, even
today, among some tribes of Polynesia, with a chanted recital
of glorious deeds, and is reminiscent of the figures of the remote, primeval poets.

The use of stupefying substances to achieve a state of incantation is a perhaps unintentional or unconscious imitation
of a process of nature; the same may be said of the lavish and
frequent use of perfumes, of colours, and of all the means
that cast a spell.

Experience teaches primitive man the means of driving
away adverse forces in the same way in which animals are
frightened off, or harmful beings and superhuman entities
driven away. A sick person is beaten and wounded, shaken
and struck, treated with drastic potions of every kind, under
the conviction that the spiteful demon can thus be driven out.
G. Zilboorg, in his *History of Psychology*, has devoted an
exhaustive study to the aggression against the sick and the
insane. Such a cure for insanity remained generally in practice as late as two centuries ago in all the institutions for the
mentally deranged.

A practice common to ancient sorcerers is that of destroying the belongings of the enemy, attempting to strike his
shadow, burning his hair and nails, writing his name and
consigning it to the flames, and smiting his image.

It was believed that adverse forces could be conquered by
diverting their attention by actions or objects likely to deflect
them violently against other objects. This accounts for the
protective value attributed to phallic images, held in great
favour by the Romans, from which amulets of various forms

were made. On the other side, the burning of images and writings representing dangerous inimical forces, as shown by recent events, bears an evident relation to this primitive idea. Books are the enemy of every irrational tendency because they constitute a written and unshakable law which it is hard to combat.

A further, equally important method of defence consisted in concealing or changing the characteristics of one's identity, as occurs in nature by assuming a protective coloration, mimicking that of one's surroundings, and in camouflage, of which there are numerous examples in the past and the present. Masks, which are attempts at transforming the personality by changing its aspect, have the same origin. To this same source may be traced frequent mutations of names, which are so important in all magic practices, and later in the religious practices deriving from them, and under other forms in political life.

Caps with showy feathers, clothes of bright and strange colours—army uniforms of ancient days—the accompaniment of loud music, are further means of changing the identity of a person, frightening off the enemy, and exercising an immediate and active spell.

Names have tremendous importance because of their power to determine and fix the place of the individual in the group and to distinguish him from its other components. Names, therefore, constitute the essence and the most important feature of the personality. Change in name is equivalent to a real and effective change of personality. Primeval man holds the belief that by changing his name he is no longer threatened by the dangers that ensnared his now abandoned personality. Frequent and interesting analogies of this are to be found in the mind of the child who believes that by changing his name or clothes he may become someone else or render himself unrecognizable. Names have a spell and a mystic power—they are both words and symbols. Things as well as persons have names: houses, weapons, rivers, mountains. It is a general practice among primitive peoples to accompany the naming of a child with a solemn ceremony during which the father, it is believed, communicates his soul, or a part of it, to his son. This is the origin of the custom of giving a child the name of his father or grandfather, and of the primitive practice of the father blowing in the face of his child. Primitive tribes believe in the existence of a fundamental relationship between the name and the year, the day, and the season in which the name is given. There are frequent instances of a secret name known only to the sorcerer or to the father, so that nobody, knowing the name, can be in a position to cast spells over the person. This conception gives rise to the prohibition to pronounce the names of the gods, of which we have an example in the Biblical interdiction to pronounce the tetragrammatic name of God. According to this conception, by changing or removing the name, one succeeds in conjuring away danger and in exorcizing fate.

According to a belief that, in modern terminology, may be called prophylactic or apotropaic, a defence is created—around the individual—which, because it consists of many components including the adjuncts of friendly persons or things or by reason of its innate virtue, fends off adverse forces just as palisades or enclosures protect an inhabited village from wild animals. Such a belief gives rise to the manifold use of amulets and talismans of every kind, and furthers apotropaic methods which deflect malevolent forces away from the individual. These methods I shall discuss more fully later; among them must be included the magic word-symbols and exorcisms and the forms of all kinds in which, in accordance with taste, epoch, and environment, the desire for protection and defence assumes an objective embodiment.

This accounts for the origin of the high-sounding titles and divine attributes given to Asiatic rulers and Roman emperors; for the taboo names *leader, Führer, Duce,* or *Son of the Sun,* which become symbolical; for such emblems as the swastika, the fasces, and innumerable others.

In conclusion, it is in nature that one finds the first example of protection and threat, the earliest foundations of magic, which may be social or antisocial, according to whether the good or evil demon is accepted and favoured or rebelled against. Antisocial magic is the alliance or the covenant with the evil demon, to whom one must subject oneself and from whom one attempts to secure the most favourable conditions or to obtain help by sacrificing, in exchange, all that one possesses or hopes to possess in this or in a better life.

4. ANALOGY AND IMITATION

In its ideation and in its practice, magic is essentially analogical and imitative. It derives, that is, from the fundamental conception that it is possible to obtain results in the struggle against invisible and unknown forces first by wishing for these results and thinking of them, then by resorting to the same means by which certain results are obtained in analogous situations brought about by known causes. Likewise, analogies to imitative magic are to be found in the thought-processes of a child, which are dominated by this principle. I may mention the practice still in use among many savage peoples for the purpose of obtaining rain, which consists in whirling a stick of wood in a pool and making the water splash, and numerous other examples. Among these the manipulations and practices aimed at facilitating pregnancy or parturition (manipulations on the belly of a screaming woman who is in labour, the simulation of parturition during which a wooden doll is hidden near the mother-to-be, simulations of suckling, etc.) are worthy of mention. All the direct or indirect practices against adjuncts (shadow, images, name, etc.) belong to imitative magic. Imitative magic has its counterpart in the thoughts and gestures of children, and is to be found in certain forms of dissociative psychopathy in which every act against one's shadow, image, or name is considered malevolent and therefore fatal. From this conception stem all the severe prohibitions against the use of images, pronouncing names, following footsteps, etc.

Analogical or imitative magic, which Frazer calls homœopathic because he believes that the term *imitative* suggests a conscious agent that imitates, is based on an association of ideas, on the principle that similar things inevitably bring about similar effects. The practices of primitive man and of the inhabitants of ancient Egypt and Babylonia are to be found today among the natives of Polynesia and Africa. The Indians of North America believe that by forming the figure of a person in sand, ashes, or clay, or by supposing an object to be the body of a person, and stabbing the form or the object with a stick, the person himself is wounded or killed. Frazer cites a form of Malayan witchcraft that consists in building a figure about thirty centimetres high out of an empty beehive. The Malays believe that by piercing the eye of the image the enemy himself is blinded, by perforating its head he suffers a headache, by transfixing the figure from head to foot and then wrapping it in a shroud as if it were a corpse and saying over it the prayers for the dead, the enemy himself is certain to die. Among the Bataks of Sumatra a sterile woman who wishes to bear a child carves the figure of a baby in wood, and it is believed that if she holds it to her breast, she is sure to have her desire fulfilled. In the archipelago of Babar when a woman wishes to have a child she holds a doll of red cotton to her breast as if nursing it. The same principle of pretence, which is dear to children, has led to the practice of performing an adoption rite in the form of a simulated birth, and also as a means of restoring life to a corpse. Diodorus recounts that Juno in adopting Hercules as her son went through the following ceremony: she took him into her bed, thrust him forth from her clothes, and let him fall to the ground, simulating a real birth. The historian adds that even in his day barbarians practise the same rite in adopting babies. It appears that this custom is still observed in Bulgaria and among the Turks of Bosnia, and there are innumerable other instances that might be adduced.

In relation to the magic conception of the virtue attributed to images, the acts of love and pity or enmity performed on the image have the same value and the same result as when directed toward the person or the animal itself. The adoration or condemnation "in effigy" stems from this conception, and to it must be attributed the prohibition of images in Biblical legislation.

In the phenomena of the mass-mind, imitation plays an eminent part. The importance it has in collective psychology is well known to those who have studied the history of the suicide of two, three, four, and entire groups of people—collective psychopathic manifestations such as the dance of St. Vitus and the mass-hysteria of the Flagellants, which occurred in 1300 after the plague that destroyed hundreds of thousands of human lives, and collective demonopathies like that of Verzeris in Friuli in 1880, described by Sighele. Imitation arises in the masses with lightning-like rapidity; individuals have no time to make use of their critical powers, just as an individual predisposed to a certain disease lacks time to immunize himself against contagion. Moreover a weak and depressed person is aware that if he fails to follow the example of the others he risks being considered either an enemy or weak and cowardly and thus, of necessity, he takes the same course. Imitation, dominant in children and primitive peoples, becomes extremely strong in the masses when in periods of depression criticism is abolished and independent personal judgment is condemned. This explains the lightning-like effect of aggressive and destructive emotionalisms on the masses and especially on organized masses. I shall speak of this more fully later.

Rites and sanguinary practices derive from the same conception. Since blood constitutes the force and the very meaning of life (it is easy to explain this belief of primitive peoples, as it corresponds to reality: we all know that a serious loss of blood results in death), magic attempts are usually connected with it. There is, in fact, no important magic practice, whether it be directed at sealing a friendship or cementing a love affair, causing death or damage to an enemy, ratifying a community of interests, or documenting the indissolubility of the bond of a sect or a close relationship of dependence and loyalty, in which blood does not play a predominant part. For the same reason, and originating in the same order of ideas, those practices which include the representation of sexual facts or organs (to be found in the most ancient drawings, in the earliest plastic images, in hieroglyphics, in the letters of the most remote alphabets, thus proving the tremendous role played by the sexual factor in primitive thought-processes) constitute a noteworthy domain of sorcery.

5. MYSTIC AND SYMBOLIC UNITY

Man's solidarity with the group, his adjuncts, and everything surrounding him, is the basis of the magic conception.

To this may be added the intuition, equally deeply rooted, of an antithesis that episodically or permanently, under the influence of known or unknown factors, arises between individuals, groups, forces, and finally between different tendencies in the mind of the same individual. We know how the concept of the simultaneous presence in two or more places of the vital force, the idea of the double personality and of the possibility that it may be embodied in different forms and at various times, constitutes one of the essential features of the primitive mentality. We know that it finds expression in the ancient portrayals of monstrous divinities with many heads, many legs, and so on, and in the tales of the possible metamorphoses of the personality, which, fundamentally, are but attempts at an escape from individuality to the plurality of persons. These are conceptions for which it is easy to find analogies in the results of the most recent scientific research regarding the existence of antithetical elements in the cell, the permanent battle between the conscious and the unconscious, between the individual who affirms his personality and his past, the essence of which centres in his ancestral heritage, between will and instinct, criticism and faith. These forms are extremely varied in appearance, but they all stem from a contrast existing in man, between elements perennially fighting against one another in the human organism, in the cell, as well as in the collectivity. It may reasonably be asserted that this primitive conception of antithetical elements fighting in mutual struggle (a struggle that later becomes fundamental in religious and moral conceptions like good and evil, heaven and hell, light and darkness, etc.) must be considered as arising from the unconscious, undefined, or exaggerated perception of an immanent biological truth.

Imitative or sympathetic magic, viewed in its determinant forces and in the conception underlying it, is not only imitative in so far as it tends to mimic causes for the purpose of achieving effects already known; it is imitative also in a wider and deeper sense. It creates its own concepts and practices on the basis of assumed relations of unity or antithesis between the elements of the cosmos, presupposing the existence of such relations of interdependence (according to Lévy-Bruhl, "the law of participation") between all beings and all elements. Imitative magic is founded on the objectified desire of the individual or of the collectivity for preservation or on the desire for aggression and the destruction and death of enemies. The creation, brought about by internal and external causes, of a particular incantational state of mind in which the critical faculties are impaired or abolished and the emotional powers intensified, constitutes both the premise and the consequence of any intense objectivation of such desires.

In a later period the magic conception gives rise, as we shall see, to a symbol representing a concrete and condensed representation of this idea of defence, escape, and aggression. Given a state of magic spell, and presupposing the fundamental law of the mystic unity between all things, real and unreal, between living or imaginary persons, symbols necessarily become of prime importance as magic factors. Nor is this to be wondered at, inasmuch as this process may be considered as a stage of the evolution of all ideas, which necessarily at a certain moment crystallize in a fixed form. The most obvious example is that of language, in which first sounds, then letters, and finally words constitute merely representations or symbols of ideas, and later assume a value and a significance often independent of the value and significance originally attributed to them.[1]

Symbolic actions become, then, equivalent to real ones because, like them, they are dictated by desire and will, the starting-points and the only truly indispensable factors of magic. The shooting of a poisoned arrow at an enemy with the intention of wounding him is equivalent, as far as desire and thought are concerned, to actually wounding him. One of the best-known magic practices, which has been in use until very recently, consists in perforating with a pin a figure to which the name and personality of the individual one wishes to harm are attributed. This same category includes the magic practices that consist in burning some hair or in melting a wax heart which are supposed to symbolize the person against

[1] Bleuler and Cassirer have published important studies of the problem of the origin of the language, and their opinions have aroused wide discussion. I refer the reader who wishes information on this fascinating question to their works.

whom the spell is directed. There are innumerable examples of these practices even today.

The symbolical conceptions relative to chaining magic forces, or transferring illnesses to others, practices that have been preserved up to present times, are no less frequent and interesting. In the humble churches of the French province of Eure-et-Loire many statues of the Virgin and the saints are covered with ribbons, every ribbon being supposed to tie the illness of a patient to the statue. A small church in one of these villages contains the statue of a local saint pierced with small nails and pins, the purpose of which is to fasten the illness to the statue. In Fleury-sur-Ambelle there is a dolmen called the Stone of St. Martin and this druidic monument is riddled with holes in which the peasants insert laces in the belief that they can thus cure their children of tubercular peritonitis. The Breton peasant with a toothache employs analogous practices to transfer pain. Following an ancient custom, he transmits his malady to a willow tree by holding a few fibres from the tree against his sore gums and then putting them back on the tree and covering them over with the bark. Others seek to tie the fever from which they suffer to the branch of a tree, the number of knots employed corresponding to the number of days of fever. This custom is connected with many practices of ancient peoples and with the secret language of knots.

6. IMITATIVE MAGIC MEDICINE

Sympathetic medicine employs symbolic actions for abbreviated proceedings whose success is equally certain. If we seek for the proofs of this conception in ancient medicine, in the attempts to cure illnesses and to conjure away death (many instances of these attempts are to be found in the medicine of primitive peoples and in popular medicine), we will find a very convincing number. But even in this field, perhaps more than in any other, the role that imagination, often supported by thousands of years of experience, played in the establishment of these practices appears important. The first attempts in the field of organotherapy which were made in prehistoric epochs have, undoubtedly, this double origin. The belief that a sick person could be endowed with the qualities ascribed to an organ or an animal if he were made to eat that organ or animal was predominant. Pliny asserts that from ancient times it was known that people eating the liver of a viper are immune to the poisonous effects of its bite, and as a consequence of this idea the flesh and the internal organs of the viper played an important part in ancient therapy. At a later date, the belief arose that the eyes of birds were an excellent remedy for eye troubles, the testicles of animals were helpful in curing impotence, the teeth of hyenas allayed toothache, and the bladders of certain animals, particularly pigs, counteracted diseases of the bladder. Stimulating substances were given to persons in an overexcited state, those suffering with jaundice were covered with yellow dust (as was the custom among the ancient Hindus), and persons with scarlet fever, according to ancient Chinese medicine, were exposed to red light. The woodcock, because of its yellow eyes, was so famous for its power to cure jaundice that venders of the bird kept its eyes bandaged for fear the sick person, seeing them, would be cured gratuitously. Gold was considered the sovereign remedy for illnesses of the kidneys, and so forth. Thus ancient organotherapy, which returns today in the modern conception of opotherapy, was founded on "imitative" magic.

From a clearly symbolical conception, sometimes originating in, or assisted by, experience, there arose, therefore, the idea of curing diseased organs with plants of the same form or colour. Thus lungwort was considered an excellent medicine for pulmonary diseases, and other plants were held to have strong healing power for other illnesses.

Ancient magic cures could be applied, according to the "imitative" idea, to the healer himself or to a relative of the sick person as well as to the sufferer. Frazer writes that a medicine-man of the Daiachi, when called to treat a case, stretches out upon the floor, pretending to be dead. He is then treated like a corpse, wrapped in a mat, carried out of the house, and laid upon the ground. After a certain time the onlookers unbind the pretended corpse and call him back to life. His pretended cure brings about the healing of the ill person. A cure for tumours is prescribed by Marcellus of Bordeaux, the physician of Theodosius I: "Take the root of verbena, cut it in two, and place half of it on the neck of the patient and the other over a smoking fire. When the verbena becomes dry the tumour also will dry up and disappear." There is an addition to the effect that if by chance the patient is not satisfied with the cure, the physician can easily punish him by throwing the verbena in water, because when the roots are wet they swell up and the tumour is formed again.

From an analogous concept of imitative magic derives the use of furs and feathers, which, through the magic law of adjuncts, endow the wearer with the virtues of the animal from which they were taken. Eagle feathers, snake-skins, tiger claws, lions' manes transfer the powers or virtues of these animals to the man who wears them.

Thus the craving of the individual and the race to preserve life, and the antithetical desire to destroy, have dominated mankind since primordial times. They subsist in the conscious and the unconscious, and magic elements persist even when the evolution of the critical faculty or concentration of emotional faculties in religious directions give a different orientation to their development. But, as we shall see, objective criticism on one side and religious faith on the other are later superstructures, which may be simultaneously present and may be suppressed, episodically or durably, when, because of special circumstances of the individual or collectivity, there occurs a throwback to conditions analogous to the ancestral one. The throwback is caused by the prevalence of incantation, psychic states over the emotional faculties, leading to hallucinations and to the emergence of the unconscious. These states to which I am referring are analogous to those which are manifested in the individual after serious contagious diseases or as a result of the use of drugs. Such states intensify the perception of the necessity for a violent defence of the individual or of the group against grave dangers. In conclusion, a sensation of isolation or of inferiority in the face of overwhelming inimical forces is present in these states, and therefore the feeling that it is necessary to grasp at any means that may lead to overcoming the danger. Thus the regression takes place: the individual and the crowd, dominated by terror, by the need for escape and the desire for aggression, revert to primeval beliefs and to practices of the most remote times.

III

Evocation and Dreams

I. THE CONTINUITY OF LIFE

IN the conception of primitive man, as we have seen, death does not mean the end but merely a transition from one state of being to another. The dead person continues to need food and drink, and to perform the functions of material life. He can feel and see what goes on among living people and can exercise over them a harmful or beneficial influence, more often harmful than beneficial because of his envy for the living or of his craving for revenge or punishment. Millet and salt are the nourishment of the dead.

According to this belief, the dead man, like the living, can be present in two or more places at once; he may appear in the form of a ghost, an animal, or a plant. When he is under the earth he feels cold and dampness and suffers from them. Life continues, particularly in the bones, because they are much less subject to putrefaction. The skull is considered to be the dead man himself; advice is asked of it and speeches and prayers are addressed to it in the name of the tribe. Trephining was a surgical operation frequently practised in the Stone Age on the wounded for the rational treatment of skull fractures. The main purpose served by this operation when performed on the skulls of cadavers (as is shown by innumerable perforated skulls discovered in Europe, Africa, and Central America) was probably that of carving the skull bones in the form of disks to be worn as amulets (rondelles). The possession of the bones, and particularly of the skulls, of one's ancestors was believed to endow the holder with extraordinary strength because it placed at his disposal all the power that had belonged to the dead man.

This accounts for the importance, in all primitive tribes, of head-hunting. It assumes a particularly interesting form among certain peoples of the equatorial countries, described by Karsten. To possess these tsantsas is equivalent to having mastery over the dead man.

According to the same conception, the vital principle may reside in the parts of the body and belongings of the dead. The natives of the islands of Torres Strait, described by Bruce, believe that the vital essence of the dead, indicated by the word *keber*, is located not only in the corpse but also in any object that was used in his funeral ceremonies or buried with him. To gain possession of a part of the corpse or of any of these objects is equivalent to obtaining control over the dead and dominating his individuality. In this lies the explanation of the custom prescribing that all things belonging to the dead, and primarily his house, must be destroyed.

Owing to this belief primitive peoples are reluctant to accept the inheritance of the dead, and the custom of putting the most highly prized and most valuable belongings of the deceased in his grave to prevent him from returning to claim them, out of dissatisfaction or envy, derives from this conception.

2. SURVIVAL AND EVOCATION

The conception held by primitive societies that the dead man may be present in two or more places at once is connected with the widespread belief that the vital principle of the individual may lead an existence separate from his body. According to the ancient Egyptians, the "ka" or vital force continues to exist near the tomb of the dead, and guards him until due honours are paid him and he is supplied with the necessary food. Only when the body is destroyed, burned, and the ashes are scattered to the winds can it be believed that he is definitely dead and no longer able to do harm, although the general conviction is that the powers or qualities of the dead survive in his belongings. Numberless legends like that of the shield of Achilles, the helmet of Mambrinus, and so forth derive from this conviction. But if the body is not destroyed, and eventually even when it has been destroyed, the dead man may return to be a participant in the life of his group and will act in a favourable or maleficent sense according to his conduct while alive. The dead may appear to the living

*Medicine-woman in Usumbura, north of Lake Tanganyika.
Painting by A. l'Ollivier*

Medicine-man of the Gla tribe in West Africa

under circumstances of the most varied kinds and even in various places at once; they assume simultaneously, at times, the form of animals and their own human aspect. Frequently they appear as serpents. Moreover, as Lévy-Bruhl, putting together the accounts of various explorers, demonstrates, the serpent-dead reassure the living as to the well-meaning disposition of their souls. Their appearance is held to be a proof of their friendly intentions.

A complex conception of the special conditions of the life of the dead is to be found in most primitive societies. The dead live in groups established on the same principles as those governing them during life, composed of their ancestors and ruled by identical laws. The individuals who die without offspring are particularly unhappy, since there is nobody who can recite prayers—invocations or evocations—for them.

As I have said, as far as the mind of primitive man is concerned, we are not entitled to speak of immortality, but of survival; and consequently the second life, like the first, which it resembles in many aspects, comes to its end. Almost all the tribes of Polynesia and Africa believe that the dead die in their turn, may be killed and recommence their life in another form. Reincarnation, a belief held by many primitive groups, completes the cycle of life by asserting that life continues, and passes from one being to another.

The role played by the dead is important both on account of the authority that they exercised in life, due to their age, experience, worth, victories won, etc., and because of the power deriving from their ability to be ever present and invisible, thus wielding a determining and uncontrollable influence. Primitive man, according to circumstances, was impelled to invoke or conjure away, to wish for or to dread, their intervention. He felt the need of summoning to his aid his ancestors or dearest friends who in life had been close to him as worthy counsellors and trusted companions, in order to avail himself of their services in moments of danger. Equally clear is the motive that prompts primitive man to deprecate the apparitions of the dead, or to attempt to foil them, fearing that the hostile spirits of deceased enemies may reappear.

This conception gives rise to the desire—in fact, the need—for entering into direct communication with these eerie, superior powers, which in dreams, deliriums, visions, hallucinations caused by illness or poison, or under the influence of certain words, gestures, or incantational practices, may reappear in various aspects. To recall them among the living, to make them constant and certain participants in daily occurrences, to have them as friends through good and bad luck, and to keep them at a distance if they are enemies; such is an essential, fundamental aim of magic.

From the psychological viewpoint, the man who fancies that he hears the voices of his ancestors, and opposes or adjusts his desires and needs to their will, or attempts to place his own will above theirs, is in reality but the instrument of a permanent strife between his conscious ego and his ancestral unconscious, from which the voices of the past continuously arise, admonishing or consoling, instructing or threatening him. He projects into the external world the events that unfold in his mind, as occurs in dreams.

To recall and identify these voices, to recapture the forms of the dead, is therefore the main purpose of the most important magic practice: evocation. We know that summonings, evocations, exorcisms, are methods aimed at accomplishing the same purpose: that of projecting or rendering more clearly perceptible those so-called inner voices which are heard by every individual, particularly in certain moods, and which express ancestral traditions, forgotten laws and images, grown faint in remembrance. The man who prepares to evoke them creates in himself a mood of collectedness, concentrates his attention on his intimate personality, listens. It is the attitude of a person who, in great and deep silence, calls a dear one, not knowing whether he be near or far, whether or not he will obey the voice instinct with both hope and anguish.

If we turn our attention to similar practices in the societies of today we perceive the suggestive importance attributed to the words of Führer and Duce, rhythmically repeated by crowds; to the name or its initial, to the invocation of the dead (as in Germany in the case of Horst Wessel), and to symbolic formulas. All these factors possess a great suggestive power, due precisely to their simplicity, which acts directly and immediately. Such facts are essentially identical with those which are to be found in the magic of all ages.

It is believed possible to evoke the spirits of familiar dead, of friends and enemies, of the protectors of the group, the family, the individual, of all the living and the deceased. Evocation reaches secret and unknown vital forces that may reside in celestial bodies, as well as in springs, rivers, trees, mountains, and the adjuncts of man and things. Primitive man, and the unconscious of every man, are instinct with a belief in a vital force that dwells in every living being and substance of the cosmos; the omnipresence of these forces makes it possible, hence necessary, to evoke them and reach them in order to propitiate or combat them.

In the magic practices of all peoples the power of a name is such that it is sufficient to pronounce it to bring about the appearance of the person to whom the name belonged; so that it is generally forbidden to name the dead or the maleficent spirits. This is the origin of the custom, still in use today, prohibiting the naming of persons reputed to be bearers of ill fortune and prescribing some gesture to exorcize the evil if the name is pronounced. A consequence of this magic conception is the fear that particularly grips Oriental peoples—Arabs, Turks, Jews, and Indians—on hearing their children praised or their names uttered by strangers, lest this may point them out to envy and to the evil arts of hostile spirits.

Evocation, properly so called, was considered at all times to be the foundation of all magic practices. Evocation—as is convincingly demonstrated by countless examples, even of modern times, quoted in recent works describing the evocations practised by the natives of Haiti, the centre of the magic cult of Voodoo—requires, like all magic rites, a special state of mind in those who perform it, a state of mind in which the emotional faculties predominate over the critical ones. It is a state of expectation of the magic event, the miracle. The sorcery exercised by the word that evokes and recalls, the death-compelling spell that causes the departed to return and to draw near to the living, are the foundation of all methods used through the centuries for bringing about evocation—that is, a direct contact between the conscious and the uncon-scious, between the individual's self-perception of his ego and the collective subconscious from which the tribal conscious-ness is reawakened. Evocation, therefore, is but the objectiva-tion of the craving for a direct relation between the individ-ual and his past.

3. DREAMS

Dreams are, so to speak, the luminous indications that from time to time arise from the depths of the unconscious and point out the way to desire. It is from dreams, perhaps, that the first conception of the possibility of a direct relation with the spirits of the dead arises. This is confirmed by the phe-nomenon of hallucination, due either to endogenous or to exogenous factors, and that of suggestion, which may be either autosuggestion or heterosuggestion. These phenomena demand the presence of a special state of mind for motives that are evident in the light of the explanations given concern-ing the relationship between the conscious and the uncon-scious. A state that leads to a deepening loss of critical self-consciousness corresponds to an intensification of emotions. Self-consciousness is suspended during sleep; active will is abolished and criticism is absent.

The reason why dreams have always played a notable role in magic is that they essentially correspond to the essence it-self of sorcery, which is, above all, the objectivation of desire. In regard to the interpretation of dreams Freud has proposed a theory that certainly contains a vision of truth. In dreams, as in magic and magic rites, impatience hastens attainment and suggestion causes the accomplishment of desire to appear tan-gible. Freud rightly observes that from the fact that magic has been practised for a thousand years, and from many ex-pressions of the language, one may deduce the importance assigned to dreams in all epochs. In all times, the saying goes: "a fact that surpassed my fondest dreams," "something I would never have dreamed of." And the most audacious desire has always been described as a beautiful dream. In considera-tion of the circumstance that not all dreams appear to be purely realizations of desires, since there are also many dreams filled with anguish, one may say that the manifestations of the subconscious, and an element of terror and menace, are always inherent in the objectivation of desire. We saw the role that fear, the initial attitude of man in the face of the unknown and the supernatural, plays in the conception of magic. This sense of fear, which is overcome or dominated by reason, is manifested in the unconscious, springs up concomitantly with every realization of desire, and probably becomes more violent when the dreamer is not in good mental health. Nightmares awake the sleeper and obsessional fears prevail even in waking hours when danger predominates in the unconscious.

The analogy between dreams and hallucinations also has an important function in magic. Inducing of sleep and dreams belongs to magic practices and has been considered by sorcerers of all epochs as a means of achieving success. This is shown not only by the accounts of travellers and missionaries, but also by many rites of healing magic, like sleeping in the temples of Æsculapius, dreaming in the cave of the prophet Elijah, etc., and by a number of experimental researches on the results of mild stimulations of the senses which eventuate in hallucinations. Coleridge tells the remarkable case of a servant who, while suffering from fever, in her delirium was wont to repeat long passages in Hebrew, a language of which she was utterly ignorant, but which she had heard spoken by a rabbi.

It is evident that, whether dreams be the expression of manifest or suppressed desires, or the result of fear or anguish, the dead often appear and play an important role in them. The affection of parents for their children, and their strong desire that the relation with them be not broken, recall the latter to life in dreams; and, vice versa, the fear of the beyond, the threat of punishment and of revenge, make awesome and bloodthirsty shadows appear. In every epoch mankind has devoted hopeful and fearful attention to dreams because there has always been a belief in their determining influence on the future. Thus dreams became a formidable weapon in the hands of the sorcerer, and they guided the actions of the ancient healer and hypnotist in a manner perhaps not unlike that which guides the understanding of the psychoanalyst of today.

The role played by dreams in the origin of primitive belief

in the continuity of life is a problem that has created much discussion among psychologists. Some of these are unwilling to admit that primitive man confused dream visions with apparitions of the dead. It is undoubtedly hard to gain a clear idea of the formation of psychological associations, which are wont to undergo numberless modifications according to individual and environmental conditions. But it seems most probable that even when primitive man frequently did not consider the figures appearing in his dreams to be the shades of the dead, in every epoch his dream visions contained, or appear to have contained, a recollection of a different form of life. This is also true because, for clearly comprehensible reasons, it is particularly the figures of the beloved or feared dead that most frequently haunted those visions; the latter, in the opinion of Freud, being merely manifestations of unconscious wishes. Roheim has examined and analysed the dreams of primitives, with their help, and has made interesting observations.

4. EVOCATION AND THE FIGURE OF THE EVOCATOR

Besides the evocation of the dead, the magic of all times was conversant with, and practised, the evocation of known and unknown forces of every kind. Evocation, as the word indicates, is a call, an appeal, in which voice and name have an important function. Hence all the living forces of animals, plants, celestial phenomena (such as light, darkness, fire, lightning, etc.), rivers, springs, mountains, stars, may be evoked. Primitive man perceived in everything surrounding him the presence of a superior power which he could put to advantage or prevent from acting against him.

It is perfectly understandable that the necessity of establishing a hierarchy of these powers should appear very early in the mind of primitive man. The law of order, of system, of the gradation of various forces, is doubtless one of the fundamental necessities imposed by the needs of life itself. Man soon wanted to distinguish beings whose influence was restricted within very narrow limits from those whose position in the cosmos indicated the vastness of their might. While the power of an animal or of an enemy is restricted to persons near by or to a group, the power of the sun, of lightning, of stars appears infinitely larger, and they necessarily assume first place in the hierarchy and keep such a place in the earliest religious structures. Such structures, as we shall see, though built on more complex associations of ideas, and with the aid of a more highly developed criticism, preserve the hierarchic systematization in its essentials. The most advanced civilizations, even the most distinctly monotheistic religions, evince this trait, which appears in the hierarchy of saints, angels, demons, and their categories and subdivisions.

The intervention of the intermediary who evokes these forces and renders their foreseen action useful is one of the consequences of this classification. Such intervention requires the knowledge of many facts, the recognition of mighty forces, the exact decision as to those which must be selected, and finally—and most important—the right application of the means needed. In the field of evocative magic occurs, fundamentally, the same phenomenon of social evolution as in industry and the arts: in early times every man was a woodcutter and smith, hunter and palisade-builder, farmer and shepherd, and so forth. With the growth of knowledge and the perfecting of techniques, which became more and more complex, and with the continuous increase in demand, each member of the group slowly assumed specific functions, in the same manner as groups of cells in the progressive evolution of an organism. The evocator is therefore the individual endowed with the necessary knowledge for summoning distant and invisible forces by acts and gestures which in early times were simpler and consisted in calling forth those forces whose intervention was desired. A series of drawings by primitive peoples, still extant, shows how the gestures and dances that accompanied song also served this purpose. This and other facts, which I shall point out, demonstrate that in the practices of evocation the main role was always given to rhythmic expressions or gestures. The rhythms of expression or movement, sometimes slow and monotonous, sometimes discordant and crashing, were always considered to be the principal factor of evocation. The origin of all the formulas of evocation, consisting in infinite rhythmical repetitions of the same words or of words of a similar sound, repeated in the same tone, must

perhaps be sought in this fact. Poetry and music probably
originate here, in the power attributed to rhythm in summoning occult and remote forces.

Thus the intervention of the intermediary appears to be a
necessary premise, and it is logical that in conformity with
the hierarchy of supernatural beings there should have been
formed the hierarchy of the evocators of those beings, according to whether the latter had under their control inferior beings only or superior ones also. A classic example of this
thought-process is the Biblical account of Pharaoh's magicians
who entered into a competition with Moses, and the demonstration of Moses' superiority and of the power invoked by
him, which was vastly greater than that of the Egyptian wizards, who succeeded in producing only the most elementary
and simple miracles.

5. THE CHARACTERISTICS OF EVOCATION

Essentially evocation is the summoning of the past, the objectivation of a desire, the exterior projection of phenomena
occurring in the individual, the need of the individual ego to
connect itself with its past and with the memories of the
events of that past. The memories of the past anticipate the
future. Evocation runs an infinite gamut, from the magic and
ceremonial calling forth of demons and dead to the modern
summoning of the figures and occurrences of the past history
of individuals or of races. Infinitely diverse in their gradations
are the states of mind which accompany or precede this evocation and which, for a moment, may superimpose on present
concepts and figures the living image of the past. Evocation
builds a bridge, creates a balance, even though temporary, in
the eternal antithesis between the conscious and the unconscious, and to this end words and music, the magic evocators
and sovereign spellbinders, serve a definite purpose.

The wizard or spellbinder evokes the past in order to draw
from it the forecast or promise of the future; he evokes the
memory of the wrongs and sorrows suffered, of the threats
made against the individual or the group, and emphasizes or
exaggerates them to demonstrate the need for defence or aggression. Antisocial magic evocation, inspired by frustration

and leading to aggression, with suggestions of revenge or reprisal in order to create a new political and economic domination, is analogous to present totalitarian propaganda, with its recalling of the German Empire, the conquests of Rome, the Jewish menace, the Bolshevik fury and so forth. Evocation of the past is a recalling of the memories and fears of the primitive unconscious in antithesis to critical reasoning.

IV

Divination

I. DIVINATION AMONG PRIMITIVE PEOPLES

DIVINATION plays an outstanding part in primitive societies. The same features survive in groups living in regions inaccessible to civilization, under conditions analogous to those of the European peoples of the Quaternary epoch.

The desire for knowledge of the occult originates, we may say, from man's perception of the insufficiency of his forces and senses and from his conviction that solely by increase of knowledge can he obtain life's necessities or assure and increase his well-being. Divination, therefore, is one form of the objectivation of the desire to live and to know.

The divination of the immediate and predetermined future, of the unknown present, and knowledge of the vanished past developed in primitive man simultaneously with the needs of his life and environment. The first necessary foreknowledge was that of the weather, of conditions favourable or unfavourable to hunting, of the outcome of battles, of the time required for healing a wound or recovering from an illness, of the discovery of the individual guilty of a theft or a murder, or of other facts harmful or dangerous to individual or group.

It is clear that divination postulates the possession of a conscious or unconscious memory of the past, of special knowledge, founded on long experience and on a keen faculty of critical observation. The most intelligent member of the group, he who had most attentively and frequently observed the phenomena which precede rain, the habits of animals, the behaviour of offenders, or the outcome of illnesses, acquired a superior position to others, who undoubtedly attributed to him supernatural powers, just as today the layman confronted with a judgment, an affirmation, or a forecast which he is certain will come true, but of which he is incapable of reconstructing the process and the causal nexus with visible facts, attributes its origin to supernatural powers. The knowledge of divination of the future may therefore be said to be partly intuition—that is, a result of the faculty of deducing from the observation of present facts their probable connection with future events. Originally the wizard, the "medicine-man," was nothing but an expert, the most intelligent member of the group, who, because of his gifts of observation, asserted his superiority and became the counsellor and most important member of the tribe. Likewise the man strongest in battle, the most agile in the hunt, the one who best endured inclement weather, became the leader of the primitive group. This plays a role in the origin of the idea of "totem," according to which the power of a group is embodied in an animal that is believed to be endowed with superior strength, agility, or cleverness and to which mysterious qualities are attributed.

Medical divination was an essential part of early medicine. The medicine-man had, above all, to perceive the secret cause of an illness, and in fact in all the extant documents of early magic medicine, which doubtless represent the primitive tradition, the first action of the wizard consisted in divining the cause of illness: "When you see such-and-such an illness," it is stated at the beginning of all the medical texts of ancient Egypt, "you shall say: such-and-such demon, or such worm, or such parasite causes the illness, and you will then proceed in the following manner. . . ." Diagnosis and prognosis are a part of magic divination; therapy is based, as we shall see in the chapter on magic medicine, chiefly on empiricism. Later, medicine developed from the germs of observation contained in this form of divination. It was thus from the divination of fate that the systematic observation of the stars developed.

We are led to admit the possibility that men living in a primitive group possess powers denoting an acute sensibility or a susceptibility to sensations which escape our senses. We may suppose that, just as primitive man's sight was keener, his olfactory senses more highly receptive, and his hearing infinitely more developed, owing to the great need for these qualities in the daily struggle for life, primitive man was also endowed with a sensibility that to us appears as inexplicable as the sense of orientation of birds or of police dogs. This sensibility may be lost or may manifest itself only in certain individuals living under peculiar psychic conditions, or under circumstances which may cause the reappearance of that sensibility.[1]

To deny the existence of divination, within the limits I have outlined, to refuse to admit that it is possible, and to classify all these facts as frauds or suggestions is certainly an easy way out of a complex problem. But from the scientific, strictly objective point of view, this classification is as inacceptable as the explanation that those facts are due to the intervention of supernatural forces. On the other hand, if we start from the idea (which seems undebatable to me) that all human conceptions have a basis in reality and are made either by intuition or by correct or erroneous conclusions based on the experience of actual facts, we must admit that divination—that is, the knowledge of matters hidden in the future—being as old as human reasoning, must have some basis of truth. The fact is that this notion has persisted unchanged for thousands of years and has been accepted by the most authoritative scholars and observers of all times.

2. SIGNS AND PRESAGES

The methods of divination are many, and vary according to the times and the environment in which they are born. The inefficacy of certain of these methods appears at first sight to the unbiased observer: almost all of them seem to have no effect in so far as the success attributed to them is concerned.

But let us not forget that if, as I have stated, the most important part of divination consists in casting a spell—that is, in the creation of a special state in which certain mental faculties may act—all these means represent stimuli which excite those faculties. It is not, therefore, very important to know what these stimuli were, but it is sufficient to keep in mind that by concentrating attention on a certain fact or object, all

[1] Freud has called the attention of his readers to this subject in his *Neue Vorlesungen*. He thinks that these dispositions may be considered as a rudimentary remainder of a sense that was highly developed in former times and appears as a so-called "subhuman" residual in the man of today.

the psychic faculties of an individual are focused in a single direction, as well as those of his audience, which, in its turn, exercises an action of collective suggestion upon the subject. Those stimuli may become the agents of suggestion in the same way in which bright metal foil, a shining piece of glass, a picture, or rhythmic music may provoke hypnotic or hypnoidal states of mind or other phenomena of a similar character.

Presages are closely connected with divination. These are premonitory signs by which it is allegedly possible to foresee the favourable or unfavourable results of an action about to be undertaken or of an imminent event. Meteorological phenomena, the flight of birds, the presence of certain animals, and numerous other facts are held to be favourable or untoward presages. In the beginning, it is evident, phenomena occurring in purely fortuitous association were interpreted as a sequence of cause and effect. The abstract idea of accident or chance did not exist. There is also a kind of divination which Renan called "collective," the divination of a great danger, for instance, the mass impulse that sometimes led to great emigrations. It is hard to discover their direct causes. In some cases, such as occurred in India, where whole cities, like ancient Delhi, were suddenly abandoned, we know that this was due to the suggestion of magic dangers supposed to be inherent in the places themselves, in presages or possibly in meteorologic factors.

The interpretation of presages, as a part of magic, was considered in ancient civilizations to be a sacerdotal function; that is, it was viewed as the interpretation of the will of the gods. The soothsayer who explained the presages, who interpreted the meaning of signs, like Chalcas, was greatly honoured and his function was considered the highest of all. Soothsayers, augurs, priests, and all who endeavoured to divine fate or to predict the future from the portents have in every epoch greatly relied for support on the psychic manifestations of the unconscious, and particularly on dreams, the interpretation of which has always been considered a basic fact of the divinatory art.

The variety of presages that in every epoch were believed

to exist is easily accounted for when we realize that the coincidence or concomitance of facts of every kind was reputed a manifestation of a superior will and a definite sign by which such a will was disclosed to the living. Astrology originated as a search for what were supposed to be direct influences exercised by the stars over the events of life; it was founded on the assumption that there exists a reciprocal connection between meteorological phenomena and the facts of life and death which they dominate, as well as on the conviction that, in the unchangeable order which early man held to be supreme law, the movements of sun and stars represented the fundamental rhythm and necessarily had repercussions on the life of individuals and groups. Divination became a social factor of tremendous importance, and the guidance of all decisive events concerning the group was entrusted to it. Drawings recently discovered in the prehistoric caves of the Dordogne represent scenes of divination and magic practices, consisting particularly in rhythmic dances around the totemic animal. Analogous scenes appear in the majority of the primitive drawings still extant.

Hunting among primitive peoples was an affair of state, because, from the economic viewpoint, it was the most important if not the only active occupation of the group. It was therefore necessary to concentrate attention upon it, to perfect the technical devices, to develop human senses to the full in order to be forewarned of any sudden attack by ferocious animals. No less important was the divination of the outcome of wars or of battles of conquest, and I shall call this prophecy, to which primitive groups assigned the greatest importance, official divination. The most powerful agents of supernatural forces, reigning over the widest domain, were called upon in this official divination: primarily the sun, then the stars, celestial phenomena, animals of great size, tall trees, mountains, and rivers.

The facts of individual existence were dominated by particular forces which later came to be considered demons, protectors, and so forth. Individual divination was entrusted to soothsayers, who often conflicted, just as individual interests often conflict with collective ones. The official caste of State augurs, having become powerful in the ancient Mediterranean civilizations, began a fiery persecution of those who had engaged in individual divination, and who were forbidden or barely tolerated by the earliest religions. Official magic is often violently averse to antisocial magic.

The belief in divination for the benefit of the individual exists uninterruptedly, however, through the centuries. The foretelling of good or evil, the validity of premonitory signs, the significance of dreams in the life of the individual, kept all their importance in the collective unconscious, perhaps because they derive from more easily ascertained and objectively true facts. Many things that were considered as presages were nothing but symptoms, correctly or falsely interpreted. Thus, for example, the importance of a presage attributed in all times to a sneeze undoubtedly is due to the observation that a sneeze is sometimes the beginning of an illness. The epileptic aura was considered to be a presage, just as the appearance of mice in houses was believed to be a forewarning of pestilence, while in reality the vermin already struck by the disease emerge from their refuges and become visible. Numberless like examples might be named. We may add the real forebodings that are frequently to be observed, especially in persons with deeply depressed nervous systems, which reflect perhaps only a physical state that cannot be controlled by the means at our command; reflecting, that is, the indications of an organic disturbance which is barely commencing.

It is needless to show that certain facts which cannot be easily ascertained may cause sensations of well-being or distress which are interpreted as presentiments. It is sufficient to mention the feeling of inexplicable and profound uneasiness that is aroused by contact with certain persons, a feeling for which one tries in vain to account, and which very often is proved correct by succeeding events. It is well known that a feeling of joy, of well-being, pervades one's soul in the presence of a person who is considered to be a friend or favourably disposed to one, or who seems to emanate an atmosphere acting on one's sensibilities. I may likewise mention the feelings stirred by the belief in the evil eye or in the power inherent in persons whose physique is often different from that of others, and who are believed to exert a maleficent influence over those near them.

If we trust the explanation given by psychoanalysis of dreams in which repressed sensations or occult desires are manifested, we can account in the same way for certain phenomena, like premonitory dreams, in which suppressed wishes or concealed fright appear.

3. HOMO DIVINANS

It is not the purpose of this book to expound all the hypotheses put forth to explain the origin of divinatory facts. Recently many accurate studies have been devoted to them, particularly by the Society of Psychical Research, of London, which has collected extremely valuable material, not perfectly arranged and evaluated as yet. A new terminology has been frequently created for dealing with these hypotheses: Driesch, who in 1933 published a work on this subject, partly accepting several of the most discussed data, called the study of occult facts "parapsychology," and brought up the problem of whether there existed original phenomena in the field of divination (*Urphänomene* in the sense of Goethe). But hypotheses and designations do not bring near the solution of the problem, whose basic facts and historical development we have felt it important to summarize.

Divination, like magic, of which it is an essential aspect, appears in all times and is tied up with the origins of society. Divination, stimulated by the desire for defence, by terror, by hope, is closely bound with the special sensibilities of certain individuals, who generally possess hypnoidal or somnambulistic dispositions; such sensibilities may be sharpened by an incantational state which, in its turn, may be caused by numberless influences acting on the nervous system. Divination stems from the necessities imposed on man by the struggle for life; from the desire to live, from the instinctive fear of death, from the need to know the future in order to regulate one's life and actions, to avoid misfortune and death. Divination chooses the means it requires, it draws and develops them from all things and beings of the cosmos. Individual and social factors are of essential importance and vary in accordance with

conditions of environment, period, and the individuals forming the world in which it exists.

Consequently the same phenomena occur in societies that
are going through a period of stress, as well as in persons suffering or convalescing from serious illnesses. They feel the
necessity of being reassured as to the future and protected
from danger. In postwar European societies, just as in those
of the Middle Ages around the year 1000, when the end of the
world was thought imminent, astrologers and palmists, prophets of every kind, increased in number and were sought and
listened to even by intelligent and sane persons. Great renown
accrued to those who predicted the future or promised healing and well-being, particularly when these forecasts were
presented in the most fantastic and bizarre forms.

V

The Personality of the Magician

I. THE FUNCTIONS OF THE MAGICIAN

WITH the formation of socially organized groups, the practice of magic grew vaster as needs, desires, and the contingencies in which it must be used increased. The emergence of increasingly vast possibilities for its application, owing to the growth of the groups and their closer interrelationships, stressed the need of regulating such practices, of establishing a hierarchy of adverse and favourable forces, and of codifying these complicated practices for preservation in the group.

The personality of signally powerful magicians or spellbinders became clearly differentiated from that of the other members of the group, so that, although in early times every individual could be a healer and carry on the practices inherent in magic medicine, with progress in knowledge, the clearer discrimination between maladies, the recognition that certain persons possessed a higher degree of qualities and knowledge than others, the number of magic healers decreased, and little by little a selective criterion was established. Just as the strongest warrior became the tribe-leader and the ablest hunter directed the hunt, the individual who knew most about stars, the virtues of plants, and the poisons of animals, who was able to help sufferers and cure illnesses and hold off death, assumed a special position in the group. Probably this position was awarded to him because of qualities different from or superior to those of others; and/or because of easily recognized physical characteristics, such as hair of a colour rare in the group, an exceptionally strong physique, or some deformity. Such qualities might be joined with or replaced by powers connected with some psychic gift because of which he was believed to have contacts with invisible forces and to dominate them. The group-member who had hallucinations, dreams, and visions and possessed the principal features of the *homo divinans* (that is, the knowledge of facts of the distant past and the future, ability to guess the meaning of presages, a suggestive power such as to induce special moods in other members of the group or to allay these moods when they were induced by other agents, a definite strength of will, and the conviction of success) focalized upon himself the faith of his companions.

The magician is created by his environment—that is, by collective suggestion, when the feeling of dependence is very strong and the guidance of an energetic and expert individual is necessary. He must at the same time act as a father-double and transmit the thought and the will of the ancestors, express the traditions of the group, and establish contact with the supernatural forces. In certain primitive tribes—as numerous examples in the islands of Polynesia and in certain regions of Africa attest—the magician was chosen and compelled by threats to accept his post and perform its functions. Many times, especially in most ancient epochs, a vast suggestion undoubtedly took place, deriving from atmospheric changes, economic conditions, or external factors of some other kind, without the presence of an intermediary acting for the whole group being perceived. But in this case the suggestion was disjoined, fragmentary, casual, and temporary. With the creation of the figure of the magician, suggestion objectivized the essential fact, discovered its ruler, and thus unfolded simultaneously from group to leader and from leader to group. As environmental conditions varied, the personality of the leader, the things suggested by him, the collective action he unloosed, were directed toward mystic, heroic, or destructive deeds. Such is the origin of mysteries, of the great heroic or economic enterprises having a heroic cast, like the Crusades or similar tragic adventures. The magician's voice is in reality nothing but the echo of the voice of the hopes and the desires of the crowd. This parallels a well-known biological phenomenon in which the results of the physiological activities of an organ become in their turn stimuli for new activities, no matter whether ordered or disordered, normal or pathological.

In primitive societies the magician directed the sexual life of the individual and the group and presided over all practices accompanying all of its manifestations, particularly fecundation, birth, and the upsurge of virility, which was considered the decisive moment in the life of the individual. He taught and practised propitiatory and initiatory acts, led magic dances and rhythmic songs. Masked, surrounded by the theatrical trappings that answered the psychological needs of a suffering or longing individual, he was the leader of the masked bands that played such an important role in all the manifestations of the group. He foresaw and presaged the future of the new-born by interpreting the positions of the stars, the flight of the birds, and many other facts concomitant with birth. He knew how to conjure away malevolent forces, how to evoke and placate the shades of the dead.

Animated by the need, the desire, and the will to exercise his power, the magician brought supernatural forces and the group into contact. From these supernatural forces, with which he was in constant contact in dreams, hallucinations, visions, and the like, he received messages and injunctions, and he transmitted commands or communicated desires to them. He taught men, with whose desires and needs he was familiar, how to submit to the influences of these forces or to overcome them. There was in the magician a certain special quality, a particular technique, which helped him to retain his position in the group. The wizard might in reality be an able physician, knowing, by long experience or acute observation or intuition, methods by which to alleviate the suffering of the sick; he might be endowed with musical talent so as to be able to produce rhythmical sounds or play music inducing the desired state of mind in an individual; or he might have known how to reproduce forms and figures with outstanding skill. He undoubtedly knew how to avail himself of the means at his disposal in order to arouse admiration, fear, and faith; he was an adept at choosing the colours of the feathers with which he was bedecked or the most suitable mask or suggestive perfume. But the main, the essential quality of the magician, in all his functions and practices, was obviously the gift of knowing how to provoke, in himself and others, the peculiar state of mind essential to magic, the "spell" of the magician, who concentrated and sharpened his will in the certainty of achieving the intended result. The charms that he cast over his subjects might be effected by various means, many of which we know and even today use in order to produce analogous states, dreamy, hypnotic, somnambulic, or hallucinatory, or, to put it more simply, states of decreased criticism and clouded awareness. Many other means, some of which were successfully practised in other times, have been forgotten or have lost their efficacy. Music and rhythm, arousing emotional reactions, perfumes, poisonous substances, the monotonous repetition of formulas, the laying on of hands, staring at bright or luminous points, and, finally, verbal suggestion were, not to speak of many others, methods by which the magic state of mind was brought about.

These methods, applied in various forms and degrees, constituted magic practices and rites. They placed the subject in a condition of readiness to submit to magic practices on the one hand, and on the other they gave to the magician the assured conviction of being endowed with superior powers, inasmuch as he was able to arouse moods that rendered the individual passively amenable to his domination and to the forces issuing from him.[1]

2. FAITH AND SUGGESTION

Enchantment may be either individual or, as is more often the case, collective. In the first case, when it is exercised on an individual, it reflects, first of all, on the magician. In the case of collective bewitchment, it manifests itself above all with a repercussion and one might almost say a contagion of enchantment in all the participants, through the effect of reciprocal and collective suggestion, which in its turn is reflected

[1] The question why the magician is generally a man is an interesting one. The person most expert in the creation of a spell is the mother, the nurse. The one who knows the most about poisons or intoxication is the cook, the midwife. The history of magic abounds with women who were devoted to magic arts (from the Witch of Endor to the witches of the Middle Ages and of recent times). Nevertheless the magician is almost always a man. It is likely that the quality of the leader, who is able to exercise a suggestion, is required for the magician, and that this quality is rarely to be found in women. The magician is, in the common conception, the person who combines the qualities necessary to the practice of witchcraft and of suggestion.

on the magician. This does not exclude the fact that, as happens with magicians of all countries and all times, their tricks are employed (tricks that are often necessary to the effect and are sometimes practised even in the most modern medical suggestion) to increase their power and success.

But faith is indispensable; only the certainty of accomplishing the desired result, deriving from the absence of criticism, can determine great success. Men with a critical and developed spirit are never true magicians. The magician who is not sure of himself can only exercise his will fleetingly or with the aid of violence. Only confidence in the success deriving from his own personal power, or from the supernatural factors to which he attributes his power, can exercise the spell that compels crowds. In the group that is subjected to the suggestion of the personality and action of the magician, reciprocal suggestion occurs through contagion and prepares the ground for the common and confident expectation of the miracle, one of the most important factors in the preparation of the individual or collective state of mind. The individual or the collectivity, imbued with faith and will, solely animated by desire for the success of the awaited magic action, is divested, from the beginning, of all critical faculty and rational action that might impede suggestion or render it difficult. Any occurrence, no matter how simple or insignificant, is interpreted according to promise and expectation, and the impression it creates is proportionate to the organization, preparation, and numerical size of the group. These facts have been studied and are well known so far as certain regularly recurring crowd-phenomena and suggestions of every kind are concerned.

Some fundamental maxims of the modern totalitarian states were closely connected with this idea. The absolute rule and the infallibility of the Leader were at the basis of such slogans as "Obey without question," "The Duce is always right"; this, in a hundred variations, was the supreme law printed, carved, painted in a thousand forms in books, on houses, in streets and squares: the dogma imposed on all. Blind faith is the necessary premise of blind obedience.

A state of collective mass-suggestion exercises, in its turn, an action over the mood of the magician and increases his power, just as the applause of a crowd and other signs of approval exercise a dynamic influence over actor, author, and artist.

Numberless miracles related by history can be explained by this constant reciprocal action between subject and object. All the facts of mass healing, for instance, which otherwise would be hard to account for, beginning with the cures effected while the patient was asleep in the temples of Æsculapius, the healing of scrofula by the royal touch, and the collective neuropsychic epidemics that have occurred in all times, and particularly during the Middle Ages (St. Vitus's dance, tarantulism, etc.). The basis of these facts, as in all magic action, consists of isolated or consecutive phenomena which have a real foundation and may be demonstrated by experience. In mass healing single cases, in the beginning, were actually cured by the proper medicine, or phenomena of nervous illness were overcome by suggestive action; such examples aroused faith in the wonder healer and confidence in his ability and in his miraculous therapeutic power. Countless examples in ancient and modern history may be cited of collective suggestion. Single facts occurring after hallucinations, or coinciding with symptoms exhibited by persons suffering from a disease or poison, aroused group-fear, uneasiness, a tendency to exaggerate light or insignificant facts.

Examples of magic medicine are better suited to this study because it is easier to check the facts. The medicine-man who, in a series of cases, by extracting a weapon from a wound stopped the hæmorrhage, or by expelling a worm from the body of a sick person or bleeding him put an end to his suffering, created the belief that all hæmorrhages were caused by a weapon or by the presence in the body of some extraneous object, either visible or invisible, that all illnesses were due to a living being which must be driven away, and that all suffering connected with inflammations could be healed by letting blood. There are countless instances of cases of hysterics being cured by a touch, and a great many medicines owe their fame to their effecting the same cure. Wonderful recoveries obtained by removing stones from the brain, a fantastic operation of which numberless descriptions and graphic figurations exist, may be quoted as an example.

Once the possibility—nay, the certainty—is, by analogical reasoning, admitted that suggestive action may contribute to success even in cases of illnesses unlike those in which the first favourable results were observed, nothing appears impossible to the believer in magic action. *"Carmina vel cœlo possunt deducere lunam"* ("Magic verses are even able to draw the moon from heaven"), sings Virgil. In reality the magic circle is a closed circle, like that of an electric current between its two poles, and within these poles countless possibilities and probabilities of circling ways exist.

3. SECRET POWER

The magician is the bearer and not only the actor in the practice of magic. Belief in his success is indispensable to him; failures are never attributed to him and his art, but to the trick of an antagonistic magician or to the presence of sinners in the crowd. His art itself, the multiplicity and contrast of desires and wills, expose him to the dangers deriving from the competition of other individuals possessing equal or greater powers, and capable of exercising suggestion over individuals and groups, and of exploiting his knowledge for their own profit. This fact, which imposes the necessity of safeguarding the magician's power, inevitably dictates the setting up of a clear differentiation between him and the group, so that his superiority may be guaranteed by making him materially and externally unlike the other group-members. A solemn bearing, perfumes, clothes, masks, showy ornaments, such as coloured stones or many-hued feathers, the accompaniment of music, house decorations of human bones or those of sacred animals—everything, in short, that is rare or difficult to obtain is proof of the superiority and power of the wizard and an efficacious factor in his prowess. Rhythm in all its forms, music, dance, song, repetitions of monotonous formulas, whose meaning is incomprehensible to the common people, complete or rather are a preparation for concentration, attention, ecstasy, or frenzy, according to the sequence of the rhythms. A magician who is poor, weak, modest, and simple in his words and unskilled in the use of music and colour is inconceivable, because he would be divested of all power and would prove manifestly inferior unless this condition had such an unusually exceptional character as to appear as a voluntary renunciation, an expression of strength and will, and unless it possessed a suggestive strength—that is, unless his parsimony in words became almost muteness, and his parsimony in food, fasting. Such elements in their turn may exercise at certain moments an equal or even more violent suggestion on individuals and crowds. This occurs whenever individuals and crowds feel the need to react against too violent manifestations of power or whenever, for other reasons, they are persuaded to accept this source of suggestion, particularly frequent among some Oriental peoples, whose imagination is more stirred by motives closely connected with ancestral ideas and with their conditions of existence. The example of Gandhi clearly demonstrates this fact.

The yearning for annihilation or the renouncement of material goods is an expression of what we may call the spell of death. The sacrifice of worldly pleasures, the rules of chastity, of fasting, of abstention from food and drink, are means of purification. The withdrawal from all earthly relations and a detachment from the passions of the group play an important role in the training of the magician. This appears logical, since communication with the dead, on which a large part of his power is based, requires a detachment from the living and an assumption, as far as possible, of those forms of renunciation which belong to the dead. Among many primitive peoples the magician must abstain from eating meat, because all contact with the bodies of animals is held to be impure. This material purification bears, in some respects, a close and interesting analogy to that ideal purification of the spirit which in more civilized epochs leads, through religious ideas, to ecstasy. In some primeval religions, when magic was being superseded by rising religion, purification included, required, and sometimes commingled both forms. An interesting study by Goldberg on the magic conception in the Bible, in which he demonstrates the identity of magic and religious sin, sheds light on this point.

The instruction of the attendants and the arrangement of the place, the choice of the victims designated for sacrifice, the complicated ritual, contribute to this real and symbolic purification which is so highly important.

All this determines the magician's detachment from and superiority to the members of the group and the necessity for jealously guarding the secret, because the action of the magician, which often has individual and antisocial aims (the magician being not only the healer and saver of life, but also the giver of death and of illness), must be carried on in darkness. Magic aims to satisfy the passions of the individual resorting to its intervention: unfettered by moral laws, which are non-existent in primitive groups, no action within the limits of taboo appears impossible or forbidden. This necessitates the constitution of a caste which is slowly formed through the transmission of the secrets of formulas and rites, with a series of initiatory procedures devised to arouse faith and terror. Through these initiatory procedures the man destined to become a member of the caste is accepted. The caste becomes the possessor of mysterious insurmountable power, through rites often sanguinary, through customs in which blood, sexual practices, fire, and destruction play an important part, since they constitute the real elements and the symbolic foundations of desire: life and the continuation of life, death and destruction.

Since earliest times blood has been the centre of the vital magic conception; the blood-sacrifice of animals, stemming from primeval human sacrifice (cannibalism, originally, being a magic practice and essentially having as its aim the incorporation of the powers of the enemy whose flesh was devoured, a fact that is proved by the widespread custom of eating the enemy's heart), assumed later the form of sacrifices, such as circumcision, endowed with a special initiatory character, and still later passed into purely symbolic acts. Sexual facts, the centre of the life of the unconscious, are emblematically expressed in a thousand forms, from ceremonies practised at the time of puberty to circumcision, a rite that is a part of collective initiation, as we know from the practices of Egyptian priesthood, and is to be found in the ceremonies of primitive African tribes.

4. THE FIGURE OF THE MAGICIAN

The caste of the spellbinding magicians, to which in remote epochs the medicine-man necessarily and naturally belonged, organized and codified its practices with the passing of time. Formulas and rites were surrounded with mystery. A special taboo with its complex prohibitions and performances guaranteed the infallibility of the caste. Thus the inaccessibility of the magicians and the inviolability of the objects belonging to the magic cult were established, and under this protection there occurred the transformation of many practices into symbols that, we may say, constitute a condensation, a conventional substitution, like that of a seal or a cipher for a name.

Magic, like all systems, eventually lost all possibilities of further development through the establishment of rigid and immutable formulas, since established formulas, known to and demanded by the group, limited and circumscribed the action of the magician. The individual and suggestive power were transferred from the personality of the magician to practices, formulas, signs, talismans, and amulets; later these themselves were believed able to perform acts of sorcery, just as the action of the legislator was transferred to the word of the law itself, and the spirit yielded to the power of the letter: *quod non est in actis, non est in mundo* (what is not in a record is non-existent). But the power of direct suggestion remained for all times connected chiefly with the personality of the magician.

With the constitution of a caste bound by rites, with the codification of practices, with increase in power, the magic healer became the chief of the group, but at the same time and for the same reasons this was the first step in the decay of what we may call official magic. This decay derived primarily from granting too much political power to the magician, thereby compromising the position of the war leaders or making it difficult. Magic's decay was also due, partly, to the development of criticism through increase of knowledge, through broadening of relations between various groups, and through reactions against the organized system, finally and mainly to the appearance of religious systems. When faith in invocation and in prayer to a powerful and remote deity prevailed over the invocations and spells forbidden by the laws of religion, the power of the caste declined. Only among peoples isolated from social contact, in whom, for various reasons, the development of the critical and intellectual powers had been arrested, did the magician remain the awarder of good and evil, of sunshine and rain, and the only healer.

The figure of the medicine-man, the sorcerer of primitive tribes, changes with and adjusts itself to the times. He becomes a black magician when monotheistic religious principles arise and dominate, or he reappears in the figure of the group-leader, the great spellbinder inciting the crowd to enthusiasm and passion, to foolish hopes and desperate actions. Throughout history the type of man who leads the masses, holding them in his power, suppressing criticism, and ignoring or abolishing social laws, remains identical; his program is the creation and stabilization of a force superior to law and religion: superman, super-state, super-race; a program that in most cases is doomed to failure because it is founded on imaginary premises antagonistic to reality. The fate to which he drives the masses is then necessarily tragic.

In its essential characteristics the personality of the magician and spellbinder persists throughout the centuries and in all peoples, as does the desire for improvement, the hope for miracles, the will to defeat adverse forces, the challenge and fear of the unknown, which cannot be entirely eradicated or legislated away. Keyserling remarks that there is no man in the world who at some time in his life does not desire to be a magician. The magician is the intermediary between the group and the invisible benevolent or hostile forces of the supernatural world. Surrounded with mystery, he is the master of all means that can determine a special state of mind in himself and in others. Dark in his words and prophecies, awesome in his aspect and actions, he appears as the mouthpiece of an inaccessible and remote world. His is an atmosphere of the supernatural, of evocations of ancestral ideas, traditions, and legends. His power is based on the establishment of the law of his inviolability and on faith in his infallibility.

History shows that no magician can afford to be fallible, and his power ceases at the moment when another magician proves himself his superior. Magicians were killed, as Frazer recounts, as were kings in ancient days, by people wishing to inherit their names and power; in sorcery as in war victory goes to the strongest. Hence no error can ever be confessed and recognized by the sorcerer, everything which has been said and done by him must at any cost be supported and defended. Every failure must be explained by errors committed by others or by a false interpretation of the orders received. Human and honest confession of mistakes, which is the foundation of developed monotheistic religions, and the principle of rational behaviour, inasmuch as they recognize and admit the inferiority and the errors of the individual or of the group, cannot be accepted by the magician and his initiates, since it would signify his end and the crumbling of his system. Many examples prove the truth of this fact; it is sufficient to quote the Biblical account of the meeting between the magicians of Pharaoh and Moses: though the former were capable of performing simple miracles (*ot*), they could not perform extraordinary miracles involving the group (*mophet*). This is an example of the yielding of inferior to more powerful magicians.

Thus throughout the centuries the figure of the magician took on distinctive lineaments, with varying names, functions, and prestige, and has persisted down to our times. He is needed for his power of casting spells; he is capable of judiciously employing all possible methods to obtain success. Always surrounded by the faith of the weak, he is the sure and convinced asserter of his own infallibility. A constructor according to Kant, a superman in the meaning attributed to the word by Nietzsche, he possesses and is aware that he possesses, and intends to use, the powers necessary to guide the herd.

Here, therefore, is the matrix of the belief in the super-race, of the doctrine of violence of Sorel and Pareto, the dogma of the superman builder who, before creating a new world-order, can destroy the present and eliminate all his opponents who, in his mind, are his irreconcilable enemies because they are free thinkers, independent critics, whereas his power must necessarily be limitless and destroy both individuality and criticism.

VI

Magic Tools—Amulets, Talismans, Fetishes

I. MAGIC PLANTS

AS we saw in our study of the action of magician and environment, in a certain number of cases magic is carried out directly with the aid of formulas, gestures, words, or complicated rites. In other cases such action is exercised through magic implements—that is, by beings or substances that are endowed with magic power and that may thus have great importance in the action itself. There are two categories of implements. The first includes those which on account of some essential characteristics of efficiency produce the desired action; among these, for example, are medicinal herbs, poisons, and so forth. The second category embraces innumerable substances that in themselves cannot exercise, objectively speaking, any appreciable action, either favourable or unfavourable, but whose power derives, exclusively or mainly, from the images to which they give rise in the mind of the actors. Many of these factors belong in both categories, inasmuch as by their origin and owing to a century-old experience they are, or may be, effective under particular conditions while in others their value needs to be intensified by suggestion and faith.

According to the mind of the primitives, factors giving material and instant protection, such as that afforded by a dog against thieves, the roof of a cabin against rain, noises or fire keeping animals at a distance, are also magical. Every occurrence of life is enclosed in the magic circle, and the use of magic is considered necessary for both protection and attack. Since, as I have said, in the primitive mind there is no rigid separation between the natural and the supernatural, the normal and the miraculous, the possible and the impossible, every act is determined, in preparation and in expectation, by necessity and desire alone.

Considering the conditions of life of primitive peoples, it is natural that the first and most important among magic factors should be those employed to combat or prevent sickness and death. Since sickness and death are conceived as magical because they imply the work of invisible or visible forces, magic action is viewed as necessary for protection. There are numberless remedies taken from the vegetable kingdom, some of which possess real therapeutic power, such as the roots of plants like garlic, cyclamen, squill, etc.; medicinal plants like rue, wormwood, mugwort, ferns, hyssop, the castor-oil plant, and verbena, to name only the most popular; flowers like peonies, asters, roses, carnations, ranunculus, and iris; seeds such as those of the thistle and the mistletoe, wood and bark like the aloe and the yew, resins like benzoin, camphor, myrrh, mastic, sweet-gum, and incense.

A great interest is attached to the history of magic plants, which may be traced down to our time uninterruptedly, because of the fact that almost all plants to which magic virtues were attributed by primitive peoples enjoy the same popularity even today. Sometimes, as I said, this popularity derives from real therapeutic powers, as, for example, in the use of cinchona bark and roots, which was sanctioned by scientific medicine; their power to cure intermittent fevers was well known in pre-Columbian America. In many other cases, trust in the powers of plants is dependent on their forms, or appearance or the resemblance between their roots, leaves, or fruit and certain aspects of diseases or organs of the human body. Ranunculus was considered excellent for curing diseases of the kidneys because of the yellow colour of its flowers, and many similar examples might be cited. This theory, which was called the theory of "signatures" because, according to it, plants reveal in their appearance signs of their curative powers, was particularly championed by Paracelsus.

The garment of magic in other cases is nothing but the official evidence, exaggerated and surrounded by a halo of mystery by the magician, of those essential qualities which empirical medicine has recognized as a result of long experience. It is no source of amazement to the expert physician that the evidence with which the medicament is presented to the trusting public tends to extol its efficacy and to amplify some aspects of it.

Let us consider the most famous magic plant, the mandrake. Almost all the extant books of prescriptions of antiquity and mediæval times praise the powers of its fruit, its leaves, and its roots, variously prepared for use as a sedative and a powerful soporific. The mandrake was more highly prized than any other remedy until the end of the Middle Ages. It was also famous an an aphrodisiac, as a narcotic, and for facilitating pregnancy. All the literature of thirty centuries, from the Persian legends down to Shakespeare, from the Bible to Machiavelli, testify to its fame. Because of the curative powers attributed to the mandrake, which appear justified to a certain degree by the most recent chemical research, showing that it contains sedative and stupefying substances analogous to hyosciamine, there was formed a legend and a magic ritual for picking the plant and digging up its roots. There are numerous accounts of searches for this plant by night, in cemeteries or under gibbets, because mandrake growing under a hanged body is particularly potent. The roots were described as representing male or female bodies, through analogy with their aphrodisiac faculties; and hence the plant became an amulet, a talisman, and was placed on the shields of warriors or wrapped around the necks of babies. This is a classic example of the building of a complicated symbolic structure, stemming from an experimental observation, which persists even today almost throughout the entire Orient.

In other cases the fame of the magic power of plants depends on completely different causes. Consider, for example, a plant which is famous for its magic powers and which even today in many houses, and especially in England, Germany, and France, is considered to possess particular apotropaic powers—that is, to avert danger or evils. Every year at Christmas or New Year millions of branches of mistletoe carry, besides good wishes, the hope that good luck will come to the house where they are hung. What is the origin of this fame, mentioned by Pliny in his narration of the worship of mistletoe by

the Gauls? And in the Nordic legends it was with a dart of
mistletoe that Balder, the mythical hero, was slain by an
enemy god. That fame is owing to the observation that mistletoe is a parasitic plant which grows on other plants and whose
roots do not touch the earth. Mistletoe was believed to exert
a magic protective action over large trees and therefore it was
held to be the symbol of supernatural force. It was believed
to exercise its magic powers against all forces that tend to
prostrate human beings, against epilepsy, abortions, and the
lightning that strikes the earth from the skies. Even today,
many thousands of years later, this faith in the magic power
of mistletoe persists everywhere, among the peasants of Brit-
tany who believe that mistletoe in a house protects it from
lightning, among the natives of Scotland who carry it on
trips as a talisman against bad luck, and finally in all the great
centres of Europe and America where mistletoe hung as an
amulet on a lamp or in a doorway is thought to protect the
house from all evil.

Tobacco, imported from America as a magic healing herb
(as it was used by the Indians), enjoyed three centuries of
renown throughout Europe as a universal and efficacious
remedy.

I have only given some examples, but there are hundreds
that might be mentioned to demonstrate the great tenacity
with which legends and superstitions persist, and the relations
that these magic ideas bear to observed and cleverly exaggerated reality, even though they cannot always be clearly
demonstrated.

2. ANIMAL AND MINERAL MAGIC REMEDIES

Almost all animals have made a contribution to magic therapy, in which, in every age, the horn of the deer, the bile of
the dog, the blood of the ass, the testicles of various animals,
the viper, the lizard, and numberless other magic remedies
have been important.

These remedies were applied in the most varied forms in
ancient magic medicine. Baths, fumigations, unguents, and
oils were used in several illnesses with the aim of defending
the sick person against witchcraft and of driving away the

cause of his illness. Powders, decoctions, aromatic waters, and different kinds of baths were given orally or applied externally, as well as compositions of every sort, in the belief that they were efficient measures against all infections.

Great power was attributed to water, and especially to the waters of rivers and seas; water in which glowing coals had been plunged was considered by ancient magic as the sovereign remedy against the evil eye. This belief in the power of water for protection and purification evidently gave rise to the Talmudic affirmation concerning the immunity of fish and their perfect health because of their living in water. From this idea stem the practice of the bathing of babies, the washing of corpses, according to the primitive concept that persists in Biblical prescriptions; the stern exhortation to throw away immediately the water in which a bath has been taken because it contains dangerous magic forces; and numberless other precepts. In the therapeutic formulas of ancient Assyria water played an important role and exorcisms often contained this formula: "Let your magic, your poison, your curse disappear with the water from my body and be wrenched from my hands with the water of purification." This conception of the magic bath removing curses, a conception naturally founded on actual truth, was preserved and enlarged in the most ancient civilizations. The water of the Jordan was believed to cure leprosy; in ancient India bathing in the Ganges or pouring water from that river over the infected parts of one's body was supposed to have the maximum efficiency. The washing of the Arabs before entering a mosque, like the purification of Egyptian priests, derives from the same origin. This concept is also to be found in ancient Celtic and Teutonic legends.

The magic power attributed to fire is no less important. From the conception of the protective power of fire and light, which keep away wild animals and exercise a beneficial action on the body, arises the idea of purification through fire, an idea fundamental among all primitive races and expressed in the burning torches prescribed in the ritual tables of ancient Babylon, and in Indian and Biblical, Persian and Spartan rites. Armies were preceded by fire-bearers; during childbirth or after death every magic practice was accompanied by the lighting of fires. In ancient Assyrian magic medicine the magician threw highly combustible objects into the fire pronouncing these words: "As these objects burn and disappear, let disease and impurities vanish from this man." The concept of attaining purification by passing through fire arises from this fundamental idea. With it, in later epochs, was connected the ancient Roman Dea Candelifera (the candle-bearing goddess), who protected childbirth by preventing evil spirits from drawing near the new-born child. The idea of purification prompted also the use of torches for weddings, festivities, funerals, and tombs.

The role attributed to the earth, considered both as goddess and as mother, from whom everything arises and to whom everything returns, is naturally outstanding. It was a frequent practice among primitive peoples to bury sick people in order to cure them, in the conviction that illnesses and their causes would remain in the soil and that the evil influence could not act through the earth.

A series of remedies, known since the earliest days, was taken from the mineral kingdom. First among these remedies are precious stones: topazes, beryls, emeralds, sapphires, and pearls. An important function is attributed to meteorites (masses fallen upon the earth from space); almost all metals, but primarily gold, silver, and iron, were reputed to have many and varied therapeutic powers.

Gold and silver are considered excellent remedies against evil influences, and this accounts for the custom of gilding the horns of victims destined for sacrifice, as well as for that of placing gold in the mouths of the dead, and for the usage of gold ornaments, rings, necklaces, crowns, masks, and so forth. Copper and bronze were held to possess exceptional magic power, but this power was considered inferior to that of iron. Iron is the material from which are forged weapons and tools, which is by itself an evidence of its protective power. Iron is believed to be a prophylactic and cure for all illnesses and dangers and is held to give protection to the individual against all malignant powers: the application of it is reputed particularly to be a cure for convulsions. Chains and rings of iron, horseshoes, knives, nails, and generally all objects made out of strong metal, whose possession represents for primitive man a powerful safeguard and precious wealth, were considered in the remotest epochs to protect the holder against the evil eye, and it is unnecessary to point out that this belief is strong and widespread to this day. A relic of this belief is the custom of touching iron, and later wood.

Subsequently other metals such as zinc, antimony, and mercury were reputed to have healing and magic powers.

3. AMULETS AND TALISMANS

I have mentioned the best-known magic implements resorted to in order to combat actual illness or to protect man from the threat of illness and death. No less noteworthy is the set of magic factors whose power derives from suggestion, which factors are entrusted with the task of protecting the individual and the collectivity from the evil eye and all other influences of malignant beings.

Amulets have undoubtedly existed since the beginning of history, and have preserved their fame through the centuries. At one time the word *amulet* indicated an object with a healing power. The etymology of the word was discussed at great length by the ancient Romans, who believed the term to have originated from the word *amoliri*—that is, to fend off (evil). Later it was believed to be a derivation of the Greek word *amma* (knot) or of *amula*, a word used in ancient times for the amber vases that were tied to the necks of children to ward off evil demons. Finally it was held to stem from the Arabic word *chamalet* or the Greek *amulon* (starch), which was believed to be an infallible remedy against poisons. The term *amulet* in common usage indicates an object possessing the magic and passive quality of protecting its wearer from evil forces. Words corresponding to *amulet* were the *bulla* of the ancient Romans, the *fascinum* (originally the phallus), to which was attributed an outstanding protective power, and the *filacteria* or apotropaic (fending off) objects of the Greeks.

We must distinguish between amulets and talismans. The word *talisman*, according to Seligmann, probably derives from the Greek *telesma* (de luxe object, a perfect thing) or from

the Arabic *tamina* (magic object), or perhaps is related to the
Indian *tali* (the gift made by a man to his wife at the marriage
ceremony), or to another apotropaic object, the Biblical
taleth or shawl in which people enfolded themselves for
prayer. The talisman exercises an active magic influence,
since it may bring fortune or success to whoever wears it.
Often the two concepts are confused and talismans are also
amulets, or vice versa. Both amulets and talismans are considered by primitive peoples as medicines, and in fact the medicine-man or shaman selects and distributes both.

The earliest amulets were formed out of parts of the body
and out of secretions of a person or an animal. Among certain
primitive peoples the father rubs his child with fatty substances taken from his own body; he ties around its neck the
claws or skins of animals and covers it with the hide of a bull,
hare, or tiger. Traces of these customs are still extant in the
protective power attributed to the teeth or feathers of certain
animals, elephant hide, and so forth.

Magic symbols drawn on the skin are held to have great importance, and this is the origin of the practice of tattooing,
which has become universal and has persisted throughout the
centuries with the same significance it has today. In early
periods organic substances of various kinds were inserted under the skin during the process of tattooing, and this caused
the pattern to stand out in relief. The prehistoric figures and
amulets of Cyprus reveal signs of tattooing, and in the worship
of Cybele the marks were engraved with red-hot needles.

The custom of tattooing starts in an early age in which
linear drawings or geometric designs predominated. The next
development shows tattooing representing strange and fantastic animals, obscene acts, symbolical figures such as birds
with wide wings which appear to be flying to the heart of the
person on whom they are tattooed, or serpents that wrap
themselves around the person's arms or legs, figures of women,
or names of beloved beings: evidently the figure is believed to
possess the same power as the object, the written word the
same virtue as the thing that it expresses.

All ornaments of the body derive from amulets and talismans. They are now signs of well-being and wealth, and in the

course of time have been transformed into ornaments whose magic significance has been forgotten, as in the case of necklaces, corals, pearls, rings, etc. The magic character attributed to amulets explains why in historical times they were not transmitted as heritages but were buried in tombs with the dead, as occurred with the marvellous jewels of the Egyptian kings or of Greek warriors, and in many other cases in more recent periods. The magic character of amulets likewise accounts for the quantity of ornaments worn by primitive peoples on all parts of their bodies—in their noses, lips, and ears, on necks, arms, and feet. This custom does not derive from any æsthetic consideration, but is intended to protect all parts of the body from threatened dangers.

Amulets must be worn next to the body, as their magic power arises from contact with the skin. According to this idea, which explains why figures drawn on the skin have greater and more immediate power, amulets and talismans form an indivisible nexus with the individual.

Mascots, animals or objects which are believed to bring luck and to protect against dangers and misfortune, and which had an enormous popularity during the last war, belong evidently to the category of amulets and talismans.

4. THE ACTION OF MAGIC FACTORS

In the beginning the power of the various amulets and talismans derived from some personal characteristic, as the result of a series of events that were believed to evince a causal nexus. An individual who noticed that he was favoured by fortune or struck by misfortune when wearing a certain garment, ornament, or object naturally tended to give credit or blame to this garment or object. This idea is still held today.

A fundamental criterion in the choice of amulets is given by the similarity between the amulet, the substance out of which it is made, and the purpose for which it is intended. Red plants and minerals protect from, and cure, diseases of the blood; antelope hide endows the wearer with swiftness; the skin of the lion or the elephant induces strength. This accounts for the importance of ivory rings and ornaments, leopards' claws, and other parts of wild animals.

It was believed that the magic force inherent in an object could be transmitted to another. This led to the making of artificial amulets and talismans, to which the wizard transferred the virtue of the original object or the power he himself possessed, according to the beliefs of certain primitive peoples, which he wielded through a series of established rites. It was considered necessary to accompany the preparation of magic objects with ceremonial observances. Some amulets must be worn in a certain way and be visible; others, instead, must be concealed and kept secret, since they lose their efficacy if anyone can see them or even imagine their existence; while still others, as I have said, are purely ornamental. An amulet and talisman *par excellence*, whose original function endows it with the power with which it is credited, is the magic wand, which is used to keep enemies away, to draw the magic circle, to point out the place where magic forces must gather, to unite and divide. The magic wand is mentioned in the Bible in connection with the miracles performed by Aaron before Pharaoh, and in connection with the water that Moses struck from the rock. The wand of Æsculapius should also be mentioned, which was wrapped in the coils of the serpent, and the divining-rod of the rhabdomancers. There is perhaps no sort of living being or inanimate object that has not been fashioned by the credence of peoples into an amulet or a talisman.

Fetishes should be distinguished from amulets and talismans. The word *fetish* may derive from the Portuguese *feitiço* (fictitious) or more probably may have the same origin as the Italian *fattura* (magic action), *fattucchiere* (wizard). In the eighteenth century it was applied by explorers and sailors to religious practices followed by primitive peoples, and more precisely to the idea of a deity residing in material objects and to the adoration of such objects. In reality it has not been proved that primitive man believes the fetish to be the seat of divinity or of superior spirits or that he worships it; there is therefore no essential difference between the idea of fetish and that of talisman and amulet; the fetish emanates a special force with which it is endowed by the magician; it is impregnated with this power, and many practices and procedures are necessary to prevent the loss of such power, because without it the fetish is utterly useless. Fetishes are often figures of men or animals of strange shape or with certain organs excessively developed. They may also be teeth, horns, or feathers of animals, parts of plants, or objects made in the most varied forms. Besides individual fetishes there are collective fetishes which are at the disposal of the whole group and are good for all purposes and protect from all evils.

The power attributed to magic factors, either because it is inherent in the object itself or because it is transmitted from other objects, persons, or animals, is in only very few cases connected with the real, recognized and tested, therapeutic or protective power, such as that of certain medicinal substances. Because of the concept of the possible transmission of this superior power it was later attributed, in a measure infinitely greater than reality, to countless objects. It was believed that the real and proved toxic power of a certain poison could be exercised by every substance infused with this power through certain practices, and analogously that the therapeutic and prophylactic virtue of a medicinal plant could be easily made to pass into another substance placed in contact with it. The value of magic means, therefore, derives largely and sometimes almost exclusively from the suggestion that leads people to believe in the existence of such virtue. Its strength depends on that of the suggestion, and is greater if collective suggestion and self-suggestion are combined. Therefore, if magic factors in themselves possess little importance, we must not forget that they become active in their turn when there emanates from them a suggestion of their power. Because of their form, strangeness, rarity, or other characteristics which appeal to the imagination, and finally and above all because of the traditional belief in the power connected with them, they influence the mind of primitive man. Acting on the unconscious through hundreds of thousands of years, in spite of the whole superstructure of civilization, they even exercise on persons whose critical faculties are well developed this power, which is almost generally accepted without discussion as a possibility to be taken into account out of necessity or prudence.

VII

Practices, Formulas, Rites, and Symbols

I. MUSIC, GESTURES, DANCES AND WORDS IN THE FASCINATION OF RHYTHM

THE history of magic practices—that is, of the procedure by means of which the magic act is initiated and brought about—illustrates the history of the adventures of the mind. With the necessary discrimination between beneficial and harmful forces, with the organization of the hierarchy of wizards and the fixation of the practices of sorcery, it appears necessary to gather together in single groups with set rules a number of rituals deriving from an identical or analogous conception. Rhythmic music, which preceded and accompanied every act of the magician, exercises an exciting or depressing effect on the emotional faculties. The dominant rhythm in a given environment or moment, expressed through music, may be considered the determining factor in magic action, inasmuch as it plays a signal role in the creation of the necessary atmosphere. The effect of colours, sometimes combined harmoniously and sometimes in glaring contrast, the use of intoxicating perfumes which help to create a special mood, intense lights in intermittent flashes illuminating horrible things or eerie scenes, are other factors used in magic practices, which are often decisive. They have the extremely important function, as we saw, of preparing the atmosphere, of concentrating the attention on a particular point, of allaying criticism, of exciting the emotional faculties of the onlookers and imbuing them with faith in the miracle. They are very active elements of magic. Music, noises, and light are magic factors that act at a distance to remove enemies, to frighten away adverse powers, or to call on the assistance of friendly ones; they are the mighty call of power which fills the magic world. Dances mark the gathering of initiates in the magic circle.

Incomprehensible formulas, often repeated at great length in a monotonous voice in the midst of profound silence, concentrate the attention of the spectators on the action. Rhythmic dances originally possess a magic and imitative character inasmuch as they partially reproduce the movements and gestures of animals (and here we recall the popularity of the goose-step in Germany), or of individuals under special conditions of excitement.[1]

These rhythmic movements accompanied by monotonous music, repeated again and again, with a sad, slow, and nostalgic melody, arouse in the listener a mood that may even become hallucinatory and determine the same mental condition in the person performing them. Hence the importance that rhythmic movements have possessed through the millenniums, in their various forms and in their union with other factors such as singing, masquerading, colours, perfumes, dances, etc. To cite a modern example, mention may be made of the suggestive importance attributed to the rhythmical snapping of the Nazi and Fascist salutes. The suggestive value of dances, which were originally a set of impressive and emotional gestures, doubtless derives from their suggestive quality as well as from the apparent or simulated changes in the aspect, and hence in the personality, of the dancer. Some ancient magic dances represented the cyclic movement of life and of death and were noteworthy in funeral rites. The origin of the mystery-plays from which drama developed is strictly connected with magic dances.

Every important act of primitive peoples is preceded or accompanied by music, which is played during the building of a

---

[1] Repetitional rhythm as a source of pleasure and suggestion to both child and primitive has been analysed convincingly by René Spitz in his *"Wiederholung, Rhythmus, Langeweile"* (*Imago*, 1937, 2). He asserts that the repetition of an action or of a tale, like that of a rhythm, gives the child a feeling of being protected from the unknown, which always appears as a danger. Anything that is well known becomes safe. The adult, when criticism is awake, finds repetitions monotonous; but in certain cases, when the unconscious is predominant, he accepts it and it becomes a way of suggestion. Ernest Lach claims that repetition is a physiological and biological law, connected with circulation.

hut or a road and the performance of all kinds of farm work, especially planting and harvesting. Dances are the prelude to the celebration of symbolic festive ceremonies as well as to wars, and are an essential part of any manifestation of the spell of life as of death.

The variety of dances among primitive peoples in various epochs is so great that it is hard to explain their origin by a general rule. Among certain peoples like the Eskimos, dances are an imitation of the movements of birds and animals; Eyre describes a kangaroo dance at Lake Victoria as a marvellous imitation. Other peoples imitate the movements of frogs in a dance for the purpose of invoking rain. Catlin writes that the Mandan Indians of Missouri, before going on a buffalo hunt, organize a buffalo dance, which lasts for many days, and is an imitation of the movements of these animals.

The devil dances that I had an opportunity to witness in Ceylon and in northern India, in which the participants are masked, are magical in origin and always possess a ritual connotation.

Other ritual dances evidently stem from the imitation of epileptics or other psychopaths and have the purpose of arousing some analogous condition in the dancers and onlookers. Often the dances are performed by intoxicated individuals and end in orgies. Sometimes the faithful fling themselves on the ground, the victims of convulsions. The dances of the whirling dervishes, accompanied by screams and like performances, which up to a few years ago took place in Scutari (Asiatic Turkey), were a derivation of primitive magic dances.

The magic use of music and dance, sound and rhythm doubtless preceded that of words, which are essentially human, whereas the magic factors thus far pointed out are patterned after nature and constitute imitations of natural rhythms or acts of animals. They represent the central action by means of which the atmosphere is prepared once and for all, or from time to time, and constantly maintained at the same temperature.

The suggestive power of words, in rhythm more than in meaning, has been recognized since earliest days. Since the most ancient epochs the words employed in magic practices have been sung. In the Old Testament (I Samuel x, 5; II Kings, iii, 15) the power of music in arousing a spell or inducing exaltation was noted: the magic word flies, according to the ancient expression, on the wings of music. The magician sings, and when he exalts his words in song, they are received as an order or as a prophecy, and his gestures take on decisive significance.

Words assume a particular value when they take the form of a ritual, a blessing, a curse, an oath, or an exorcism. A blessing is equivalent to an accomplished fact; what seems to us to be only the manifestation of a wish is in ancient times the certain and irremediable objectivation of the wish. Nobody can interfere with this accomplished fact, as is to be seen in the example of the blessing erroneously given to Jacob by Abraham, which Jacob obtained by fraud, but whose effects nobody could ever annul.

Curses and invocations of adverse forces or of terrible events are likewise considered to be facts among facts: curses are often combined with oaths. Negelein remarks with reason that primitive peoples consider an oath to be a demoniacal force, an extraneous object emerging from the mouth, which produces an immediate effect and which burns the tongue and lips if used falsely. The Kpelle tribe of Africa attribute the destruction of the tissues of mouth, nose, and lips caused by leprosy, lupus, or syphilis to the effects of the beverage given to persons who are being tested as to the veracity of their oaths.

Exorcism—that is, the invocation with which dangers or adverse forces are driven away or the safety of the individual or group is defended—has very remote origins, whose traces may be found in the most ancient graphic representations of prehistoric epochs: symbolic drawings of wounded animals, of violent scenes, of plants and objects whose only purpose is to express violent desire. This expression of desire is, however, through the power of magic, a commandment at the same time —like the orders of sovereign rulers which are expressed in the form of wishes.

2. FORMULAS AND SYMBOLS

What I said demonstrates clearly how, with the organization of magic, with the formation of a classification of magic practices, and with the fixation of these practices, formulas and rites were slowly brought to create symbols.

The origin of many symbols is nature itself. The cross, the most ancient and widely known symbol, is the oldest symbol of fertility, representing fruits hanging on trees. But it also originates from the crossing of two antithetical lines: the horizontal indicating stability, quiet, water; the perpendicular signifying movement, birth, fire: dualism and bipolarity, the union born of two fundamental contrasts, the ancient symbol of the Egyptians, of the Cretans, and of more ancient peoples. The circle, a symbol of eternity and infinity, most likely derives its significance from the great stars ruling the universe: sun and moon. The circle expresses the concept of that cyclic law of life, from death to rebirth, of which ancient peoples believed the serpent to be an emblem. The hexagon, symbol of perfection, is present in flowers, in snowflakes; the pentagon is one of the forms of living nature and becomes the symbol of humanity.

The most eloquent example of a universally accepted symbol is the altar, which from early periods has been considered as highly suggestive, the symbol of the slab, or sacred table holding the food consecrated to the god, the sacrifices, and the eternal fire.

The Roman fasces, the symbol of power, because in ancient Rome they represented in the hands of the lictors the close union of the various tribes, have become in the modern totalitarian state the emblematic taboo expression of absolutism, binding the various wills with the tie of indissoluble power. The swastika, originally among the ancient Hindus the symbol of the solar movement, is closely connected with all ancient solar myths, and has risen to new life as the token of a personal cult that, in order to strengthen itself, resorts to the legend of the Aryan super-race.

Writing is magic in origin. The first signs carved on rocks, magic figures of invoked or feared divinities, were symbolical.

Ideograms representing portions of the body, sexual facts, phenomena of life, were drawn; every sign stood for a term or a concept. In a word the first letter (and later every letter) is a symbol. Writing in primitive epochs was emblematic and secret, intelligible to the initiated alone.

There is a set of other symbolic signs which have the same origin and are founded on the concept of the relationship between the visible and the occult virtues of things. The real and material power of the chain that binds one or more individuals to a place or to a fixed aim is emblematically expressed by rings, girdles, and necklaces; the drawing of the circle that blocks the penetration of adverse forces, stemming from the custom of erecting palisades or perhaps its originative idea, still persists in various regions of the world in the daily custom of peasants who mark a circle around the feet of animals in order to prevent evil forces from drawing near. Likewise formulas and words are the abbreviated symbolizations of long invocations, just as in the early alphabets the form of every letter briefly summarized many and varied concepts.

The representations of stars, of plants, and of magic animals are used to symbolize forces, desires, attractions and antipathies, sympathy and hatred. Just as its tracks symbolize and represent an animal, and the name and even the shadow of a man symbolize and represent him, so the depiction of stars represents the power attributed to them and possesses the same quality as they. The symbols of plants are endowed with healing virtues, and those of animals constitute a threat or a danger. Freud asserts that the value of a symbol derives from the fact that it is the material persisting in the unconscious. And every symbol, in fact, suggests, recalls, or defends some instinct, wish, or hope.

3. THE POWER OF MAGIC SYMBOLS

With the progress of time, magic practices become codified and tend more and more toward standardization, just as the laws of gestures, language, writing, music, and reciprocal social relations become fixed as the intellectual faculties become perfected. Wishes, needs, and the means employed by man to satisfy them increase constantly, and as the dangers deriving from the struggle that threatens man and the group are intensified, symbols assume an ever greater importance. One of the principal reasons for this is the faith that preserves countless magic practices in orderly collections, and the fear that creating any new procedures may be dangerous. Just as in language a relatively restricted number of words must represent a number of ideas varying in breadth (inasmuch as a constant increase demands constant subdivisions), so a certain number of symbols must constitute the foundation of the magic repertoire. Up to a certain point this renders indispensable the intervention of an expert, who alone knows how to interpret and utilize the symbols, while primitive man was able, or was believed to be able, to perform the necessary practices by simple imitation.

The magician of the ages in which magic is ruled by symbolism stands, in relation to his predecessors, in the same position as the scientist of today, with his knowledge of the meaning of formulas, stands in relation to the experimenter or practitioner of past centuries. And just as the formulas expressing elementary forces are the best known even to the layman, and are, we might say, the most popular, so the most widely spread and accepted symbolic figures are also the simplest. Geometric figures that suggest the protected house, the closed and perfect place, and the self-bounded circular line that gives the idea of complete union and leaves no means of ingress or egress to the enemy, are the most simple and eloquent symbols. The forms of the letters of primitive alphabets, preserved in the Semitic languages, the numbers which symbolize in their rigid form the concept of rhythm, and which rule in nature a set of phenomena known to primitive man and perfectly observed by him because they regulated his life and actions and constituted the fixed foundation of them, assume outstanding symbolic importance in this language. Figures being the fundamental basis of all geometrical mystic theology, and the circle, the square, the triangle, and the straight line constituting its principal elements, there must be added to these all the concepts of numerical mysticism and the different meanings of numbers: perfect numbers, propitious and unpropitious numbers, and so forth. Among primitive peoples the power of signs and geometric figures is limited to simple numbers and figures, but countless combinations and associations of numbers and figures, of numbers and stars, of numbers and letters were soon formed. Extraordinary and rare conjunctions attracted the attention of primitive man and sometimes terrorized him; they were impressed on his memory and became presages of rare, fortunate, or disastrous future events.

In its earliest forms the alphabet made a new and important contribution to symbolic formulas: every letter, either in itself or because of the position assigned to it in connection with numbers or geometric forms, assumes a special significance, and every one of the elements mentioned contributes to the formation of a complex magic ritual, which differs in time and place, but is identical in its fundamental lines. This ritual is composed of all the essential factors of magic, which slowly became set in the artificial structure of magic dogmatism. Rites and formulas, practices and procedures, dances and rhythmic songs, imprecations and exortations are combined in the closed circle of the new structure. This persists, unchanged in form as in purpose, as a characteristic and systematic note in all the great antisocial adventures of the mind of the present. It is protected by the class which wields power and guards its secret, which is guaranteed by complicated and often terrible initiatory laws. The historical evidences of many of these laws are still extant, including the fundamental one of taboo, the belief that forbids contact with wizards and with magic objects, prohibits or regulates the employment of magic procedures, affirms the inviolability of names, images, words, and numbers, and establishes the most serious penalties for transgressors, identifying, as is demonstrated by the identity of these words in many ancient languages, the concept of sacred with that of horrible, that of holy with that of forbidden, and enclosing the persons and things possessing magic power in a strongly defended position. Other laws of magic origin and character assume symbolical significance: first among these is the law of totem, which I shall describe later.

4. BLACK MAGIC AND WHITE MAGIC

The conception of demons and spirits is certainly much later than that of primitive magic, and represents, like symbolism and jointly with symbolism, the necessity for classification and regulation that is typical of the animistic and anthropomorphic evolution of the system. Every being assumes particular functions, good or bad, favourable or adverse, in this new demonistic concept, which represents a phase of development following the animistic. With the assumption of the existence of demons, and because of the essential antithesis between the magic and the religious idea which arose later as the logical evolution of the demonistic idea, the decay of magic began. It was perhaps determined also by political and social factors. Magic found itself in a position contrary to the political conception of the State and its leaders. From this point of view the intestine battles of the most ancient states, the constant struggle between military and political might and the power of the magicians, with victory won sometimes by one and sometimes by another, is evidence of this evolution.

There is no doubt that the religious idea in the beginning, and in its detachment from demonism allied with polytheistic systems, gets support from the magic conception. The religious idea accepts, logically, the mystic symbolism of magic, partially assumes its rites and practices, and, above all, employs its fundamental procedure—that is, the preparation of the atmosphere by means of suggestion. Very soon, however, the religious element detached itself fundamentally from magic and later, and particularly in monotheistic structures, assumed absolute predominance. This is proved by a set of prescriptions which tend to extirpate magic conceptions from the minds of the people, sometimes by means of adjustments, disguises, and transformations of magic ideas into new religious structures, as is shown by certain Biblical accounts, for instance that of the bronze serpent, the Witch of Endor, and so forth. However, when solidly organized ethnic groups affirm the necessity of ethical laws which alone can guarantee the life, the well-being, the commerce, and the progress of the group, the battle against magic is more violently fought by religion, the bearer and guarantor of these laws. In this manner occurred the rupture between white magic, permitted or tolerated by religious laws because it works for moral and social ends, and black magic, which crystallizes antisocial and antireligious interests.

VIII

The Secret Societies and
Their Laws

I. THE LAWS OF THE PRIMITIVE SOCIETIES

PRIMITIVE societies, in which, as we have seen, magic conception is fundamental for all forms of individual and social life, are governed by a set of laws which differ according to place, epoch, and ethnic group, in form and application, but are analogous and partially identical in their fundamental structure. We may easily prove the identity of these laws with those which regulate the life of social groups and particularly of the first tribal societies. Traces of them are still extant today.

With the systematization of magic there were formed in some areas of primitive cultures castes of sorcerers, or magic brotherhoods with varied attributions, upheld by complicated rites, and these castes were established like real secret societies, composed of the initiated, to whom were entrusted various functions, the most prevalent of which was a political and juridical one. Webster, in his book on secret primitive societies, devotes a very interesting chapter to these magic brotherhoods, which still exist among all primitive groups. Particularly noteworthy is the information collected by the Cambridge anthropological expedition among the tribes of New Guinea and the islands of the Torres Straits. In Pulu the *kwod*, or the house of the men, is the setting of an important funeral ceremony or dance of death, a yearly rite in honour of the recently deceased members of the tribe, which non-initiates are not permitted to attend. The leader of the ceremony, a hero who, according to the popular legend, has come from New Guinea, is represented in the ceremony by an eyeless, earless figure of wood, which can be seen only by initiates. The performers, with their heads hidden by leafy masks, represent the spirits of the members of the tribe who died but a short time before, and imitate the characteristic gait and gestures of the deceased, thus imbuing the celebrants with the certainty that the spirits of the dead have come to visit their friends.

In some primitive tribes the intervention of the magic brotherhoods is credited with a therapeutic power. When a chief or some other important person is ill, the Duk-duk of the islands of the Bismarck Archipelago hold ceremonies, lasting for a week, which are connected with the propitiation of evil spirits. In the island of Florida the secret societies provide periodical sacrifices and feasts, intended to curry favour with the spirits presiding over vegetation, which are held to inaugurate the season when the first fruits of certain trees are eaten.

Among the Areoi, a society that appears to have spread in part of the Polynesian area, Webster claims the existence of a magic brotherhood of tremendous importance, stemming probably from an ancient secret association of the Melanesian type. The first Christian missionaries considered it to be a diabolical band in whose rites the worst infamies were practised; men and women lived together in a state of complete promiscuity. The natives paid mysterious respect to the members of the society, and those who held superior positions enjoyed the greatest privileges; after their death they were assigned to the loftiest places in paradise. The initiate admitted to the sacred group assumed a new name, which could only be uttered by his brother members. The festivals in honour of Oro, the divine founder and protector of the society, had the character of dramatic mysteries, with interludes of songs and dances. In the temples, which also served as tombs for the highest members of the society, human sacrifices were offered on the altars. These sacrifices, practised by the natives up to the introduction of Christianity, were the occasions for meetings of the most influential men. One of the most important studies of these rites is that by Montgomery.

There are analogous societies in other regions of the Pacific islands, such as the Uritoi of the Marianas Islands and the Maori brotherhood of New Zealand, which have an essentially esoteric character. There are also certain essentially magic societies in western Africa, such as the Kufong, a society of the Mende which devotes itself to witchcraft and practices of sorcery, and particularly to the preparation of filters.

The ceremonies of initiation in certain parts of Africa, and especially in the Congo, are different. They are entrusted to the medicine-men, who form an association on their own account. Under their surveillance boys at the age of puberty are segregated in the forest, where they are circumcised and given special instruction. In some tribes, as among the Kaffirs, there is a real school for the preparation of magicians or shamans, who must prove at the very beginning that they are subject to visions or hallucinations. Admission to the brotherhood is obtained after a long novitiate and after the performance of rites exactly analogous to those practised in the ancient tribal initiations. Among a tribe of South America there also existed certain magic initiatory ceremonies, which have not been altogether abandoned as yet. Before the arrival of the missionaries the *knina*, the place where boys were segregated during the period of puberty, was the setting for mysterious scenes of ancient origin in which the roles were played exclusively by men who, disguised in various fashions, stained with blood, with their faces covered, leaped and sang and emitted savage cries, attempting to render themselves as frightful as possible.

The practices of the magic brotherhoods of the Northern American Indians are extremely interesting. At the beginning of the new year some of these societies celebrate ceremonies for a period of four days and four nights, during which magic medicines are prepared and all persons who are sick gather in the meeting-places of the society to be treated. The society of the False Faces of the *Akonwarah*, which was widespread among the Iroquois tribes of North America, according to Boyle, is a society of masked men founded on the supposed relations between its members and certain spirits whose power is wholly concentrated in their horrible aspect, and who are capable of inducing various complaints or illnesses. A society of the Omaha Indians possesses and prepares, according to Dorsey, a special medicine, which before battle is rubbed on rifles and bullets so that they may kill the enemy, and on horses to increase their vigour.

Many of these brotherhoods, besides their medical functions, perform rites especially connected with the ripening of crops, the rainfall, and the fecundity of domestic animals. I may cite the Buffalo society among the Omahas and the Snake society among the Sioux, which celebrate exceedingly complicated ceremonies intended to induce rainfall. In many of these ceremonies the practices are closely related to more ancient sorcerous customs, such as the dances in which the performers cover themselves with the skins of various beasts representing the totemic animals of their clan, whose gestures and attitudes they imitate; dances, rhythmic songs, and blood-sacrifices are the means for communicating with the great spirits.

2. THE CULT OF THE TOTEM

These rites of savage and primitive peoples, as is shown by the constant reference to the customs of animals, the imitation and, in many practices, the symbolization of animals and plants, bear a direct relation to the first and most ancient magic system, which among certain tribes still takes the place of religion: namely, totemism, first studied by a Scotchman, McLennan, in 1869, and later closely examined, discussed, and analysed by psychologists, sociologists, and physicians, including Wundt, Reina, Frazer, and Freud. Reina made a résumé of the code of totemism in the following prescriptions accepted by a great number of tribes: the prohibition against killing certain animals revered and respected by the members of the group; the obligation to pay funeral honours to the totem animal when it dies and to bury it like a member of the group; the prohibition against eating the meat of the totem animal except in special cases when to eat meat of the totem is prescribed; the obligation to perform expiatory ceremonies if the animal is unavoidably killed; the adoption of the name of the totem animal by a part of the group and by single individuals; the use of symbols of the totem on the banner of the group, on weapons, and on the body; the belief that the totem will not harm the members of its tribe; confidence that the totem protects its group from danger and foresees the future; and, finally, the conviction that all members of the tribe are tied to the totem by the bond of a common and equal duty.

Some additional indications must be given to complete the picture of totemism. Frazer, in his book *Totemism and Exogamy*, states that the totem is a material being, usually either animal or vegetable, for which primitive peoples feel a superstitious veneration due to their belief that between the totem, the men of its group, and every being of the same species, there exists a special reciprocal relationship of protection and attachment. The totem is distinguished from the fetish in that it is never a single plant or animal, but always a whole species; never a bull, but *the* bull; never an oak, but *the* oak. Totemism may be considered both as a magic and as a civil system. There are tribal totems that belong to an entire clan and are transmitted from generation to generation, and sexual totems that belong to all the male or female members of a tribe to the exclusion of members of the opposite sex.

There are two important fundamental laws in this social code. The first is the prohibition of sexual union between members of the same group. This exogamy has been differently interpreted by various writers. Freud maintains that it was inspired by the necessity of combating the tendency to incest of the primitives, whereas other writers consider this a secondary motive. In reality it is evident from both old and modern research that this prescription constitutes one of the fundamental canons of totemism.

The second noteworthy law was referred to by Robertson Smith in *The Religion of the Semites* (London, 1907). He assumed that the so-called totemic banquet was an important and characteristic ceremony of totemism. At this banquet a sacrifice was offered in the form of a communion between the believers and the totem. The ceremony was guided by the idea that at the totemic banquet the spiritual leader of the group and the faithful materially affirmed their communion, eating and drinking together the flesh and blood of the totem and thus evidencing their close bond. Robertson Smith maintains that an individual was forbidden to kill the animal victim, and that its killing was justified only when, on the occasion of the banquet, the entire group assumed the responsibility. Robertson Smith thinks that the victim is identical with the sacred animal which was originally considered to be a superior being sacrificed to cement the relationship between the group and its totem. Eating together the flesh of a sacred victim is the basic proof of the original meaning of the sacrifice and accounts for the sense of mystery surrounding the death of the victim, strengthening the blood ties binding the faithful to the superior being. Thus in the sorcery of death the spell of life is formed and dissolved.

This rite, which initially stemmed from the magic conception of the belongings, discussed in a previous chapter, and from the idea of the transmission of the characteristic qualities of a man or of an animal to the person eating his flesh, constitutes an essential part of the *Intichiuma* of the Central Australian tribes, which Spencer and Gillen observed among the Arunta. Frazer discovered typical examples of the common meal, at which the flesh of the sacred animal is consumed, among some tribes of western Africa.

The explanations of the nominalistic, sociological, and psychological origins of totemism are, as I have said, so many and varied that the reader must refer to the books of the writers mentioned. They have treated the subject with great depth of observation and reasoning. Freud's psychoanalytical theory (*Totem and Taboo*, Leipzig, 1922) is based on analogous ideas of children and neuropathics, and particularly on the examination of the animal phobias that are rather frequent in childhood and may be explained as a projection; in other words, as a transposition such as that which occurs in the mind of a child who substitutes an animal in lieu of his father as the object of his fear. The analogy which certainly exists—as I pointed out—between the ideas of children, neuropathics, and primitive peoples concerning psychological facts, suggests that Freud's doctrine is the hypothesis explaining this interesting ensemble of phenomena most plausibly. It must be pointed out that all this social system, of the greatest importance to the history of ideas and religions, is essentially magic. It is founded on the desire to connect facts and individualities of various character and origin, without any rational causal nexus, in a mystic linkage in order to establish a reciprocal relationship for the purpose of guaranteeing protection and defence against unreachable or invisible forces. The fact that the concept of sacred and that of forbidden (which occurs also in the taboo) are simultaneously combined in the idea of the totem proves that magic is founded on an association of ideas that we are able to understand today. Magic is determined by the coexistence of diverse and contrary feelings, such as love and hate, respect for and hostility to the same object. This psychological fact, which is called ambivalence (Bleuler), was particularly studied and elucidated by Freud and his school. One may perhaps affirm that this conception, which combines in all its manifestations antithetical tendencies stemming from antagonistic reasons, originates in the spell of life and of death, and is ambivalent *par excellence.* A simultaneous existence of opposing feelings is to be found in both the child and the primitive, and is evidenced by the existence of words having two meanings, one of which is the opposite of the other, and by the existence of two contrary feelings, one or the other of which becomes prevalent. In this latter case the aim of one feeling is often changed in order to suppress the adverse feeling, which in its turn is projected onto another object.

3. THE LAW OF TABOO AND ITS ORIGINS

Social law, which rules all aspects of the lives of primitive peoples and which in part determines those aspects, constitutes the foundation of an entire legislation and represents an important system of protection and defence: tabooism. The word *taboo,* Polynesian in origin, indicates a concept familiar to primitive peoples but alien to our way of thinking. It signifies both the sacred and worshipped, and the impure, forbidden, and dangerous thing; "sacred horror" perhaps partially interprets its meaning. A thing that a person cannot approach, touch, or name without incurring grave dangers is taboo, and the prohibition does not derive from a moral or divine law, but from the thing itself. The prohibition, in other words, is one of its essential qualities, the most important substantial quality, immutable, unceasing, not subject to either human or supernatural will or action; it is the law in itself. Wundt states that the taboo is the most ancient legislative code of humanity: it stems from the sacred character (and in this case the word *sacred* has the Latin meaning of *sacer*, the Hebrew meaning of *kadosch*, and the Greek meaning of ἁγιός—that is, sacred and fear-inspiring at the same time) which gives rise to the prohibitions, and the punishments with which those who do not obey those prohibitions are threatened. There is an essential difference between the natural taboo ascribed to a mysterious force (*mana*), which is inherent, as I have said, in the person or the object, and the indirect taboo, which may be either acquired or transmitted to others by a leader, a priest, or any other person or thing possessing it. The possibility of this transfer appears natural to those who are familiar with the primitive belief that every quality inherent in a person can be validly and completely transmitted to another person or object, voluntarily or accidentally, by means of practices, rites, or words, as in the case of a blessing, an exorcism, a transmission of illness or death to another animal (*Kapara'* of the Hebrews) through contact, a magic wand, and so on.

The law of taboo defends and protects the important members of the group, the animals that symbolize or represent its origins, the objects to which particular importance is attributed, from every contact representing a violation. The law of taboo, on the other hand, protects the weak from the magic power of the priests, from the persons, the animals, and the things that are taboo and that would imperil their existence by contact. The law of taboo safeguards man from the dangers deriving from contact with dangerous things such as corpses or poisonous foods, or from the threats that may hang over important acts of his life, primarily sexual acts, and protects man from demons or supernatural beings opposed to him (this is important as it proves the magic quality of the conception). The punishment received by those who transgress this law is, originally, automatic; that is, it derives from the very fact that the transgression is an offence against the law, and it is only later that penalty for the violation of the taboo is exacted by society.

The persons or things that are taboo, therefore, possess, according to this conception, an awesome power that is communicated through contact and has frightful consequences for the individual or object unable to bear it. It may be likened to a strong electric discharge. The intensity of this magic force depends on the person or object from which it issues, and the effects differ according to the strength possessed by the person or object with which the magic force comes in contact. Thus the taboo of the king or of the high priests would kill the member of the group who came in contact with them, but could be borne, in various degrees, by a priest or a leader of the group, who in their turn must be approached only under certain conditions by other individuals to whom they can harmlessly transmit a part of their magic power.

The taboo may be permanent, as with high priests, objects inherent in the cult, leaders, sacred animals, the dead, and everything that belongs or belonged to them. On the other hand the taboo is temporary when it is connected with special conditions such as menstruation, childbirth, preparation for battle, and so forth.

The taboo consists in a countless number of limitations and prohibitions, which may be infinitely multiplied without explanation or justification. Persons who involuntarily transgress the laws are inexcusable for so doing and are struck with the gravest penalties. Wundt explains the origins of the taboo by stating that this conception comprises all those customs which evince the fear of contact with persons or objects connected with ritual practices or possessing this character. Wundt holds that the taboo derives from the fear and from the objectivation of the fear of the demoniac or magical power residing in the taboo person or object. He claims that later the taboo constituted a power in itself, independent of the demonistic concept.

Freud has made a brilliant study of the conception of taboo from the psychoanalytical point of view. He compares it with the ideas of neurotics with *idées fixes,* which from a certain viewpoint may be likened to taboo prohibitions. In the illness known as *délire de toucher* the patient is the victim of an imaginary compulsion forbidding him to come into contact with a certain object or person, or even to think of it or speak its name. The patient believes he would be struck dead if he touched this object or person. As Freud himself states, the analogy between these prohibitions and the taboo is more formal than essential. The analogy is a real one, however, as attested by the comparison that Freud draws between a Maori chief's conception of taboo (the Maori chief being afraid to blow on a fire lest his breath impart to the fire his magic power, which in its turn would be transmitted to the vessel on the fire, the food cooking in it, and the person eating the food, who would die of it) and the case of a sick woman who wishes to remove a certain object from her house for the sole reason that it was bought in a street bearing the name of a friend living in a distant city toward whom is directed her *idée fixe*, preventing her from coming in contact with the friend. The interesting point in Freud's theory is that in both cases it is a question of ambivalence; that is, the strong desire to touch or possess a person or thing is followed by a prohibition that becomes stronger than the desire. This perpetual conflict between desire and prohibition is the genesis of taboo, according to Freud; and the prohibitions of taboo are the fundamental laws of totemism, which forbid the things that are the most greatly desired—that is, the killing of the totem animal, and sexual relations between members of the same group.

The magic power of taboo consists, therefore, in the bewitchment, the fascination, the suggestion emanating from it and tempting the most acute desires of the unconscious, which is naturally infectious, since suggestion and example are contagious.

In taboo legislation, which was profoundly and extensively studied by Frazer, there was created, on these fundamental principles, an entire system of prohibitions and of rites for obtaining pardon for persons transgressing those prohibitions. Thus among almost all primitive peoples a ritual ceremony is performed by the man who has killed an enemy in order to obtain forgiveness for the death. The head of a slaughtered enemy is treated with the highest regard by the savages of Borneo and the Indians of North America, and a set of expiatory ceremonies is performed around it. The victor who has killed an enemy cannot return to his house for several months, nor can he have contact with his woman: he is considered impure and is forbidden to return to his place in the family and the group until ceremonies intended to conciliate the spirit of the dead have been performed.

The taboo surrounding kings, which manifests itself in the magic power issuing from them, is a notable self-defense against danger. The leader is enclosed in a network of usages and prescriptions, prohibitions and ceremonies, not only protecting him, but also preventing him from acting in any way but the one that his subjects desire. The strictly taboo ceremonial that surrounded, in relatively recent days, the mikado of Japan, who was forbidden to touch the ground with his feet, expose himself to the air, or have his hair or nails cut, and was obliged to remain motionless on his throne for hours on end like a statue, gives an idea of the severity of this law, which was originally intended to protect the sovereign, but became later, in the rigidity of systematization, a real torture. Some examples demonstrate how the limitations relating not only to movements and contacts, but also to diet and performance of the most elementary acts of organic life, have been codified by superior civilizations. The high priest of Jupiter in ancient Rome, the *flamen Dialis*, was surrounded by a set of taboo prohibitions; he was forbidden to ride horseback, to see armed warriors, to touch fermented flour and dough, to eat or even mention meat, beans, and certain other food; he was not permitted to touch a corpse or leave the temple with uncovered head. No less complicated were the prohibitions surrounding the ancient kings of Ireland, who, for example, were forbidden to visit certain cities on certain days, to cross certain rivers, and so forth. The extremely severe legislation that even today controls relations between castes in India, strictly prohibiting contact with untouchables and maintaining that their presence or even their shadow renders all things impure, is a derivation of the concept of taboo.

The severity of the taboo that still surrounds the dead among some primitive peoples is partially due to the belief in the extraordinary powers of the dead. Contact with a corpse results in the immediate segregation from the group of all the persons who have been near it. These persons are forbidden to enter houses, to touch other individuals, or to talk with them, and only after rites of a clearly magic character are the relatives or friends of the deceased permitted to return to social life. It is interesting to note that mention of a dead person's name is forbidden, and the breaking of this prohibition is considered a crime equal in seriousness to homicide. The practice of changing the name of a dying person, and also that of other persons, animals, and things having the same name, was generally established for this reason. Among primitive peoples the name is an essential and in fact the most important belonging of man, and the uttering of the name is considered as an immediate and direct invocation and as an action equal to, or more important than, that of contact with the individual. In Hawaii after the death of the king all words containing his name were eliminated from the language (F. Mauthner).

The conceptions of the totem and of taboo, with their complex organization, affecting every event and almost every moment of life, are suggestive factors of the first order, exercising a lasting influence and creating a special state of mind. A member of a group practising the totem religion, in either its original or modified form, who belongs to a clan ruled by numberless taboo prohibitions, is held by unbreakable bonds. His physical, social, and moral life is bounded by strict limits, which he cannot cross even in his thoughts. This condition obviously is created by a psychological state in which he is compelled to recognize that these limitations are real and immutable. In this state the objectivation of his suppressed desire to free himself becomes more violent, a frustration that generates a need for aggression. This accounts for the fact that magic on the one hand is the essential force of the ruling and adverse powers, and on the other becomes the only possibility of liberation. Magic is the instrument by which primitive man seeks to subject supernatural forces, change the actions of spirits or demons, of leaders or of the dead, and attain those desires whose barest formulation is forbidden by law.

The *id* (psychoanalytical terminology calls the instinctive unconscious by this neuter pronoun) or, according to Jung's terminology, the archaic subconscious rebels against the limitations, the checks, and the control of the superego, the reasoning individuality. In primitive days the most powerful weapon in this struggle was magic, which was fought by religion and, more recently, by science.

4. MASKS

Masks were adopted, through an analogical and imitative conception, in order to protect the individual through an escape from his personality. A man wrapping himself in the skin of the totem, hiding his face under a mask representing a wild animal, decorating himself with strange and fearsome pictures, or otherwise making himself unrecognizable is convinced that he has assumed the personality of his disguise. Thus he escapes the menaces of supernatural beings, of spirits, of inimical forces, who do not recognize him under this changed aspect. Such a belief is analogous to the idea that one is immunized against threats by changing one's name. Primitive man believes, besides, that by assuming another individuality he also gains all its characteristics, and particularly its power. A person wearing the mask of a wild beast is believed to acquire its strength just as he does by drinking its blood or eating its flesh; and he utilizes this force to intimidate or conquer his enemies. This accounts for the enormous importance of masks in all magic practices, their variety, the strangeness of their patterns, the establishment of typical masks representing individualities particularly desirable for their power or other characteristics. The use of masks antedates the historical epoch, at least in its simplest form of changing one's facial traits with paints, with the addition of ornaments, of particoloured feathers, ribbons, and other strange objects. This custom has persisted in varying degrees and forms throughout the ages and among all peoples, and we may rightly affirm that all artificial colouring of the skin, hair, eyelashes, and so forth stems from the same initial conception,—that of personality change and of the wish to assume the personality of another for reasons of protection or profit, in order to intimidate others or make oneself unrecognizable, to conquer enemies by terrorizing them, or to win over indifferent people by seductive means.

Masks are only the objectivation of the desire existing in

*Mask of the African Habbe tribe representing the crocodile
(Congo Museum, Brussels)*

Meeting of the False-Face Society of the Iroquois

the mind of man to escape from his own personality. Such a desire manifests itself in a simple and obvious form in primitive man, and in a complex form, deriving from tormenting doubt, in intelligent and cultured individuals. The attempt at an escape from one's personality is very clearly expressed in a theatrical predilection for stage-effects (which is but a single or collective attempt to escape from one's individuality through the suggestion of the changed personality of the actors). This attempt at escape is one of the dominant and fundamental laws of magic. It is the desire to change one's life and personality that animates and directs magic practices; and it is through the changing of the individual's personality, through a mutation brought about by sorcery, which is transitory but believed to be permanent by primitives, that magic exerts its action. Metamorphosis, in ancient times, was the magic action *par excellence*, and later became metempsychosis—that is, "a mutation of the personality in the life beyond the grave."

Finally, it is by means of passing beyond his own limited personality that the magician acquires his greatest power, and it is only at the moment when the suggestion of this mutation is widespread and accepted that his power in the group is established. The leader becomes the god of the group or of the crowd. The possibility, opportunity, and necessity for a change of personality are a means, at the same time, of defence and attack, an infallible weapon in life and in death, and are an essential basis of magic. There is no doubt that the origins and example of this change are to be found in the life and behaviour of plants and animals which hide their individuality in order to defend themselves or attack others, or which change their individuality by assuming by imitation the color and aspect of their surroundings.

Suggestion may be most effectively exercised in secret societies. The secret, masks, taboo, totem, initiatory rites, and the grave threats to persons who dare to violate them form an enclosure. This barrier prevents escape and therefore multiplies the effects of collective suggestion. This is why later the group or political party is governed by inflexible laws.

IX

The Magic Circle

IN early times man felt at one with nature, closely bound to the earth on which he lived and to the living beings that surrounded him and from which hundreds of thousands of years had differentiated him. The progressive evolution of the personality of the individual was a necessary consequence of this biological process. At a remote date he broke away from his animal-like habits and created a new life of his own. Later the individual differentiated himself from the other members of his group and conceived a desire to become stronger than they or to dominate them. This progressive rise of the individual man is underlaid by the growth of self-consciousness, of dignity and the desire for superiority, which becomes more apparent when man realizes the possibility of rising above his surroundings. In a more recent period the ethical sense and the spirit of justice were formed, stemming from man's desire and necessity to create a stable order for the purpose of protecting and defending himself, his family and belongings. This evolution includes a set of superstructures arising from the social and economic conditions of existence and is connected with a countless number of accidental facts. It is accompanied by an adjustment of physical and psychic powers; by a sharpening of intelligence and of criticism, the need for which is increasingly felt; by a weakening of those powers which under changed conditions of life and environment are much less exercised and therefore become atrophied, as with organs that have become inactive.

The lack of adjustment, when changes in social or individual life, due to progress in techniques or transformations in climatic or cultural conditions, are too rapid, creates what Ogburn called a "cultural lag." Doubtless human nature is endowed with the possibility and the premise of a slow adjustment which may take place in hundreds or thousands of years. It is equally certain and evident that the changes in our life caused by an extremely rapid growth of technical appliances and by their individual economic and social consequences have been enormous. Even if we are not willing to admit this as the sole cause of the modern lack of adjustment, we are bound to realize that it may account for the persistence of the mental habits of the past which recent facts have been powerless to obliterate or change.

Openness to suggestion, one of the characteristics of an over-emotional nature, absence of criticism, and therefore lack of awareness of borders between the real and the unreal, natural and supernatural, possible and impossible, are also elements accounting for some apparently strange, mysterious facts regarding individuals who have preserved or increased the primitive sensibilities of the human race. Special sensibility to temperature and to storms, forebodings of earthquakes, the gift of divining the location of water under the ground, and other phenomena of rhabdomancy, over-acute perception of meteorological phenomena, and so forth, give us an indication of the qualities that were attributed to *homo divinans* and that decreased when man detached himself from his intimate contact with nature.

This sensibility and all the facts connected with and dependent upon it contribute to creating an atmosphere in which every manifestation is profoundly felt, a magic world accessible to the influence of sounds, words, and visual sensations whose interpretation is dictated by the will of the person exercising the spell. Contact with the invisible appears possible and real: the close solidarity of the individual with the group and with its past, the link of the living with the dead and those yet to be born, of the present with the absent, form the ground-plan according to which the sorcerer's acts take place and are directed. Dreams and hallucinations are not only interpreted but directly considered as actual facts. The conception of the miracle, as we imagine it, is not existent at this stage, because even the simplest fact is always inexplicable and miraculous, and nothing is absolutely impossible. Since the logical premise and the concept of the causal nexus, which are the basis of experimental science, do not exist, the cause of every fact, the origin of every event, is wish, the wish of an individual or of his enemy, of one group or of an opposing group. Life appears to be a perpetual battle between adverse wills and wishes generating contrary forces.

Does not the clear luminousness of the atmosphere in certain regions apparently explain why physiological hypersensitiveness is joined to a profound, clear sensibility, just as the presence of fog, producing a murky gloom that makes visibility difficult, undoubtedly influences the limpidity of intellectual perceptions? The direct influence of environment is obvious and certain: the high degree of sensibility of men living in contact with nature, removed from all noise, in a perfectly transparent and clear atmosphere, is, as a consequence, easily explainable.

If we consider architectural monuments as attesting to the sensitivity of a people or an epoch, let us think—to cite a few of many examples—of the magic, luminous character of Hindu architecture, with its grotesque, innumerable forms of animals climbing up fantastic columns, in the transparent atmosphere of India, where vegetation springs up rapidly and amazingly. The Greek temple, with the exactness of its structure and the pure harmony of its beauty, evidently expresses the critical and speculative cast of mind that is the product of a meteorologically and intellectually temperate environment. The Gothic bell-tower marks the indefinite search for a mystic light above and beyond the clouds that darken the view of reality.

2. GROUP MIND AND GROUP-SUGGESTION

If the sorcerer rises above the group and affirms his superiority to it because he possesses not only greater sensibility, but also ability to make use of it, those around him close the magic circle, awaiting magic action, which appears as certain and necessary as the rising of the sun, rain, or food, and represents the objectivation of a wish. With insistence and absolute faith the group demands magic action of the living and the dead and is ready to wreak brutal revenge on all who oppose its imperious will. The surrounding milieu, therefore, constantly acts on the magician, who dominates and is dominated by it. There is reciprocal action between two forces which, working toward each other, strengthen each other as much as possible in the will to create a fact believed to be indispensable to the existence of each of them. The fellow members of the group to which the sorcerer belongs attempt to persuade one another that the event took place according to their own desire and will. They explain every lack of success by the intervention of new hostile forces or by errors committed in the performance of the rites, and agree in creating facts that, even when existing only in the imagination, may be productive of the desired consequences. According to the saying of Buddha, everything in man is desire; desire creates will, and will determines the events of life. This is the fundamental definition of the interaction of magician and environment which takes place within the compass of the "spell."

In early societies the first formation was that of the primordial horde (*Urhorde*), of the herd, which instinctively feels the need (according to Le Bon and Sighele) of placing itself at the orders of a leader. When the leader possesses the personal qualities necessary to dominate the mass, and, in particular, the fascination deriving from his absolute faith in success and a sure and strong will capable of overpowering the mass-will, the essential requisites for the interrelations of leader and group are established.

According to W. McDougall, the aggregate that forms a society has, as a result of its past history, primitive tendencies which do not stem from the single units that composed it at various times. The aggregate acts in a very different way from that in which each individual would have acted had he been alone. Every society possesses a mental life that is not the sum of its individual units. Crowds act in a way unlike that of single persons. Hence we speak of a collective or group mind, which constantly differs from the individual mind.

Totemism is the basic example of the group-spirit that is developed by the life, traditions, unconscious instincts, and the suggestive powers of the super-individual. Another typical example of the traditional group-spirit as it develops in closed or stagnant societies is the Hindu caste-system.

It is characteristic that in the mass the individual loses his conscious personality. Tendency toward the immediate realization of suggested ideas gets the upper hand. An individual belonging to a mass has a sensation of power and irresponsibility that increases his strength. Contagion, an easily ascertained phenomenon analogous to hypnoidal conditions, spellbinds the masses to the extent that the single individuals lose not only their critical faculty but any comprehension of their own particular interests. The individual becomes, as Le Bon says, a will-less automaton, and even persons who, when taken alone, are cultured and refined identify themselves with the herd when part of the mass, and their critical and intellectual faculties are noticeably impaired. The mass, as Freud so cleverly observes, is easily swayed and therefore nothing appears improbable to it; it knows no doubt or uncertainty; it thinks of concrete images and not of abstract concepts, and these images succeed one another through uncontrolled association, as in dreams and hallucinations. The mass lacks the feeling of censorship deriving from reasoning and from a sense of reality; every hypothesis becomes a certainty, every suspicion hatred. The mass demands power and violence of its heroes, and feels the necessity of being dominated by and simultaneously of fearing and worshipping its leader. The unreal, observes Le Bon, always takes precedence over the real; the fantastic element and illusions predominate.

In our times conquered and enslaved groups, even when not homogeneous and organic, may be subjected to suggestion, though this is harder, because suggestion exercised by means of the press or radio can never be so violent and decisive; it lacks the factor of immediate contagion between the listeners, direct contact with the leader. The homogeneous crowd is more open to suggestion, and its reactions are more violent and lasting. Organized and disciplined crowds act compactly and with order, when criticism tends to be weak or is suppressed. One of the secrets of success consists in the preparation of homogeneous and compact masses, or of masses guided by homogeneous and strongly predominant "rings," belonging to the sect or the party, held together by personal interests and fear, by oaths and threats, bound in an unassailable solidarity.

The spells characteristic of the influence of drugs or of special psychological moods, congenital or accidental, become, through contagion and the reciprocal action of individuals and group, a collective fact; and thus the group or the mass provides the particular milieu favourable to magic. Let us see what an important role this plays in the history of all magic practices, when adjustment between the social heritage and the original nature of man is absent.

Mass is a plurality of individuals manifesting group behaviour: the society may be the tribe, the clan, the political party, the labour union; all are open to mass suggestion. Freud has asserted that often escape from conflict may lead to neurosis, hysteria, morbid compulsion, anxiety neurosis, or to insanity like paranoia, melancholia, and manic depression. In groups and in crowds a similar imitated or suggested pathological state may be brought about by the surroundings or by psychological causes rather than by physiological factors. Crowds then live in a world essentially unreal or imaginary and their conception of facts is essentially fantastic. Aggressive nationalism, the mystic conception of the super-state (Hegel, Fichte, Treitschke), contribute to the creation of the mythology of the State.

The emotional slogans instigating hatred of the Jews, of democracy, or of plutocracy stem from this fantastic conception of the superior race, which is not accepted by more tolerant Latin peoples, who, with flexible minds, have never been fertile ground for the development of mysticism. ?, Bull!

In Oriental races the emotional factor predominates. The sense of dependence, the need for paternal protection and guidance by an adult or a stronger person, the need for dictatorship, develop from this conception, and appear indispensable also when the struggle for life becomes intensified. Worship of one's ancestors is a characteristic of Oriental races, but in the Occidental world this has slowly disappeared with the feverish rhythm of existence.

There is a typical example of dependence on ancestors or

on powerful leaders in the Japanese mentality, which clings to a discipline of loyalty to dictatorship—dictatorship of the ancestors or the emperor—resulting in emotions that seem pathological to us. The suicide-escape is considered as the only acceptable solution by those who either voluntarily or involuntarily have broken the supreme law.

The collective mind in its interest in the necessities of the living-conditions of the primitive group is dominated by the will of the leader. Such necessities are: contests with neighbouring or enemy groups, alliances with friendly groups, and, finally, the needs of material life. They are originally determined by meteorological facts and other conditions connected with the raising of stock, hunting, business, and so forth. Every accidental external factor may have an influence on some separate members of the group or directly on the whole group, and creates or influences, in its turn, the surroundings required for the expectation, the development, and the success of the magic act. Sorcery is then considered as the remedy and means of salvation; it is therefore the focal point of all desires and efforts, since magic action is imperatively demanded in behalf of the individual and the group. It is not easy to analyse individually all the factors that contribute to the creation of a special milieu and to the formation of its action; it is evident, however, that this situation is in many ways analogous to that of the present day, when groups aroused by passion and driven by economic necessities demand seemingly impossible and miraculous interventions. Here the role played by violent collective suggestion in the development of events becomes evident. Complying with the action of the human mass, always ready to applaud the victor and to kill the sorcerer who is unable to accomplish the desired results, the leader is compelled to employ any means, to succeed at any cost, or, if he cannot succeed, to disguise his failure, casting the blame on others. He protects himself through a structure that may be the tribe, community, state, or party, which will defend, support, and surround him. From the beginning he seeks the help of forces that can be provided and maintained by the groups for which the miracle has been accomplished; by these the sorcerer tries to defend his person and his work

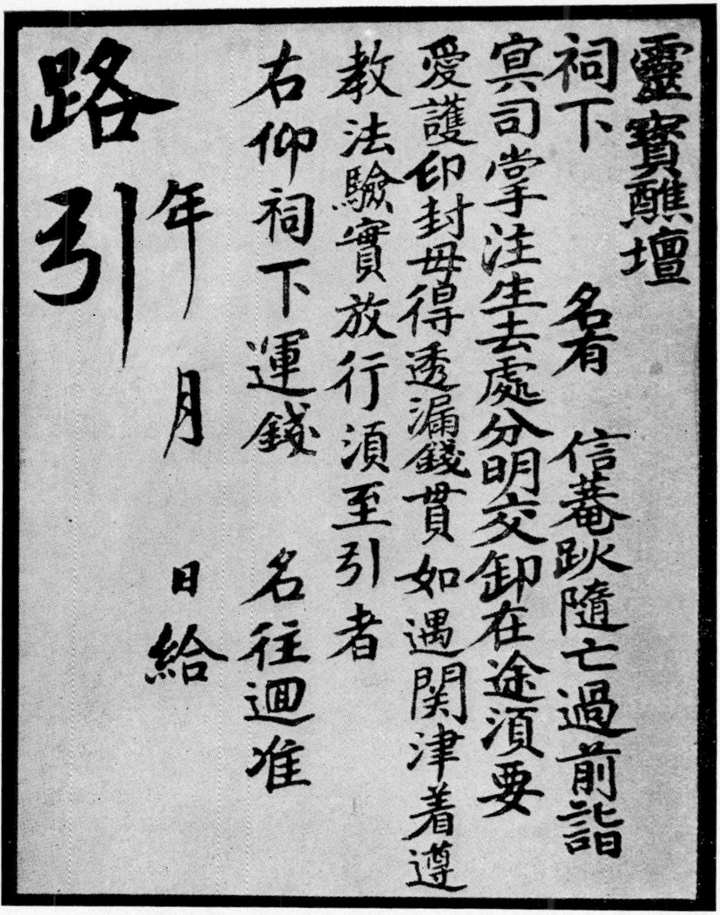

靈寶醮壇

祠下　名者　信蕃跋隨亡過前詣

宴司掌注生去處分明交卸在途須要

愛護印封毋得透漏錢貫如遇關津着遵

教法驗實放行須至引者

右仰祠下運錢　名往迴准

年　月　　日　給

路引

Passport of the soul, Lou-Yng Tan-tse, which grants passage to the beyond. The name of the deceased and the date of death are inscribed.

The women-birds. Tattooed clay figures found at Ur in Meso-
potamia by the Woolley Expedition (British Museum,
London)

in the moment of danger. Fear is created on a vast scale by means of such an organization, and threats deriving from it constitute an important factor of compulsive cohesion and have always been a most powerful weapon.

His spectacular position within the group generates the necessity for the magician to surround his practices with mystery, to maintain his secret, so that none but those whom the magician completely trusts may repeat or check it. By these means he strengthens his suggestive influence and succeeds in winning the blind faith, the certain expectation, the unconditional dedication, the absence of criticism on the part of the group, which is the pledge of success. The magician clothes his expressions in ambiguity so that his words may be interpreted according to the outcome of events. Every member of the group who is sincerely convinced of the sorcerer's power, who gains personal advantages from it, becomes in his turn the sorcerer's helper. He repeats with conviction and— as may be proved by numberless examples—sometimes with unconscious exaggeration the miracles accomplished by the magician, and makes the magician's power over the group more firm because he guarantees it with all the strength of his unshakable faith.

Identification or clear designation of enemies is indispensable. The destruction of races, parties, dissenters who may be, according to the period, other clans, socialists or democrats, plutocrats, Jews, Bolsheviks, or what not, is a necessary part of a group magic action, in our age as in the ancient world. All these facts recur in history and exhibit features that are sometimes identical and constantly analogous.

3. THE MAGICIAN'S RISE AND DECLINE

Any mutation in the formation of a group, and especially every alteration in its homogeneity, reflects on the relations between the magician and the group and on the power of his magic action. The influence of elements extraneous to the group who do not have absolute faith in the power of the magician and in whom the critical faculty is active, individuals accustomed to considering facts and persons with attention and courageous liberty of judgment or with scepticism, immediately changes the situation. Increase in travel and in contacts with other peoples, improvement of economic conditions, a victorious war, have also been factors that contributed to an increase in the individual and social critical sense. Consequently the power of the magician declined and gradually at the same time the group or individual lost faith in magic action of which they no longer felt the need or which they no longer believed to be dangerous. The same occurs in modern manifestations of collective suggestion, when the presence of sceptics or persons who do not feel the need of recourse to such means is generally considered a cause for lack of success. On the other hand, history proves that all facts which by worsening the conditions of individual or collective life first stimulate, then lower the critical faculty, bring about, as a consequence, a greater need for the supernatural, and hence increase any magician's power. One might say that the power of the magician in a certain epoch and among a certain people is a gauge of their economic and spiritual conditions. This is also the case with the individual who after a serious illness, or grave disturbances in his economic, physical, or emotional existence, becomes an easier victim of hallucinations, allows suggestion to dominate him, and resorts to what is rightly called an artificial paradise— that is, to intoxicating drugs.

The assumption of power by a great mass-ruler is always preceded by symptoms clearly indicative of the right moment —that is, by the rise of superstitions and the rapid increase in the number of minor magicians. To quote a recent example: Berlin between 1930 and 1938 was flooded by an unexpected spate of superstitious beliefs, of astrologers and prophets, of seers and palmists, who drew great crowds of believers or, at least, of curious people. About twenty newspapers on astrology were published at the same time, with wide circulation, and all magic practices became popular. These were certainly attempts to escape from the unpleasant reality of existence and from the bondage of painful necessity. These facts always mark the beginning of the dominance of a great magician who assumes leadership and suppresses the will and criticism of the masses, directing their emotions toward a single goal.

There is a continuity in the idea and in the practice of mass-suggestion which is constantly re-enacted whenever there is a recurrence of the circumstances determining it.

Thus we may interpret more correctly and profoundly the statements of the ancient treatise-writers according to which magic action can take place in the closed magic circle alone, within which are to be found those who possess the required qualities. No outsider may penetrate within this line, and this explains the necessity for the chain that symbolically and actually encloses and draws together those who await the magic action. The critical objection of even a single individual whose mind is perfectly dispassionate would be sufficient to upset the conditions required for that action. Magic action can take place only when the relationship is perfect and there is a strong co-operation of forces within and without the group and when such a relationship is established in close connection with the factors determining the life of the group.

If we examine the essential and characteristic facts of anti-social magic we shall see that they may be grouped in the following manner:

1. The external climatic or economic conditions creating a state of depression, or mistrust in the social laws, which appear unjust, useless, or harmful.

2. The conditions of the individual or the crowd which render them open to any suggestion of possible escape from a danger or menace by making available to them superhuman or supernatural assistance as mysterious or unknown, improbable, and inexplicable as the danger or threat itself.

3. The presence of a suggester, wizard, seer, or leader (or of more than one), convinced of the truth of his opinion, his point of view, and of the infallibility of his success. He exercises a collective suggestion through promises, threats, all the arsenal of suggestive means that arouse the instincts of the unconscious, inflame the emotions, and suppress criticism.

4. The construction of a system of terms, figures, or objects which acquire symbolic and magic power and are used rigidly to establish, in a directly suggestive form, the essential principles of the antisocial laws and their aims.

5. The creation of a state of collective spell, of mass-sug-

gestion, analogous to conditions of intoxication or of contagious infection, in which the critical faculty is abolished or diminished. This phenomenon is cleverly exploited by persons able to judge the consequences and profit by them for the purpose of increasing their own power and enchaining the masses by violent means, which are suggested by danger and rendered acceptable by the state of depression.

6. The formation of a state of reciprocal suggestion between the leader and the masses. The latter, through their collective action and their violent support, which implies a threat in case of failure, strongly bind the leader to his program and promises and at the same time menace him if his system should crumble and his promises fail.

I have attempted to collect in these chapters the most important data that, in my opinion, explain the formation of the idea of magic in primitive epochs, selecting only those facts which appear the most interesting among the many frequently cited, generally known, or easily accessible.

This rapid exposition of a set of complex phenomena which took place during the thousands of years before the creation of religious systems can be nothing but a summary sketch of the evolution of the idea of magic in primitive epochs. The analysis of their evolution which I have given is attested to by the documents of prehistoric ages and by the mentality of primitives. It presupposes, not the identity, which would be an error, but the analogy between the beliefs of the man of early epochs and those of men in whom, though changed, the ancient ideas survive in their essential traits. Just as the history of the cell and of its components alone can lead to an explanation or concept—if not complete, at least approximately exact—of our organism and its functions, likewise the examination of the elementary ideas formed and contesting in the mind of the primitive can alone explain the survival of certain ideas, and the complex formation of ways of thinking which, to the superficial observer, might appear as psychological creations of the present, whereas they differ in their manifestations, in extension and depth, but not in their origins, from the ancient beliefs.

PART TWO

ASPECTS OF MAGIC IN ANTIQUITY
AND THE MIDDLE AGES

X

Chinese Magic of Numbers and Letters

IT is a difficult task to write the history of magic and of the various aspects it assumes in the adventures of the mind, and to group together facts that, owing to different causes, unfold in dissimilar forms. It is hard, above all, clearly to distinguish between happenings with an antisocial and destructive magic tendency and events belonging to opposite categories. A change in these tendencies occurs, at times, in one sense or another while such adventures unfold under the influence of causal factors acting in a determined direction.

I shall attempt to divide the history of magic according to ethnic groups and epochs; this division, however, like any other, is inevitably artificial: events develop differently according to country and epoch; contagious diseases, likewise, break out sometimes in small groups, at other times spread with lightning-like speed, and at others vanish without any apparent reason. A study of the history of leprosy, plague, typhus, and other infectious diseases reveals that in certain epochs, for reasons that we can surmise but seldom definitely substantiate, the forms, symptoms, and courses of these epidemics change their character. Doubtless preventive measures and the increased physical resistance of individuals and groups, as well as the immunity that time has developed, are largely responsible for these changes, but they are not enough to explain certain unusual facts.

Similar phenomena take place in the history of the adventures of the collective mind: a complex defence system arises, groups become more impervious to magic action, and a kind of immunity, occasioned by the progressive development of critical intelligence, is built up.

In ancient times social and moral laws oppose magic; later the strong organizations of society and Church and finally, in a more recent period, the results of experimental research combat it and interrupt its action, without, however, destroying it. According to economic and social conditions, group-solidarity, and the development of scientific study, the magic idea flourishes or declines, gains or loses power.

I shall attempt to define three types of ethnic groups: the Pacific, the Oriental, and the Mediterranean. The contacts of the first group with other currents of thought are less evident and certain than those of the last two. We know, through our knowledge of their recent history, that the Oriental and Mediterranean peoples had frequent and often decisive contacts with each other, although the picture is incomplete because the study of the history of beliefs and suggestions among the Arabs, Slavs, Teutons, and other races among these peoples offers an endless field for similar research. I believe that by selecting certain ethnic groups and historical periods one may form a sufficiently clear picture of the evolution of these ideas.

The periods into which, to my mind, one may divide this history are: the ancient, up to the spread of Christianity, marking the first decay of magic; the Middle Ages, when, especially after the terrible plague of the fourteenth century, every type of magic flourished with renewed vigour; the Renaissance, which, with the advent of individualism, historical criticism, the concept of the State, and the dawn of experimental science, triumphantly asserted the victory of reasoning over instinct; and finally the modern age, in which vast economic, political, and social crises once more brought forth multiple manifestations of adventures of the collective mind, in which various social groups have found themselves involved.

1. THE SPELL OF NUMBERS

There is a close analogy between the ideas of the peoples living on the shores of the Great Ocean, whose mutual contacts in remote times we cannot investigate here. Their magic, which I shall call of the Pacific, apparently is dominated by a fundamental tendency toward numerical or geometric systematization, examples of which we have already noted in the Aztec sorcery of pre-Columbian America. This tendency likewise dominates the art, literature, and religious notions of the peoples of the Far East.

Before the introduction of Buddhism into China two systems ruled that country: Taoism and Confucianism. The latter is both a political and an ethical body of teachings, raised to a State system by Confucius (550–478 B.C.), whereas Taoism is a mystic-religious doctrine in which Lao-tse (580–530 B.C.), its legislator, grouped ancient traditional concepts, reclothing them in mystic form and adding philosophical reasonings. In this epoch, magic is present in all the manifestations of the life of the people. The idea of two principal, constant, and opposite forces, *yang*, masculine and active, *yin*, feminine and passive, is essentially magical. *Yang* is energetic, exciting, *yin* is soft and yielding; the former is at its apogee in summer, the latter predominates in winter. Man is ruled now by one, now by the other. All the powers of the universe live in him and he is but an image of the cosmos: each of his parts, his organs, his functions, corresponds to parts, organs, and functions of the universe. The correspondence between the elements is intimate and constant, their classification and subdivision perfect. The five elements, wood, fire, earth, metal, and water, have their counterparts in five colours, green, red, yellow, white, and black; in five regions, east, south, centre, west, and north; in five organs, the spleen, lungs, heart, liver, and kidneys; in five forms of being, in five tones, five numbers, five plant species, five spirits, five odours, and so forth. Every element corresponds to an organ, a colour, a tone, a number, and so on. The entire cosmos is enclosed in a rigid system, in which the position of every individual and part has the greatest bearing on the reciprocal relations deriving from it. This system is dominated by the symbolism of numbers and their combinations, which control the life of men and stars. Some numbers have a favourable or unfavourable significance. Chinese music is dominated by five tones, corresponding to the five planets.

This systematic conception accounts for the veneration surrounding certain animals, regarded as symbols of the whole system. Thus it is believed that the convex shell of the turtle corresponds to the sky, his underside to the surface of the earth, the twenty-four lateral plastrons representing the twenty-four stations of the moon, the five central squares the five planets, and so forth.

It is obvious that in a system constructed in this manner astrology plays the most important role, because the laws of the cosmos ruling the life of men may be discovered through it. The arrangement of the Chinese calendar is similar to the Aztec: signs and symbols govern the periods, the days are divided into propitious and unpropitious, and the calendar possesses the power and significance of a talisman.

The enormous propagation of Confucianism among the people, the pagodas built by order of the emperors, the statues, tables, and pictures, the illustrated biographies of Confucius and his followers, multiplied so fast that images assumed preponderance, and every figure and sign acquired a very clear significance. The history of Confucius' life, in which magic had a notable part (suffice it to mention his meeting with the symbolical buckets which occasioned his maxim concerning the mutability of human life, the gold statue with sealed lips that Confucius found in a temple, symbolizing the obligation of the wise man to keep silent, the story, often told in his biographies, that Confucius, having heard ancient tunes played and tarrying to listen, lost his taste for meat, and many others), is told to the people, repeated century after century, and fixed in images. The four members, twelve disciples, and sixty-four sages of the Gallery of the East become symbolic personages, each one invoked in magic practices.

Taoism, though assuming the dignity of a system of government, leans heavily on the doctrine of the doubleness of the soul, the first formulations of which are to be found in the writings of Tse-tchan, a philosopher of the time of Confucius. According to this doctrine, every man has two souls, the inferior soul (*Pe'*) ruling over material life, and the superior soul (*Hon*) ruling over the spiritual. This doctrine was generally adopted and constituted a point of departure for magic practices.

2. MAGIC PRACTICES

Magic practices are collected in the Book of the Transformations or Book of Changes (*Y King*). This book is divided into sixty-four chapters, each one of which is devoted to a sign, a sort of hieroglyphic, of which the explanation is given. These signs, called hexagrams, are composed of six parallel lines, some of which are broken; they symbolize, in the interpretations of hundreds of commentators, the past and future history of all individuals and events, and their origin is connected either with the spots and lines appearing on the skin of a legendary dragon emerging from the Yellow River or with the patterns on a tortoise shell. This is a very complicated system, based on mathematics or geometry, for explaining or symbolizing all the laws governing the universe.

Many of the best-known magic practices have been extensively studied and described by P. Henry Doré, a Jesuit who lived in China for many years. In his excellent book *Recherches sur les superstitions en Chine* (Shanghai, 1919), the author relates, with many reproductions of prints and statues which he found in houses and temples, a great number of ancient ceremonies still practised in China. A study of this book and of other literature on the subject enables us to gain a clear perception of the characteristics of Chinese magic. All magic practices are exceedingly detailed, exactly specified down to the most minute item, with countless subtle distinctions. It appears evident that the predominant idea of Chinese magic is the absolute power of the sign, the letter, the written word. Any illness can be prevented, any happy event can be brought about, and any unhappy one averted, by swallowing the ashes of a paper upon which an exorcism or invocation has been written. The magic method *par excellence*, exercising the most profound and immediate influence over all classes of people, is writing. Amulets consisting of pieces of parchment or of paper bearing written formulas are the most widely used form. In all houses magic images, with explanatory, invocative, or deprecatory writings, take an important place. Finally, another characteristic of Chinese magic is the importance that it attaches to numbers, which, as we saw, dominate the entire structure of religion as well as that of medicine and, in general, of all aspects of life.

Magic practices, preserved through the centuries almost unchanged, rigid in form, and arranged in a complicated system, accompany the life of the Chinese from the moment they are conceived until their death, and are followed by numberless rites devoted to the dead. The greatest desire of every Chinese is for numerous offspring, and to this end magic rites require the intervention of fantastic animals such as the unicorn and the phœnix. The place of honour in the chamber of a newly wedded couple is occupied by the image of Koan-Kong, a celebrated Chinese scholar, offering to the couple a child wearing the cap of learning. When childbirth does not proceed rapidly, a table taken from the pagoda is carried into the house, and the woman in labour places her clothes upon it. Talismans and amulets written on pieces of paper by the priests are placed or pasted on the woman's body. A small copper mirror hung around the neck of a young mother allows her to enter a house containing a dead person without risk of bewitchment.

As soon as a child is born, his horoscope is cast in order to discover the obstacles he will encounter during his life. Arrows made of the wood of a peach tree, considered excellent for putting malignant demons to flight, are shot in every direction. Parents always fear the visit of a witch who may steal their children, or of an evil genius who sometimes assumes the shape of a yellow dog and brings misfortune. In certain regions of China it is the custom to sacrifice a rooster to the spirits of the dead three days after the birth of a child. Children are often given the name of an animal in the belief that the evil spirits will thus be fooled. The custom of tying small bells to the feet of children in order to frighten off malicious demons is very common. A great number of amulets of every form, and particularly earrings, pendants, medallions placed on caps and garments, are used to protect children from the evil eye. One of the most curious of these amulets, described by Doré, is the so-called "garment of the hundred families." The mother asks each of her neighbours for a piece of cloth and some thread; then with these many-coloured fabrics and threads she makes a garment which is certain to protect the child, since everybody has contributed something for this purpose.

There are countless amulets of all kinds and shapes for the purpose of protecting children from illness, and particular amulets are designed for every ailment. Clearly defined rites, worked out to the last detail, are practised. The amulet against headache, for example, cannot serve against earache or sore throat.

One of the most interesting rites, connected with the magic beliefs of pre-Columbian America, inasmuch as it bears the characteristics of arithmetically arranged and, I may say, literary Chinese magic, is that of the custom-houses, which has been described with special care by the writers on Chinese usages. According to a widespread notion, every child must pass through a set of custom-houses—that is, departments in which he is checked, examined, entertained, and allowed to pass or detained by the spirits which perform this particular task and molest travellers on the road of life. There are thirty custom-houses, each with its own name. Exact rules establish the time of passage, as well as the means required for passing through them: amulets, figurines, or written magic words serve as a passport and guarantee free transit. There is, for example, the custom-house of the gold hen, that of the hundred days, those of the five devils, the iron serpent, the white tiger, and so forth. At the age of sixteen, when the youth has passed through the thirtieth custom-house, the danger from malicious spirits is notably lessened and he feels more tranquil and safe, but even so it is no less necessary for him to keep on with practices of defence. All rites accompanying betrothal and marriage and the entrance of a bride into her husband's house are a thoroughly organized set of magic ceremonies, distinctly and exactly prescribed.

The magic practices prescribed for serious illnesses and death are equally precise. For example, when the end is visibly approaching, the dying man is divested of his sash, an essential and indispensable part of his clothing. The reason for this is that the word *sash* (*tai-tse*) has the same pronunciation in

Chinese as the word *t'ai-tse*, meaning to steal or carry away children. Therefore, in order to prevent the word from assuming the latter signification, and to make it impossible for anybody, on seeing the sash, to utter this word, which might act as an invocation, the danger is avoided by removing the object.

All the magic ceremonies performed after death, accompanying the symbolic custom of the "crossing of the bridge," which represents the passage from this life to the next, and during burial, substantiate the importance attributed to the cult of the dead. In order to show how some of these practices are directly connected with the magic beliefs of the primitive period and of classic antiquity, I may mention that of the "house of paper." On the forty-ninth day after death a house is built of paper, containing paper models of furniture, servants, utensils, and in general of everything that was a part of the life of the deceased. The house is then burned, in the belief that it is thus transferred to the world beyond, where it can be used by the spirit of the dead. This notion is analogous to that of the primitives who were wont to bury weapons in graves, and of the ancient Egyptians who placed exact reproductions of houses, servants, animals, and so forth in the tombs of the dead. Another ceremony of the same type is that of the straw crown placed on the graves of children to prevent the celestial dog from devouring them. These crowns are like a magic circle into which the evil demon is believed to be unable to penetrate. A custom widely in use in China and Japan is that of placing coins or paper money, or rather imitations of paper money, in graves. This money, called the "right of passage," is intended to enable the dead to pay his fare to the Charon of Chinese belief.

I have chosen a few of the magic practices described by the hundreds in European and Chinese books devoted to this subject, in order to demonstrate that China not only has preserved religiously its magic beliefs in their most minute forms and manifestations, but has also organized in a manner unparalleled in its exactitude the practices connected with them. The Chinese mentality is characterized by the strictest faithfulness to all traditions, and particularly to the written word.

This faithfulness to the written word stems perhaps from the respect and profound devotion felt, since the ancient days of the Celestial Empire, for learned men, who in no other country in the world occupy such a high and well-established social position. Moreover, this faith in the sovereign power of the written word, in the magic efficacy of a sign drawn by a learned man, creates and consolidates the scholar's influence. The magician, in Chinese belief, is the scholar: every written or printed word is a magic tool of the greatest importance, and hence books, or even printed pieces of paper, are looked upon with respect and fear. The book is the taboo *par excellence*.

The thorough, mathematical arrangement of Chinese magic ceremonies, analogous to the practices of American Indian magic, derives in its turn from the proclivity to minute compliance with and respect for all forms and gestures, no matter how small or insignificant, which is well known to be one of the fundamental characteristics of the Chinese mentality. In its turn this observance of minute and exact practices renders necessary and explains the tenacious passion of the Chinese for all detailed descriptions, endless lists, and distinctions bordering on the metaphysical. China abounds in titles, methods, standards. In diagnostics five hundred different kinds of pulse are distinguished; there are one thousand different points for the acupuncture, a therapeutic practice widely employed in Chinese medicine.

Chinese magic beliefs, orderly, mathematical, boundless in their aspects and forms, interminable in their subdivisions, crystallized by centuries, rooted in the unchangeable faith of the people, present one of the most interesting spectacles of the history of magic. They clearly show how, in a country impervious to foreign influences and to the movement of great currents of ideas, there occurs a proliferation by subdivision of magic ideas, and how, as a result of that imperviousness, form, or the letter, may assume predominance over spirit.

XI

Magic Systems of the American Indians

AMERICA is one of the most interesting fields for the study of the psychology of primitive peoples. Until a relatively short time ago America was inhabited by groups of interrelated peoples who had been isolated from all other civilizations for thousands of years. In these pages I shall attempt to give a summary picture of the evolution of ideas of magic among the pre-Columbian Americans. These ideas are expressed in their monuments and in the beliefs of their descendants.

One of the most notable traits is the dualistic conception of nature that exists among the Kagaba of South America as well as among the Arowak Indians living in the Sierra Nevada in Colombia, who have been studied by Preuss, an outstanding modern ethnologist. The religious idea of these people is characterized by the belief that the supreme deity is female. The great goddess Hava Sibalaneuman is the mother of all men, races, rocks, animals, and plants. She rules over rain, the sun, and the moon. It is interesting to note that all women are believed to derive from this female deity, a universal mother who recalls the ancient matriarchal societies—reminding one of the social organizations of certain insects, such as bees, where the queen is the universal mother. Men, instead, issue from another deity or supernatural being, who is male. There is a clear dualistic distinction between the race of men and that of women, a distinction that goes back to the time when primitive peoples did not understand fecundation and believed that it was due to eating certain foods or originated from contact with animals or with plants. The belief that one sex was *taboo*, sacred, to the other sex of the same tribe arose from (accord-

[132]

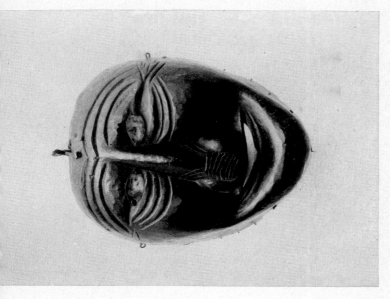

Mask representing a female, with small child mask attached, used by the Seneca Indians, Cattaranga Reservation, in prenatal maternity rites

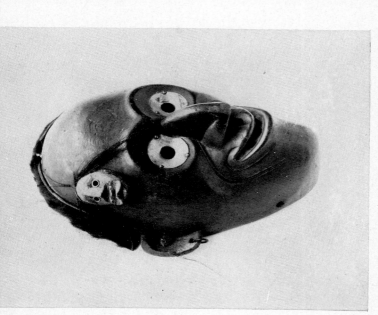

False Society mask, Seneca tribe, Ontario. The eyeholes are blank. The wearer looks through the nose (Both masks in Museum of the American Indian, New York)

Medicine-man mask, Onondagas, New York (Both masks in Museum of the American Indian, N. Y. city)

Dance mask, originally doctor mask, Seneca tribe, New York

ing to Preuss or at least according to the inferences one may draw from his explanation of sexual totemism) or gave rise to the law of totemic exogamy—that is, the prohibition against sexual union between men and women of the same tribe.

The idea of the California Indians, described by Gayton, that life and creation are due to great animals, and that the eagle rules the universe, is thoroughly magic. The medicine-man (shaman) has a great power; the owl, the totem of the group, is believed to be the ancient medicine-man protecting the tribe. The occult faculties of the shaman are believed to derive from a dream, during which he receives the revelation of his power.

The extant monuments of ancient Aztec culture present particular aspects that are interesting for their magic character. At the time of the Spanish conquest the Aztecs had attained a high degree of culture, attested to by their monuments, art objects, drawings, and weapons. Aztec writing was essentially ideographic; names were symbolized by animals or objects having an identical sound. Music was considered as an appurtenance of the cult and was supervised by priests or sorcerers.

The culture of the Mayans was in many respects like that of the Aztecs, but was more developed in the fields of mathematics and astronomy.

Typical of the magic of the Aztecs, whose ideas are directly linked with those of the primitives, is its systematic evolution. A nation of warriors and organizers, conquering vast rich regions and subjecting them to their rule, the Aztecs undoubtedly possessed the qualities of outstanding legislators. Like all peoples whose well-being is based on agriculture, they devoted the greatest care to the establishment of dates—that is, to the setting up of a calendar. The fundamental idea of good and bad days, according to which work in the fields, and all other activities, are ordered or discountenanced, dominates the Aztec calendar, which in its turn regulated the religious and civil life of the people. In magic, the knowledge of propitious or unpropitious days assumed unusual importance. These qualities were determined and indicated by animals or meteorological phenomena ruling the individual periods. The solar year was known to the inhabitants of ancient Mexico; it was divided into alternating periods of thirteen and twenty days. The periods whose extent is fixed by twenty days—the number that indicates the total number of fingers and toes on the human hand and foot—are ruled over by animals, such as the crocodile, the serpent, the deer, the dog, the jaguar, the vulture, or by water, wind, or rain. Moreover, every day is entrusted to the protection of a particular deity, and the system appears extremely complicated when one thinks that during the entire year the periods of sixty-five days and those of three days are in their turn under the control of a supernatural being, endowed with particular functions.

There are five great periods in the history of the world: namely, the periods of water, jaguar, rain of fire, wind, and earthquake. In the most ancient period, according to Mexican belief, tremendous rains fell and the earth was inhabited by gigantic beings who were completely destroyed. This, it is obvious, is the same idea that is found among other peoples, such as the Babylonians and the Hebrews. The second age, that of the jaguar, ended with the fall of the sky, the darkening of the sun, and the appearance of the jaguars, which destroyed men. The third age, that of the rain of fire, was brought to a close by torrents of fire raining down from the sky and annihilating every living thing upon the earth. The fourth period ended in terrible winds, sweeping away life almost completely and transforming men into monkeys. The last period, in which we are now living, is that of the earthquakes, which will come to a termination through a frightful earthquake destroying every form of life.

It is interesting to observe that this idea of the great epochs is to be found also in Babylonian lore and, according to Danzel, among certain Polynesian tribes. It reflects the idea of the four elements, earth, water, fire, and air, existing in the ancient classic conception. The idea of the world in space is no less systematic and, we might say, almost mathematical. According to this conception, there are thirteen skies above the earth and the world below, the last of which, the sky of darkness, is the dwelling-place of the dead. A river composed of nine torrents surrounds the kingdom of the dead. In Aztec art the world is portrayed as an enormous pyramid in the form of steps, supported by a serpent.[1]

2. TOTEM BIRDS

Mexican mythology is monumental and systematic. The deities are strictly divided and classified according to the regions in which they exist, and to each one are assigned special characteristics. The god of fire, for example, is enthroned in the centre of the earth. The central theme of this cult was human sacrifice; at all festivals prisoners were sacrificed to the gods. Music and games, the most popular of which were ball games, played on a field near the temples and symbolizing solar and lunar motions, were an integral part of the ritual.

In Mexican architecture the pattern of stair-steps, symbolizing the phases of life, is predominant. The temples are almost all in the form of great pyramids, with the shrine at the top. The shrine is reached by three hundred and sixty steps, the number of days in the Mexican year. These structures are strongly reminiscent of Babylonian and Buddhistic temples, and represent the gradual purification required for approaching the deity.

The religious and magic buildings of the ancient Incas, who ruled Peru up to the Spanish conquest, bear a clear analogy to Mexican structures. The Incas were divided into groups, or *dan*, each of which was headed by a chief entrusted with administrative, judiciary, and religious functions. In the Inca kingdom the State not only controlled the administration and protection of all movable and immovable property, but also, through its officials, exercised surveillance over all citizens whose duties were definitely prescribed. The worship of the sun was the centre of the religious idea; the Inca was believed to be the son of the sun, whose name could be uttered only on certain occasions and with the greatest reverence. The priest-sorcerer played an important role in social life: he foretold the future by observing the flight of birds and by scrutinizing the

[1] G. Roheim has made an important contribution to the study of the magic of the American Indians and especially that of the Aruntas, and has described in a remarkable way the Intichiuma ceremonies from the viewpoint of the psychoanalyst. This very careful and exhaustive study on the subject places a great part of these magic practices in a new light.

entrails of the sacrificial animals, the blood clots on their lungs, and various plants. These sorcerers performed their ceremonies while in a state of ecstasy, induced by eating certain vegetable substances.

The history of the magic of the South American peoples is marked by the mental characteristics of bold men inured to hardship, who lived in a constant fight with danger, on high plateaus of the Andes or on the banks of great impetuous rivers, prior to the time when the richness of the earth was revealed by intensive cultivation. The totem dominating all America is the great bird of prey which soars high above the tallest mountains, an eloquent symbol of unattainable power. Appearing as the eagle of the United States and of Mexico, as the condor of Bolivia and the multicoloured quetzal of Guatemala, this bird has assumed a thousand shapes through thousands of years, and has been imprinted on coins, medals, and stamps. This ancient totem, symbolizing also the yearning for wider horizons, exercises its spell over the whole history of the peoples of both American continents. The history of ancient America constantly refers to the strength, beauty, and audacity of these great birds: the throne of the Inca had the shape of a gigantic egg; feathers of a thousand colours were the most prized ornaments in all the temples, the sign of authority of the chief in all tribes from the redskins to the Quechuas of Chile. The Mexican totem was the plumed serpent, which is extremely important in Mexican folklore.

I believe that the ruling characteristic of pre-Columbian America is today perfectly apparent to those who attempt to penetrate the way of thinking of the peoples who have preserved their age-old traditions. It is more difficult to judge the repercussions of these beliefs on modern currents of ideas and on political and social aspirations. Undoubtedly the ideas set forth in Keyserling's *South American Meditations*, a book that successfully points out, with a deep understanding, the motifs forming an ideal unity, or at least the continuity that links the magic ideas of ancient Indian tribes with those of the modern inhabitants of South America, are convincing. Paul Morand's pages in which he indicates the close connection between the passion of modern America for airplanes and that of America's early dwellers for birds of prey are very alluring, because undoubtedly a relationship exists between the fascination of the remote and unknown exerted by the eagle in its magnificent flight and that which captivates modern man in the sight of a plane. But even without drawing any conclusions from the ideas of the philosopher and from the words of the poet, or from some trend of thought of the men living in that country, without attaching a supreme importance to such movements as Andinism, Indianism, or to the return to the ancient traditions of the Aztecs manifested in certain regions of Mexico, we are forced to admit that the ancient magic notions, so powerful in those regions, still thrive in the countries where Western civilization has not destroyed, even with three centuries of the yoke of the Inquisition, the ancient soul. Perhaps in the archaic collective unconscious the marvellous treasures of the Incas, described in ancient narratives, which the fierce greed of the conquistadors was unable to discover, still lie hidden.

3. MAGIC MEDICINE

The medicine of pre-Columbian America was, as far as may be judged from extant documents, essentially magic. The Aztecs and the Incas believed that illness was caused by evil demons; exorcisms, talismans, and amulets played an important part in their therapy, and magic rituals were performed during childbirth and over the new-born infant. Surgical instruments were made of flint, and the ancient surgeons had great technical skill. Pictorial representations, impressively realistic, of pathological cases and especially of skin diseases are frequently to be found on clay vases, the famous *huacos,* suggesting that they may have had a particular significance and a specific function in the treatment of disease, probably because to each one of them a demon was attributed. Sorcerers, as among all ancient peoples, possessed a knowledge of the virtues of plants; they were familiar with the effects produced by the narcotic seeds of the datura tree, and by the stimulating leaves of the coca, the venerated and sacred tree, which in ancient days could be used only by princes and members of the court, and later were widely employed by the people because of their intoxicating properties. Even today among the Indians of Peru the *calahuata* or *kamili* (medicine-man) surrounds all his magic practices with mystery: he places a number of coca leaves on the chest of his patient, then spreads a black cloth on the floor on which he lets them fall, examining the pattern they form thereby. After uttering mysterious words he states that the illness is caused by the evil influence of an animal, whose identity he will discover. This is followed by many ceremonies dedicated to the search for the animal, all tending to neutralize the effects of the evil spell. Such sorcerers are still very popular today among the peasants, who firmly believe in their power.

The history of coca, one of the most interesting aspects of South American magic, is a chapter in itself. In ancient days coca was offered to the deity, and its use was restricted to kings and great magicians, as it was known to be a powerful drug, producing hallucinations. Later coca became very popular, and today its consumption is remarkably widespread. The prohibitions and limitations imposed by Spanish viceroys and modern laws have only succeeded in limiting its use. Coca is still, as in the days of the Incas, the sacred leaf bestowing the magic sensation of a better life and imbuing the sufferer with new hope. The great sorcery of the rulers has become the common magic of every day.

H. Valdizan, who made an accurate study of the popular medicine of Peru, discovered how extensive magic beliefs are: some animals, such as the sparrow and the turkey, are considered as harbingers of death; it is believed that a dog howls in the presence of death, and that a skittish horse has seen the soul of a dead person. Demons protecting the harvest, and domestic animals, are extremely important in the life of the Indians; in some regions the *achachilas* are the primitive fathers of the tribe, the guiding spirits and pious protectors of the life and health of man, animal, and plant. They live hidden in hills and woods. At certain times of the year these spirits are offered sacrifices and a banquet, presided over by men experienced in the secret rites, who utter mysterious formulas. The centre of this cult is the Island of the Sun on Lake Titicaca, where the *achachilas* are believed to gather in council. Paredes studied and described analogous beliefs of the Bolivians.

The conviction of the Indians of certain sections of Peru that in dangerous mountain passes a person may lose his soul if he fails to make a votive offering of fresh boughs stems directly from a primitive conception. According to the natives, this loss of the soul results in the most serious illnesses, especially mental, which can be cured only by recovering the soul through magic rites performed at night-time by sorcerers.

The sickness of animals is also believed to be caused by malignant demons, and to be curable only by magic practices.

The cult of the dead is accompanied by long and complicated rites. Funerals last for many days, and the belief is held that the dead can return to life and work good or evil in various ways.

The centre of primitive Peruvian religion is the *supay*, the malignant spirit who is believed guilty of all illness and misfortune. This powerful demon, opposed to the good gods, has many names and forms among the Indian tribes of South America; but the belief is widespread that danger can be conjured off by magic practices alone, and all the present-day medicine of these tribes, which have preserved almost completely the beliefs of the ancient inhabitants of the country, has a magic character. A whole medical mythology has grown up, and a group of individuals devote themselves to medical practices. One of the most interesting of these individuals is the *bruja*, a sorceress or witch, who practises her art with complicated rites and prescribes remedies for all ailments. She advises the use of talismans, amulets, and formulas in which Catholic practices are strangely commingled with magic.

The rituals accompanying childbirth and the care of the new-born infant are very interesting. In these, imitative magic rites are performed by the *recibidora*, the midwife, who performs a particularly complicated ceremony in cutting and tying the umbilical cord, which, symbolizing the conjunction of the life of the mother with that of the child, is considered as the central event of the birth.

The magic medicines of the Aztecs are characterized by their antiquity and by their extraordinary hold on the Indians. Narcotic and exciting substances are important, and many studies have been devoted to *ololiqui* and *peyotl*, which have worked their magic charms for centuries. The Church has unsuccessfully tried to purge the Indians of their belief in the black magic powers of these two plants. *Peyotl* and *ololiqui* are used for their effects upon the mind and the nervous system as well as for magic rites. *Peyotl*, which Havelock Ellis took as an experiment, contains a powerful alkaloid (mescalin). *Ololiqui*, whose botanical name is *Rivea corymbosa*, is closely related to our common morning-glory. The god of the *ololiqui* is frequently invoked and its flowers are gathered with special rites. The plant has diverse functions: as a narcotic, and as a part of the ritual of divination, as it was believed to confer special powers. Nothing is known about the chemistry of *ololiqui*, but it has been found to induce a kind of hypnotic sleep accompanied by hallucinations, leading to euphoric bliss. *Ololiqui* and *peyotl* induce the same kind of visions.

Briefly summing up the most notable traits emerging from an examination of the magic of the American Indians, we may conclude that it has a particular character in that it is dominated by a fantastic note. Even though the magic currents among the various peoples are enormously different, owing to the essential differences in climatic and social conditions, there is a certain aspect that is common especially to the magic of the Pacific regions, which are most under the influence of that particular current of ideas. Narcotic plants are extensively used, because of the desire to expel the "green pain." The idea of the totem dominates magic, and among the totems the place of honour is taken by a bird of prey of many-coloured plumage.

In no other country, perhaps, is ancient magic so alive as in the small, still undispersed ethnic groups or has it exerted such a profound influence over the invaders. These beliefs and the images that lived in the minds of the conquered peoples revive, though in other guises, in the ideas of the conquerors. These new and ancient ideas, reminiscent of traditions that seemed to us completely obliterated or as deeply buried as the ancient temples of the sun, are without number, and, under particular circumstances, notions believed to have vanished for ever spring up with unexpected vigour and clearly point to their remote origins.

Chief of the fakirs of Panokakki (Aurangabad, India)

A Hindu Guru and the symbol of linga (Calcutta)

XII

Fantastic Magic of the Hindus

I. A LIFE OF ANGUISH

IF we consider the influence exerted by external conditions, which determine the forms and laws of individual and social life, over the creation of the magic atmosphere, we shall see that nowhere is that influence so evident and predominant as in India, a country of extreme climatic contrasts enclosed and protected by the ocean and by a chain of mountains—a crucible in which melt the passions, hopes, and thoughts of many racial groups, mutually hostile and swayed by one faction after another.

A study of its history, contact with its peoples, and understanding of their thoughts reveal that no other country is so essentially pervaded by magic as India. India is a complete historical museum of magic, exhibiting, vividly engendered by symbolic thinking, all expressions of the magic idea, all aspects of sorcery, all customs and rites of magic. India is perhaps the only country in which the reality of Western life, the creations of modern mechanical civilization, exist side by side with myth and legend, which have assumed an appearance of reality and often seem to overcome or supersede the ideas, forms, and laws of the modern age.

Profound fear of supernatural forces dominates the collective mind of India. Hinduism, with its worship of thousands upon thousands of deified animals, of monstrous gods evincing no trace of goodness or mercy, is but the fantastic construction of minds terrorized by the fear of unknown and terrible things. The whole of Indian art expresses this magic belief: the grotesque figures of animals carved in stone or painted on the walls of caves are magic; the origin of the blood-sacrifice demanded by a bloodthirsty goddess, in which today an animal is substituted for a human being, is likewise magic. The conception of belongings, of the shadow (an impure man cannot even allow his shadow to fall over an object without rendering it impure), of the names of ancestors, which are invoked and repeated with respect and fear, exists in India today as it did among the primitives. The magic and cruel law of taboo, establishing frightful penalties for those who dare to violate it, is expressed in the system of Indian castes. The Indian lives in the magic circle from which the serene philosophy of Buddhism, preaching the suppression of desire and the victory of the spirit, vainly attempted to liberate him.

The history of magic in India can be sketched only episodically, by selecting the most notable facts and features, since it unfolds in different forms according to epochs and to the religious, political, and national currents that at various times dominate individual and social life and sometimes seem completely to upset the ancient ideas.

The collective mind of India evolved from an early magic conception and from a systematic demonism, engendering an ethical and philosophical belief that, from certain viewpoints, may be considered one of the most perfect. From the ancient religion of the Vedas through the epoch of Brahmanism and that of the great philosophic-religious currents which gave rise to Jainism and Buddhism, down to the return of Brahmanism, which merged into Hinduism, disparate conceptions succeed one another or alternate. These conceptions are often so complex that it is difficult to discover their origins without taking into account profound and determining foreign interferences. All these conceptions, however, evidence the particularly imaginative mentality of peoples influenced by their surroundings and climate, just as vegetation is most luxuriant and colours more brilliant, development more rapid, and the forms of all living things more varied under a burning sun. All means appear to be directed toward the attainment of an end which is often beyond the compass of reality. Totemism is to be found in the early worship of animals (the cow, serpent, tiger, elephant, monkey are totems), which later, owing to the widespread idea of metempsychosis, assume a dominant importance, manifested in symbolism. The cult of numbers, forms, and signs is developed to the highest degree and finds its expression in the Vedas, the sacred songs accompanying ritual practices and containing magic formulas purported to cure the sick, stave off death, avoid dangers, and weaken enemies.

Perhaps in India more than in any other country magic shows itself primarily (a fact easily explained by the conditions of life) in those forms of incantation requiring a special state of mind in which the critical faculties are abolished or notably impaired and the emotional faculties are in a state of ecstasy or under the direct or indirect suggestive impression of music, words, shapes, or signs, individual or collective. The Soma, belonging to the cult of the moon, is one of the most ancient and important magic practices. An essential part is the drinking of soma by the magicians and other participants. This beverage induces a state of excitation: "We have drunk the soma and have entered the celestial light." A further passage of the text quoted by Hauer reads: "I have risen from the back of the earth into the celestial space, from the celestial space into the sky, and from the sky into the world of supernatural light, where I am one with the sun." The ceremony of fire, accompanying a set of magic practices, and particularly those ceremonies, still extant, devoted to the cult of the ancestors, belong to this same category, as well as other ancient practices in which music, dances, repetition of formulas, and various manipulations on the bodies of the faithful cast a spell upon the onlookers.

Indra, the god of sun and war, threatening and terrible, the conqueror of every foe, plays the central role in Indian mythology. Indra is accompanied by Varuna, the moon god, who regulates time and events, rewarding good and punishing evil. Numberless other gods and demons appear in the Indian pantheon. An important position is held by Puruscha, the first man sacrificed to the gods in a great ceremony. This sacrifice was the origin of the world, inasmuch as the sun was created from the eye of Puruscha, the sky from his head, warriors from his arms, peasants from his thighs, so that, according to this ancient legend, the life of the universe is reflected in the individual.

Animals play a primary role in the enormous fantastic portrayals of strange forms, simultaneously mythical and mystical, in which all the natural lines appear exaggerated and as such become crystallized and rigid in the sculpture and architecture of India.

2. MAGIC DANCES — THE FASCINATION EXERTED BY ANIMALS AND PLANTS

The Indian dance is perhaps the most perfect example of a magic rite. Diabolical dances with strange and ferocious masks, or reproductions of skeletons or monsters, dances strange in their rhythmic, monotonous continuity, which are performed in all solemn ceremonies, are pre-eminent aspects of national life in the north of India and the valleys of Tibet. These dances have no apparently dominant musical motif, and do not express any passion, but only a remote and nostalgic state of mind, swayed by profound sorrow. This state of mind appears to be one of bewitchment, and casts a strong spell over all who observe it. More than a dance, this performance is a set of symbolic gestures whose hidden significance escapes one: a constant and rhythmic evocation of ecstasy, an affirmation of strange beauty, having the almost moving simplicity of a fable. This dance is truly the language of a remote naïveté, apparently inconclusive, the music of a legend whose elusive meaning we cannot grasp, the expression of one of those stories without beginning or end which children love and of which memory retains but the rhythm and cadence. It is a movement that barely detaches itself from the static line, and then reverts to it, and it is evidently connected with the recitation of the formulas or with the rhythm of the dance. These dances apparently reveal no trace of eroticism, and any erotic meaning that may be concealed in them acts through symbolic evocation. Perhaps this is why the Indian dancer is the least coquettish in her attitudes. Many times, while observing these dances, I have had the strange sensation of feeling the pulsation of a life beyond my knowledge, such an impression as one receives when hearing unexpectedly in the silence of night the throbbing voices of distant streets.

The impression is borne in on one that the difference in the way of thinking between the men of the West and those of

the East when untouched by Occidental civilization arises
from the fact that the men of the East feel and act by disregarding causal relations, experimental knowledge, and mathematical approach. Magic, according to Schopenhauer, is the
objectivation of a desire outside the causal nexus, and the Indian conception of life is fundamentally magic.

The fascination and bewitchment of nature in her forms,
colours, fragrances, and in the infinite luminousness of the air
is in India so profound and magnificent that it is easy to understand why the magic belief is alive and constant and the people is permanently enclosed in its circle. Anybody who knows
India has the deep sensation that to be a scientist, an acute observer, or a scholar is not sufficient for an understanding of
this state of mind. One must have felt directly the action of
those remote and close forces, which even our most perfect
instruments cannot measure. In India one understands how the
forms of intellectual and group life are closely bound to the
whole of nature. This living and present power of all things
explains and justifies the worship of mountains, trees, animals,
which are all enclosed in the great magic circle and are all
under the same spell. Great far-away mountain ranges and
rivers represent in the minds and feelings of the believers the
supreme forces, to which their thoughts turn constantly and
of whose presence and threat they are constantly aware. Trees
are believed to be symbols of the laws governing the life of
men. There is a profound affinity, an intimate relationship,
between the great palms with their wide drooping leaves and
the men who rest in their shade and gather their fruit. In all
legends and rituals the sacred tree *aswatta* plays an important
role. The aswatta is the *Ficus religiosa*, and is also called the
banyan tree, because Indian merchants (*banyan*) used to
transact their business in its shade. The Hindus believe that
this tree is a supernatural being. Its large pale-green leaves are
so light that they stir in the softest breeze; the ends of the tall
branches bend to the ground and take root and little by little
new trunks spring up and bear new branches, so that often
hundreds of trunks, covering a vast area and fashioning with
their thick leaves a tunnel of unique beauty under which the
traveller may rest protected from the sun, are formed from a

single tree. The aswatta is sacred to Vishnu. According to certain writers, Vishnu himself assumed the form of this tree, and often, in certain regions of India, the aswatta is consecrated to the god in a long and complicated ceremony.

The sacred tree is often decorated with the triple white cord which distinguishes the Brahmans; one of the most ancient and curious ceremonies is that which solemnly celebrates its marriage to another sacred tree dedicated to Siva, which has been chosen as its spouse. The nuptial rite is performed with the same solemnity as is the matrimony of a Brahman couple: the trees are bound together in such a way as to cause them to grow one beside the other. The blind faith of the peasants is satisfied with the anthropomorphic significance of this rite, but the sacred books read a symbolical meaning into the life of aswatta, the great tree. The boughs which bend to the ground, take root, and form other trees symbolize the spirit descending from a god and entering the body, which is formed from the earth. The tree is an emblem of the universe with its thousand living shapes, appearing always new, yet stemming constantly from a single trunk; a manifestation of the fundamental idea, mentioned in a more or less veiled fashion by all ancient books, that life is a rhythmic cycle.

Animals are hardly less important. The people of India believe every animal to be the possible abode of a deity, to possess a manifest or hidden force, and to exert a power over the life of man. The cow is the centre of worship, and is held to be sacred above all other animals. In the crowded and noisy streets of the great cities all traffic is often brought to a standstill by the insurmountable obstacle, which nobody dares to remove, of a cow tranquilly lying in the middle of the road. People are forbidden to kill cows or eat them. The most ferocious battles between Mussulmans and Hindus have at all times been fought over the problem of food. Everything about the cow is sacred. Its secretions and excrements, mixed together, form the *pancha gavia,* a compound believed to be a remedy for all ills, since it derives from the body of the sacred animal and contains all substances necessary for the complete purification of the believer. The safest method of curing all ailments, and acquitting oneself of all blame, is to rub one's body with this mixture and swallow some of it. Looking after the well-being of the cow, even when old and sick, is in India one of the greatest works of piety, and many hospitals are devoted exclusively to the care of weak animals. Thus the totem of ancient peoples retains its inviolability throughout the centuries, thanks to the tenacity of tradition.

The cow is not the only animal worshipped by the faithful. Serpents, the infernal deities of prehistoric times, are conspicuous in the multitudinous world of Indian deities. The serpent is worshipped in India's famous temples, and countless reptiles are kept and fed by priests. Fish and monkeys, the Garuda bird worshipped by the followers of Vishnu, the sacred bull and the tiger, and all living beings are entitled to a place upon the altar. This is easily explained by the belief (traces of which are to be found in the history of all peoples) that all forms of life are manifestations of a supreme being. In Indian cosmogony this belief blossoms out in an exaggerated and fantastic form. According to it, every being, to a greater or lesser degree, partakes of the deity.

Observation of the stars is joined to that of the major constellations, and throughout India it is believed that desires expressed by a person watching a falling star will be fulfilled. In India this idea, which is also common in the Occident, is reflected in the magic rite of closing one's mouth and sticking a finger into it for greater security, so that one's soul cannot leave the body to accompany the falling star, which is but a spirit returning to earth from paradise.

Indian medicine, called *ayurveda* inasmuch as its lessons are drawn from the ancient Vedas and its classic text is the book of *Susruta*, is magic in type. It is taught officially in the Hindu medical schools, nevertheless, and is legally recognized by the British Government. Even though ancestral traditions, psychological observations, and psychical influences are more important in Indian medicine than the results of experimental science, it has a solid foundation of experience and keen clinical observation.

It is very important to notice the manner in which ancient Indian medicine—clearly of astrological origin—regarded patients suffering from mental troubles. Usually a person in a hallucinatory condition, and generally the psychopath, are feared and revered and sometimes considered sacred. In the case of individuals affected by a violent mania, dangerous to others, exorcisms are practised, and in order to drive out the demon who is in possession of the sufferer, a stronger demon is invoked. This therapeutic demon is sometimes locked up in a bamboo cane and sold in the market-place by sorcerers.

Healing by soul-treatment is an important part of Indian medicine. The medical texts state that a woman in labour should be kept in good spirits, and persons suffering from tuberculosis should be attended by friends, entertaining them with music, perfumes, and pleasant stories. Alcoholic beverages, generally prohibited, are prescribed for certain illnesses.

The personality of the physician is of prime importance. A follower of ancient Indian medicine and its practices, he makes great use of suggestive therapy.

Countless other traditions of ancient magic persist in India. The direction of the flight of birds is looked upon as an omen. The elephant symbolizes the god of wisdom, Ganesa. Serpents are considered sacred, and persons of high caste are not permitted to kill even the most poisonous. Clear indications of the deification of serpents are to be found in the Atharva-Veda.

Water and fire are important factors of Indian magic.

One of the most typical characteristics of Indian magic is that, in keeping with the most exact and severe prescriptions, it is necessary for man to have faith, *schraddha*, in order to obtain what he desires. Negelein remarks that this does not mean faith in the goodness or justness of God, but faith in the magic power of rites, the repetition of the lines of the Vedas, the value of sacrificial ceremonies, and the power of the Brahmans. All Indian rituals postulate the necessity of faith; all miracles are possible and are believed.

The entire Indian world is populated by demons and wizards, with beliefs stemming from strange and fantastic totemistic ideas, such as that of tigeranthropy—the possible metamorphosis of a man into a tiger.

All magic practices known in the history of primitives are still in existence in India. All forms of divination by dice, shells, words, signs, fire, trial by ordeal (by means of water and poison), and exorcism still flourish.

3. THE MAGIC RELIGION

The struggle of Buddhism against magic is expressed in all the sayings and actions of the Enlightened One, who despised the laws of caste, denied all value to magic practices, and maintained that sanctity derives from works. This may explain why Buddhism never took complete possession of India and after a few centuries was suffocated by the belief in magic, which spread again throughout the country under the protection of Brahmanism.

The accomplishments of the Enlightened One are truly unique in the history of the great adventure of the mind. Buddha abolished, or attempted to abolish, the people's belief in magic and taught them the spiritual value of moral laws, courageously abandoning symbolic worship. By his own example Buddha taught the beauty of sacrifice and justice as well as the joys of life and religiosity. Through supreme irony, as L. H. Elliott says, he found a place on the altar, which he wanted to suppress. This historical fact eloquently proves that, especially among peoples organized in closed systems such as the Indian castes, faith in symbols, miracles, and the supernatural can with difficulty be displaced by belief in ethical and moral ideas. The poverty of the agricultural classes, forming almost the whole of the population of India, and the frequency of natural catastrophes and epidemics may perhaps account for this fact.

The close kinship between magic and religion (the religion is really but magic) is substantiated by the fact that the name *Brahman* derives from a word meaning "magic force." This concept is inherent in the belief that when the priests touch a sick person with a finger he recovers, and that their curses have immediate results and cannot be revoked (like the blessing of Jacob). The formulas uttered by the priests take immediate effect: such is, for example, the prophecy of a long life whispered in the ear of a new-born child.

The taking of all nourishment is accompanied by magic prescriptions. *Ghi*, liquid butter, is said to be the best and most

sacred food, and to prolong life; fathers give it to their babies
with a gold spoon. The new-born child, according to Susruta,
should be fed a mixture of butter, honey, and pulverized gold.

A narcotic beverage made of the juice of the soma plant
(*Asclepias acida*), which is said to induce patience in the
drinker, is considered to possess particular virtue. The flesh of
all animals without exception is strictly prohibited, and since
the most serious clashes between Hindus and Moslems almost
always derive from the contempt shown by Hindus for persons eating meat, this is an evidence that the magic idea still
dominates the whole life of India.

The ancient notion of present and eternal magic and of the
overpowering or animating spell of supernatural forces per-
meates Brahmanism, an initiatory religion characterized by
belief in the necessity of self-sacrifice and of ascetic living.
These two basic beliefs assume different forms and constitute
the nucleus of a new conception of religion. The rituals are
particularly aimed at removing from the mind of man all interest in earthly concerns. All the mental faculties of man are
directed toward complete self-mastery, so as to detach his
spiritual life from his physical life and render it independent.
This tendency toward the annihilation of desire, toward
searching and ascetic contemplation, toward the spiritualiza-
tion of life, finds expression in the modern age in the practices
of Yoga.

4. THE DOCTRINE AND PRACTICE OF YOGA

The primitive belief in the continuance of life after death
assumed, in the religion of Brahma, the form of the doctrine of
the migration of the soul. According to Brahmanism, the soul
of the departed goes through a series of existences, and becomes in turn plant, animal, man, demon, and deity. An honest
life, conforming to religious precepts, is the best pledge of the
transmigration of the soul. This idea dictated practices liber-
ating the soul from impure thoughts and desires. The state in
which purification may be obtained is called *atman*, an ecstatic
mood in which the communion of the individual with the All
is realized.

The aim of the Buddhist idea, analogously, is to free the individual from countless transmigrations, to suppress desire and pleasure. Happiness is represented by *nirvana*, the end of all suffering, which, according to Danzel, goes beyond being and non-being. In this idea, a return from Buddhism to popular religion and magic is evident. Hinduism, in its evolution, claims the existence of a trinity composed of Siva, Krishna, and Vishnu, but admits the presence of countless demons and supernatural beings, which may be controlled by various means and practices.[1]

Belief in the necessity to create a special state of mind, an ego-suppressing spell, persists in the Indian mind at all epochs and in spite of all hindrances. We witness the systematic intensification and amplification of subconscious thoughts, and the slow formation of a method, variable in form and result, according to time and person, but remaining identical in purpose: escape. This method brings about an escape from personality and from material life, and, despite a thousand obstacles and difficulties, effects the achievement of a conjunction with the purely spiritual life. Thus from without, from a position of absolute superiority, magic rules over the whole of organic life, over individuals, animals, plants, over time and space.

All the complex practices of Yoga, about which so much has been written and which have successively been considered as expressions of a high philosophical idea, as severe ritual practices, or as complex quackery and refined swindles, and which in recent times have given rise to various doctrines and schools, are linked with this central notion. One of the most interesting books on this subject is that of Vasant G. Rele, an Indian physician, who has devoted himself particularly to the study of *Kundalini* or Laya Yoga. This is one of the most ancient Yogas, and is founded on the magic power of the serpent. It requires several preparations which eventuate in different phenomena, including that of apparent death, or, better, of the suspension of life for a certain lapse of time. This practice is very well known in Europe also. After the demon-

[1] F. Alexander published a remarkable paper, "*Die Versenkung des Buddhas*" (*Imago*, 1924), discussing the problem of Yoga from the psychoanalytical viewpoint.

stration afforded by experiments on a patient at the Medical Association of Bombay, during which the pulse of the radial and temporal arteries of the patient, and his heart-beat were suspended for several seconds, owing to the suggestive power of Yoga, Rele subjected the patient to a set of objective observations under severe scientific control by X-ray, sphygmograph, etc. Making a very exact study of all the physiological phenomena, Rele reached certain conclusions which should be noted, because, although possibly they are not entirely acceptable and do not give a complete explanation of all the facts, they doubtless indicate the path that is to be followed in relating these phenomena to our positive, scientific knowledge of anatomy and physiology.

The word *Yoga* is a derivative from the stem *juja*, meaning to unite or commingle, to dominate. This has the same root as the Latin *jugum*, yoke. Just as two pieces of metal can be united through fusion, a process of calefaction, and through manipulation, in Yoga the spirit *Iivàtma*, which is part of the universal spirit Paramatma, is joined to the Universal Spirit by means of physical and mental exercises. Certain writers define Yoga as a concentration purposing to free the spirit from matter. Other writers define it better as "the science which increases human capacity to respond to higher vibrations and to perceive and assimilate motions and events manifested in the universe." According to the individuals practising it, Yoga is a method for slowly raising the initiate to where he can meet the object constituting the goal of his research and yearning. There are many ways of obtaining this aim: Karma-Yoga, which prescribes devotion of every action and thought to God; Bhakti-Yoga, which teaches renunciation of all hopes and aspirations in order to concentrate one's every thought on the divinity; and finally the most perfect form, Jnana-Yoga, according to which the soul must identify itself with the deity.

The studies to which I have referred prove that this system, whose most important practices I have rapidly indicated, succeeds in bringing about control of the autonomous nervous system and thus, as in the experiment held in Bombay, may stop even peripheral arterial pulses, such as the temporal pulse, a thing which one can hardly believe could be done by muscular contraction. Rele, closely studying the postures and methods of Yoga, proves that undoubtedly the ancient sages who invented this method possessed a wide knowledge of the nervous system, and that their ideas on the functions of the central system, and especially of the sympathetic and pneumogastric system, were not far removed from those we have reached, thanks to the most recent scientific research. The excitation of all the nervous centres (*chakras*) is always accomplished through the mysterious *kundalini* from which all supernatural power stems. Divine power is communicated to the human body through the *kundalini* and the six *chakras* and their derivatives. The *kundalini* is normally dormant, and it is only when it is awakened or aroused to activity by means of the Yoga that man can perceive all supernatural virtues, his soul rise from the tomb of lies, and the perfection of beauty fill his heart with joy. *Kundalini* is the leader of all the vital functions, the centre of energy, the individual representative of the cosmic power that creates and sustains the universe. Where does this dormant force reside? According to the classic texts it dwells in the Brahman-Randkra—that is, in the cavity of the skull (the fourth ventricle). Until it is awakened no one can see the soul living in the body, nor is it allowed to join itself to the universal soul. Various texts assign different positions to the dormant *kundalini*, and we cannot here examine all the grounds that led Rele to the conclusion that it should be identified with the vagus, or pneumogastric, the tenth cranial nerve. It arises under the fourth ventricle, issues from the cranium through the small jugular hole forming the jugular or knotted ganglia, and passes through the spine to the abdomen, where it is a concurrent factor in innervating the various intestines: it is connected with the solar ganglia.

A study of the relations between the pneumogastric and the sympathetic nerve, and a comparison of them with the *kundalini*, show that Rele's hypothesis is highly tenable and that all the phenomena I have pointed out are due to an excitation of the pneumogastric nerve, which is the same as the *kundalini*. The aim and effect of Yoga and its practices consist, therefore, in the suppression of all other sources of sensation and excitation and in the achievement of conscious control over the pneumogastric nerve and, through it, over all the most important functions of organic life. An examination of the various positions occupied by the person performing these practices, and above all a study of the position of his tongue behind the uvula, by means of which he brings about a cessation of breathing and the appearance of death, prove that the most important element in all these practices is the mastery, precluded to normal man, of the nervous centres.

I have said that this hypothesis may not, in all its particulars, be sufficient to furnish an exact explanation of all the phenomena characterizing the practice of Yoga and, equally typical, of what is generally called fakirism. There is no doubt, however, that Yoga, in order to detach the soul from the body and join it to the universal spirit, tends to create a state of physical repose and of introversion of attention and will, which leads to perfect mastery and conscious control over the main nerve centres. This state, therefore, corresponds to a passive spell in the sense that all critical faculties are obliterated so that attention and will may concentrate on an idea or supernatural fact. Propounding a wider interpretation than Rele's, one might perhaps imagine that, through control of the action of the vagus nerve, Yoga attempts to awaken the subconscious, and that in reality the mysterious power of the *kundalini* consists in the subconscious which may be awakened through a complete suppression of sensation, the abolition of all individual psychic activity, and the re-establishment of relations, existent but lying dormant in the subconscious, between the individual and the cosmos.

The reader may be convinced of this fact by going over the prescriptions for the fourth grade: "One's eyes should be fixed, without closing or opening them too much, on a point of the body corresponding to that which one must see internally (these points are marked by mystic circles). If the yogi succeeds in concentrating his consciousness and breathing on the internal things that he wishes to know, and, bowing his head, fixes his gaze on a point, without, however, thinking of the object at which he is looking, inasmuch as in reality his entire attention is totally absorbed by the internally percepti-

ble things, he will be on the path to supreme reality, characterized by liberation."

It is clear, therefore, that this long procedure, which is
taught accurately today in many schools, is but the creation
of a passive spell by means of profound self-suggestion, leading finally to threefold wisdom and thus to mastery of the
occult powers.

Self-suggestion or awakening of the individual's subconscious, the purest and most strictly spiritual expression of
Yoga, may become, in certain practices of fakirism, heterosuggestion or awakening of the collective subconscious, and
in these manifestations Yoga employs all the rites of magic.
Hindu magic, which certain writers, such as Eliphas Levi,
consider as the origin and core of black magic, employs, like
primitive sorcery, but with a more highly complete system,
group-suggestion by means of words, actions, perfumes, talismans, amulets, and rhythms. Group-suggestion explains all
manifestations which, like the trick of the tree growing before
one's eyes under the influence of magic formulas, and that of
the baby thrown into the air by a bamboo stick, who falls to
pieces and is put together again by the fakir, belong, undoubtedly, to the countless list of miracles existing only in the eyes
of the spectators under a spell, consciously prepared by environment, by other inexplicable facts, objectively controlled,
which they have witnessed, and by intense expectation. These
facts belong to the sphere of collective hallucinations, and are
based on the magic suggestion.

If we wish to penetrate more profoundly into the study of
these interesting facts, which certainly cannot be better studied than in the country in which they have had a thousand
years of physical and psychical preparation and which supplies an ideal environment for them, we may finally inquire
whether the whole idea of Yoga and its practices does not
stem from primitive magic notions, and does not represent at
bottom but an outgrowth of them. This hypothesis is perhaps
the most justified. Among all peoples and in all times magic
belief has been temporarily dominated by mysticism or metaphysics; and has undergone many transformations due to the

influences to which it has been subjected. Among Occidental peoples, however, mystic magic has been implemented in religion, and discontinued or broken off in its development, thanks to experimental science and objective criticism. These have almost utterly destroyed many ideas founded on the unreal, or rather they have thrust back the boundaries of consciousness, constantly creating new superstructures and manifestations of the ego. In India experimental scientific reasoning never gained a foothold among the people, and the limits between real and unreal, subject and object, conscious and subconscious, have never been clearly drawn. This is due perhaps, as I have said before, to the conditions of the country, the closed life of its valleys and mountains, to the translucence of its atmosphere, its climate, to the social life, rigidly divided into castes. For this reason, if I am not mistaken, the Hindu is the only conception that preserves uninterrupted continuity. In it dominant mysticism perfects itself in exact rites, which become a system, the most perfect system of transcendental mysticism known to man. Consequently I feel that it may be stated that the mind and civilization of India are essentially, fundamentally magic, and as such have remained intact throughout the millenniums.

XIII

State Magic of Egypt

I. TOTEMISM

EGYPT, since the remotest times, has been the country of symbols, mysteries, magic, alchemy, and all the occult arts. No other people has left us such a treasure of perfectly preserved precious monuments of its distant past; of no country do so many voices speak, so eloquently, to recall mysteries that were inexplicable for many centuries, and to describe rites, temples, and tombs that should have remained for ever sealed to the profane. The clear idea—later a religious canon—of the soul which can detach itself from the body, abandoning it and continuing to live after its death, probably originated in Egypt. The belief in a judgment after death is expressed for the first time in the paintings and carvings on Egyptian tombs. In the legend of Osiris, undoubtedly a solar myth, the idea of the battle against death rises from the knowledge of death and from the more ancient notion of possible mutations and of new forms deriving from it.

Magic dominated the whole life of ancient Egypt; there it was believed to have originated, and there it later developed into a religious system. It helps to explain the two central problems of Egyptian metaphysics: that of the creation of the world (the doctrine of Heliopolis) and that of life and death (the myth of Osiris). All myths—and particularly that of the sun, the scarab which wanders in the sky, the youth Horus, who is born from the lotus flower, fights against the serpent, departs from men, riding on the back of his mother, the heavenly cow—are founded on magic beliefs. The most ancient portrayals of superior beings, the falcon of Horus, the dog of Anubis, the ibis of Thot, the Theban crocodile, the cow of Hathor, and numberless others, derive from the totemistic idea. Later the deity assumes a hybrid form and is represented by the body of a man or woman with the head of an animal.

[157]

Shortly after, the animal disappears and remains in only one detail of the portrayal, such as the small horn of Amon, Isis, and Hathor. The evolution of magic, according to Moret, marks stages of human thought that may be fairly accurately dated. The monuments of the prehistoric epoch disclose only totemic figures—animals, plants, and objects. Toward the beginning of the First Dynasty the hawks and fish assume human traits; at the end of the Second Dynasty human bodies with ancient totem heads, transformed into anthropomorphic gods, begin to appear. From then on, the trend toward depictions of human forms is rapid, and in the sanctuaries the ancient gods yield to new divine beings, not to reappear until the age of Egyptian decadence.

In the iconography of every period animals and totemic idols are preserved. Depictions of the totem protector of the clan are primarily preserved in the heraldic emblems of different regions. Some of these totems were paid divine honours. The ox was worshipped in the Temple of Phtah, from Rameses II up to the Ptolemaic epoch. Other animals were devoutly worshipped in single cities and regions, mummified after death, and buried in sacred graves. The penalty for killing an ibis or a hawk was death. But, according to Herodotus, the power of these sacred animals was strictly confined to a single city or region; beyond these boundaries the law does not protect them, and no scruples are felt about eating them. The survival of the totemistic conception is evident.

2. THE CULT AND THE EVOCATION OF THE DEAD

In a later epoch, when all of Egypt was united under the sceptre of the rulers, whose power extended beyond the borders of the kingdom, the religious idea becomes loftier and more elaborated. The gods assume a cosmogonic significance and represent the forces of nature. But the sacred rites are faithfully preserved and contain all the essential magic characteristics. The mystery of Osiris, the main episodes of which are the death, burial, and resurrection of the god, was portrayed throughout Egypt, outdoors and in special buildings connected with the temples of the gods. The ancient texts contain the magic formulas for the purifying and shrouding of the corpse, for restoring the form of the cadaver, and for the presentation of offerings. Magic formulas, preserved in the *Book of the Dead*, were uttered before Osiris, the judge of the souls of those who have passed beyond. There is no fear of death in the Egyptian belief. When all the sacred rites have been performed, and the dead man's tomb has been provided with all the essential foods and the objects that gave him pleasure in his earthly existence, he passes from one life to another, in which all joys await him. It is necessary, therefore, to preserve the corpse by a procedure identical, according to tradition, with that employed by Anubis, the god, to preserve the body of Osiris. An exact ritual prescribes the manner in which the corpse must be prepared, placed in a solution of salt and soda, then soaked with oil, rubbed with unguents, and bound with strips of linen upon which the formulas are inscribed. This is the procedure for the preparation of the body; in the beginning the entrails and heart were removed and placed in vases protected by the four sons of Horus. The most important ceremony, performed secretly in the temple, was the opening of the mouth and eyes of the corpse. A priest, covered with a panther skin, touched with his wand the face, mouth, and eyes of the corpse, while another priest recited the magic formula, and immediately after, the body was sealed within its tomb.

Lexa in his book on the magic of ancient Egypt (Paris, 1925), which is a mine of information for the study of texts, practices, and images, states that for the inhabitant of ancient Egypt life after death is more important than that on earth, which in his opinion is but a brief passage. This belief explains the exactness with which the Egyptians made their preparations for future life, laying all the necessary plans for burial rites so that life after death would be arranged in the best way possible.

The statuettes placed in tombs are meant eventually to replace the body when it passes on to another life; the figures of the servants, peasants, animals, and even those of the gods are meant to accompany the dead and protect him.

Texts found in the pyramids have preserved for us the magic formulas bearing on resurrection. Plutarch describes the magic performance of the *cysta mystica*: a gold vase was carried to the Nile, where it was filled with water; a little earth was mixed with the water, and this substance was fashioned into figures containing seeds of grain. Grain grew from the figures, and this was a symbol of rebirth, in which, in the most obvious form, a manifestation of the life of nature, the coming of spring, symbolized the belief in resurrection.

In his book *Egyptian Magic* Budge states that magic influenced the entire Egyptian civilization, from early days down to the last period, in a manner so profound, so lasting, that it is very hard exactly to evaluate its importance. During the Fourth Dynasty magic art was officially recognized; magic practices, however, were not only pre-dynastic but older than any deistic conception. The magic content of the texts written in hieroglyphics on the pyramids is so apparent that Breasted claims that all these inscriptions represent but a collection of magic texts. The magic power of the written and spoken word, of amulets and talismans, formed an important part of Egyptian magic.

Magic in Egyptian life is closely connected with religion, though with the passing of time a separation between priest and magician takes place, which is intensified when religion becomes connected with political and moral ideas. The gods are undoubtedly the inventors of the magic formulas; Thot is the "god with the creating voice, the master of words and books," Isis is the great prophetess knowing all the secrets, Khonsou carries out magic rites and works spells by order of the gods. The gods possess the maximum power; the lower, invisible beings that inhabit earth or sea cannot match the force of the gods, but their power may bring illness and misfortune, effect the death of man and beast, and ruin crops. Men who are wise, who know the names of the gods, spirits, and genii can wield a great power by exactly uttering the formulas. Word, name, intonation, and rhythm have enormous importance in all sacerdotal and magic practices. According to Egyptian belief, the name of god or king, spirit or sacred animal, is in itself creative; uttering a name is an act of the utmost importance and may have serious results if all the prescribed rules are not observed. The extremely severe prohibition—the taboo of the name—against uttering the sacred names of the deities, codified for the Jews in the Biblical text, doubtless originates in the terror of the results that may occur from pronouncing a mighty name inadvertently, which is tantamount to an invocation made in vain or without the required precautions. In the invocation of dead kings, in the formulas containing their titles, in the *Book of the Dead*, in the medical texts, uttering a name is equivalent to invoking it. There are many rules specifying with the greatest minuteness the manner in which a powerful and feared name must be spoken in order to achieve the desired result.

3. AMULETS, SYMBOLS, AND MYSTERIES

The Egyptian sorcerer employed formulas to protect his life and that of his followers. With these formulas, to which he almost always added practices revealing a basic knowledge of medicine, he cured the sick by driving out malignant demons. Talismans and amulets could be images of gods, kings, or animals; often they were simply tablets carved with the symbols of life, health, power, or beauty, hieroglyphs embodying the idea of help or protection or of the healing of infirmities. The same value was attached to wearing a symbolic object as to uttering the sacred word or the magic formula.

Signs, especially those carved on scarabs or other amulets, had tremendous importance. The scarab symbolized life and immortality, since it has the shape of a heart, and often a stone scarab with the magic formula carved on it was placed in a mummy, whose heart had been removed and, together with the entrails, placed in an alabaster vase. Besides these signs on plastic amulets, there were others written on parchment or papyrus, which were rolled up and tied around the neck of the corpse, or knotted. The knot was one of the most highly prized amulets. The hieroglyph *dmz*, which means "to tie," "to unite," "to join," has the form of a knot. Various objects were preserved in knots—for example, scarabs, and parts of small animals.

The Cairo Museum contains a splendid collection of scarabs, with the name of a Pharaoh carved within a small circle. It was a taboo name; it conferred a magic power on the person bear-

ing it, speaking it, or wearing it in written form. Thousands
of amulets, extended fingers and painted eyes, in shining
enamel, of every size and colour; trees, symbolizing life; small
statues of men and of animals; talismans, which the curiosity
of archæologists and the irreverence of modern civilization
have snatched from ancient tombs and displayed in showcases,
where they silently exhibit the memory of their power, document the history of the vast and complex magical beliefs of the
ancient Egyptians.

Ritual formulas and exorcisms are recorded in the *Book of
the Dead* and in the magic papyri. There is a formula and a
remedy for every situation, against every danger.

Egyptian sorcery was important in the protection of children. The following is the text of an exorcism taken from the
Book of Magic Formulas for Mother and Child, published by
Maspero: "Vanish, O death living in darkness, O you whose
nose is turned backwards, disappear without accomplishing
what you set out to do. If you are come to kiss this child I will
not permit you to do it. If you are come to stop his crying I
will not permit you to stop it; if you are come to take him I
will not permit you to take him. For his sake I have cast spells
against you with pricking lettuce, with garlic which you cannot smell, with honey which is sweet to man and repulsive to
the dead, with a spool of thread. Vanish without accomplishing
the purpose of your coming!" Magic formulas against illness
have a notable place in the medical papyri. This formula
against rheumatism is contained in the Ebers papyrus: "Disappear, O rheumatism, son of rheumatism, who breaks the bones
and bursts the skull and painfully wounds the seven openings
of the head! Such is the remedy: the milk of a woman who has
given birth to a child; such is the sweet perfume that will expel
you from the body of your victim. Go forth and fall to the
earth, filthy that which does such harm."

Other magic formulas were uttered when the physician
took the vase of medicines in his hand. With a formula on his
lips he prepared the barley, honey, or fat which were the in-
gredients of the medicine, applied the bandage to the wound,
and removed it. Prayers, threats, commands, prohibitions, and
exorcisms alternated in the formulas.

A characteristic trait of Egyptian magic medicine is that it was intelligently combined with rational empirical medicine. The sick person did not resort to magic alone, but entrusted himself simultaneously to a physician. The Ebers papyrus states that a magic formula must be coupled with the medicament, but it adds that every magic practice must be either accompanied or followed by the proper medicament. Lexa cites many sources that illustrate the custom of accompanying the cure of sickness, as well as the act of provoking it, with magic rites.

The introduction to the Ebers papyrus reads: "If the remedy is given, it is also necessary that the inimical forces be exorcized from my heart and body. Magic formulas together with the remedies are efficacious and the remedies are potent when they operate in conjunction with the magic formulas."

The magic ritual intended to blind man or drive him insane is preserved in the demotic papyri of London and of Leiden, and the ceremony intended to kill him is to be found in more than one funeral inscription.

All the magic remedies, all the ideas of belongings, all the beliefs that, as we saw, were familiar to primitive peoples, were to be found in Egyptian medical magic. Gout was treated by tying an amulet of deerskin to the feet, since it was believed that the agility of the animal's feet would pass into those of the invalid. Cat grease was used to drive away mice, the blood of a black calf or a black bull to prevent one's hair from turning white. Countless examples of like prescriptions might be quoted. Blood, milk, and saliva were much used as ritual remedies.

Originally the formulas had to be uttered by the physician or sorcerer, but later the conviction grew that the same result could be obtained by writing the formula on a papyrus to be swallowed by the sick person, or by having him drink beer in which the papyrus had been washed. Still later, further simplifying the procedure, magicians recited the formulas over beer, water, or wine, which, when drunk by the patient, introduced into his body the magic virtue transmitted to the beverage and assured his recovery. These procedures are obviously reminiscent of the practices of quack doctors or of modern healers.

There is one magic rite that I feel it is particularly important to mention because of its evident analogy with some modern practices. This is the rite, described in the demotic papyri of London and of Leiden, intended to evoke the gods, the luminous spirits, and the ghosts of the damned. I summarize from Lexa's book. The sorcerer avails himself of a youth who has had no contact with women and after examining him and finding him suitable, gives him the amulets that protect him from all dangers during the evocation of the spirits, and opens the rite with a prayer in which he asks the gods to favour the undertaking. He then lights a lamp in a dark room and places the youth before it so that he faces it with closed eyes. The sorcerer then stands beside or behind him, bows his head over him, and repeats the proper formula seven times, gently tapping him on the head and then asking: "Do you see the light?" When the youth replies: "I see the light," he questions him about all he wishes to know. In order to induce the desired condition quickly, the sorcerer proceeds to burn incense or other fragrant materials. When the rite is at an end and the spirits have responded to his call, the sorcerer, who remains near the youth with his head bowed over him, again repeats the magic formula seven times, ordering the youth to open his eyes.

Lexa's book also contains the prescriptions for a rite by which the magician, placing himself before a lantern and repeating the formulas, can put himself to sleep, and in his sleep glimpse the gods and the spirits of the dead.

It appears from this and other sources that hypnoidal practices for establishing contact with the gods and with the spirits of the dead were perfectly known to Egyptian sorcerers, and Semitic names in the formulas indicate that some of the wizards were of foreign origin. These evocatory procedures must have been familiar to the people of Israel.

The Egyptian idea of religion in its purest form assumes the character of a philosophic system, and by a slow process, in the most recondite of its mysteries, reserved to initiates, approaches monotheism. Symbolic practices continue, up to the decay which marks the end, or rather the new evolution, of

Egyptian civilization, to be the expression of the religious idea, the means by which the believers communicate with the deity.

Later, in the centuries immediately preceding Christianity, in the Hellenistic Alexandrian epoch, organized and systematized magic begets the mysteries. Aram cites the story of Clement the Roman (A.D. 200), describing his desire to know the mystery of life and of the soul after death, and relating how he learned it from an Egyptian high priest and a sorcerer who, for a large sum of money, was persuaded to evoke a soul and question it about immortality. Clement the Roman is one of the so-called Apostolic Fathers, and the legend says that he was the third Bishop of Rome after Peter, and a fiery opponent of St. Paul. It is interesting that that age also believed it possible to evoke the souls of the dead by the rites of the mysteries. Juvenal refers to this fact when he describes the popularity of the Chaldean astrologers in Rome, who were sought after by all the citizens, and particularly by women.

Evidence regarding the Egyptian mysteries is very scarce, since the magic papyri found in Theban tombs, whose contents go back to the last centuries before Christ, have been deciphered only partially and imperfectly. One of these papyri, translated by Hopfner of Prague and cited by Aram, mentions a letter to Pharaoh Psammeticus, which describes a black magic rite for the evocation of the infernal divinity Set, the enemy of Osiris, called by the Greek name of Typhon. One may gather from this and other examples that magic evocations of deities were practised according to an exactly defined system, which included a magic practice of divination, which deserves to be dwelt on because of its close analogy with modern phenomena. In the centre of a tripod of bronze, upon which was portrayed Hecate, the goddess of all magicians, there was an orifice through which was inserted a rod bearing a magic disk, carved with Greek, Hebrew, and hieroglyphic letters in several squares. Beside the disk a bronze nail was affixed to the wall in such a way that a ring, hanging from a string tied to the nail, stopped in its oscillations over one point or another of the magic disk, which in its turn could be rotated. The letters pointed to by the ring were noted, and this practice was continued until the letters and signs formed words and phrases, which were held to be replies to the questions asked of the magician.

We shall later see how Egyptian sorcery of the Alexandrian epoch exercised a notable influence over the mysteries of the first centuries of Christianity, and how through these mysteries the magic idea, wrapped in secrecy, assumed new forms and expressions, preserving some of its basic notions even down to our time.

XIV

Assyro-Babylonian Speculative Magic

I. MAGIC MYTHS

THE history of magic may be most easily traced among the Babylonians, who dwelt in the region between the Tigris and Euphrates rivers. Sufficient elements are extant to mark this development through art and epic poetry. The most ancient figurations of the Babylonians document again and again, with technically flawless examples, the fundamental magic ideas on the relationship and alliance between man and animal. The entire Babylonian pantheon, all the streets of their monumental city, are filled with animals of strange, stylized forms, probably deriving from the ineffaceable memories of the primitive mind. Individuals engage in magic battles against fate, battles that are eloquently described throughout the epic of Gilgamesh, one third man and two thirds god, who fights to be a man and then asks the gods for salvation and immortality. Gilgamesh's is a tragic drama which relates with transcendent passion the history of thousands of years of the life of man slowly detaching himself from primitive magic ideas. It is the drama of Prometheus and of Hercules—the battle of man for an escape and against death. By every means Gilgamesh attempts to avoid sleep, which he fears like death. The epic effort of his evoking his dead brother from the shadows is vividly portrayed. Finally Gilgamesh returns to earth with the resignation of a man who, brooding on rebellion, accepts his destiny. This marvellous epic is a summation of the history of man, always fearing and always hoping, strong in his alliance with supernatural beings or confident of his power to conquer them; of man wishing to obtain immortality and failing in his desire. The perennial fight in man of flesh and spirit, the breathless return to the primordial astrological idea, the search for the secrets of the sky, which generates the myth of the sun and, after many centuries, the magic calendar, are all represented with impelling beauty in Gilgamesh's epic.

The Babylonians very early manifested powers of reasoning founded on experience. The development of their agriculture was surprisingly rapid, commerce was established and became important, civil and administrative legislation was founded, and speculative and practical systems based on a profound observation of nature, of the stars and their movements, of rivers and their changes, were formed. This activity was evinced not only in the creation of a political and legislative machinery, in the promulgation of hygienic measures, in the invention of measures of protection against floods by perfect canalization, and in the organization of trades, but also in the formation of a developed religious system. In this system sorcery, based on the archaic subconscious and the collective memory of the past, played an important part; but sorcery itself was torn by the conflict between the religious and the magic idea, brought about by the progressive growth of the observation of nature and of scientific reasoning. Among the Assyro-Babylonians we find traces of well-organized sorcery, which underlay for centuries the power of the priestcraft exercising it and simultaneously, under the influence of observation, determined scientific reasoning and stimulated the growth of the occult sciences, in which sorcery assumed, perhaps for the first time in history, an orientation based on close observation of nature and on critical thinking.

In the Babylonian pantheon, the gods dwelt in the sky, the waters, and the air. The god of the sky, Anu, the god of the earth, En-lil (Bel), the god of the waters, Ea, constituted the supreme trinity. The powers with which these gods were believed to be endowed were different in various regions and cities, and each god was recognized as the protector of a certain locality and invested with particular characteristics. The three main divinities were surrounded by others, which were thought of as subject to and dependent on them. Some of these minor divinities, like Marduk, the god of Babylon, and the son of Ea, were later held worthy of greater honours. But of all the gods, as Lenormand and Lehmann point out, the most interesting from the viewpoint of the history of magic is Ea. He presides over all magic practices, probably because he is the god of water, which is of prime importance in the magic world. Ea is the divine sorcerer and hence the god of wisdom, the master of all the arts. It was he who shaped man out of clay and gave him life; he created the earth out of water so that, according to popular credence and official belief (codified by the texts preserved in the clay tablets of the Library of Nineveh), he is credited with possessing a tremendously great power. Ea is the expert in all magic formulas and exorcisms; his son Marduk, the sun god and the god of fire, are subordinated to him.

Besides the gods, an important role is played in Babylonian religion by malignant demons, who are held responsible for serious atmospheric disturbances, eclipses, and storms. They unsettle the lives of men and animals, prevent, according to the texts of Nineveh, the fecundation of women, and snatch children from their mothers' breasts. They force doves to abandon their nests, compel swallows to flee to remotest regions, and induce the two most feared illnesses of ancient Chaldea, pestilence and fever. "Cursed Asak directs his power against the head of man, the cruel Namtar against his life, the infamous Tuk against his neck, the bearer of misfortunes Alu against man's breast, the wicked Ekin against his intestines, and the terrible Galu against his hands." Every demon has clearly defined functions. An exact system, calculated down to the last detail, specifies the might of these beings, their location, and their method of combat. As a necessary consequence, the idea became prevalent that an eternal battle goes on between favourable and adverse demons, good and evil forces. The gods are entrusted with directing these struggles and deciding the outcome by their supreme power.

2. EVOCATIONS, EXORCISMS, AND DIVINATION

The importance of sorcery in the face of this demonistic system is very clear. Sorcery is one of the most important elements in the religion of the Sumerians, Akkadians, and Assyrians. Their rites are rich in magic. The gods often perform magic acts, and man attempts to influence their will with magic means. Since every disease argues the presence of a malignant spirit in the body, magic is *pars magna* of the art of medicine. Magic acts are preferably performed at night, and a horoscope is necessary for the choice of the suitable hour. A man upon whom a spell has been cast becomes impure, and it is therefore necessary to hold cathartic or purgative rites, in which milk, butter, cream, and various metals such as gold, silver, and brass are used. A rite must be performed for protection or defence. The amulet is the fixation of the magic action, and for this reason it is worn on the body, hung over the doorway, or placed on the threshold of the house. Amulets enable man to escape from demons and to obtain the favour of the gods. Clay statuettes of demons and apotropaic animals are believed to protect houses and to defend their inhabitants from illness. These statuettes represent mermen, bird-headed men, men with the tail and hoofs of a bull, cat-headed men, and so forth. Magic contrivances include curses and blessings. Knots are likewise a method for binding, both physically and morally, and the untying of knots indicates the breaking of the spell. Exorcism and related sacrifices are accompanied by magic rites.

Sorcery invokes divine protection against evil demons and exorcizes them to defend man in the war he wages against them. Magic action, therefore, is strictly connected with religion and its cult: the priest is a magician as well, because he is the only one who knows the formulas and exorcism, can avert dangers and establish contact with superior beings. The priest-magician takes over all the functions of the physician, and performs all the practices to drive away evil demons and paralyse adverse magic forces. These functions are mostly performed by means of exorcisms, a large number of formulas of which are still extant. Exorcisms usually begin with a description of the illness, after which the deity is invoked and an account of the deity's accomplishments is given, as witnessed by the following example quoted by Lehmann:

"The disease of the forehead (insanity?) is sent by the ruler of hell; the destructive demon will not permit man to sleep or find beneficent slumber. This is a complaint that lasts day and night; it attacks the old and bends them like reeds, and kills the young like lambs. Marduk perceives and helps the sick person. He goes to the house of his father, Ea, and speaks to him: 'My father, headaches come from hell. What should this man do, how can he overcome them?' Ea replies: 'Go, my son. Take a pail, fill it with water at the mouth of two rivers, endow this water with your great magic power, bathe the man, creature of your god, with it, and bind his head with a scarf. Let this madness disappear. Let the illness of this man's head vanish like the short night rain. Let the prescription of Ea heal him. Let Marduk, the first-born of the ocean, purify him!' "

This formula testifies to practices still widely used in popular medicine—namely, that of knot-tying and that of purification by water. Another very popular practice in Babylonian magic consists in the use of clay figures representing demons of various maladies. These figures are tied to the body of the sufferer in the belief that the evil demon will be put to flight by the sight of his bound image. Talismans and amulets, simulacra of divinities, often of gigantic size, which are placed before houses or palaces to protect the entrance, and tables of clay or of stone upon which exorcisms are written are widespread methods of the priestly sorcery of Chaldea.

It is interesting to observe the role of myths in the magic religion of Chaldea. These myths disclose traces of remote events whose memory has been preserved. The myth of Gilgamesh, two thirds god and one third man, is recounted in the tablets of the Library of King Assurbanipal (*circa* 600 B.C.). These tablets, now in the British Museum, were translated by Ungnad. The myth describes the amazement of Gilgamesh when seeing death for the first time as it strikes his friend Engidu. Gilgamesh goes in search of his ancestor Ut-Napishtim to ask him for help against death. Ut-Napishtim tells him the story of the flood (which in Babylonian mythology is almost identical with that in the Biblical narrative), but can suggest no remedy against death. As a consequence Gilgamesh returns to his native land and, by invoking Ea, succeeds in seeing the Kingdom of Death, talking with the spirit of Engidu, and receiving his advice. In many respects the figure of Ut-Napishtim corresponds to that of Noah in the Biblical narrative; in the Babylonian legend Ut-Napishtim is the representation of ancient man, for whom death did not exist, and he is in constant and eternal contact with the things of the sky and of the earth. Engidu lives with the animals, eats grass like the gazelles, drinks with the quadrupeds, and dies like the animals. The entire myth is pervaded with magic ideas, and appears to us, like all conceptions of ancient epochs, to be inwoven in a set of symbolizations, like those of the early initiatory mysteries of primeval days.

The myth of the great flood, willed by the gods for the destruction of the human race, is so narrated in the Babylonian tablets as to convince one that the tale refers to an event that really took place in the glacial period. There is no evidence that this myth refers to a flood which occurred in the region between the Tigris and the Euphrates, as is maintained by some scholars. The different relations of this myth point to a catastrophe occasioned by a terrible downpour which lasted six days and six nights. In the Babylonian account the hero, Ut-Napishtim, on the advice of Ea, builds a boat with which he saves his own life and that of the animals living with him. On the seventh day the sky clears and the hero sends out first a pigeon, then a swallow, which return to the boat, then a raven, which does not come back. Ut-Napishtim then abandons the boat, taking with him everything he has saved, and offers a sacrifice to the gods on the summit of the mountain.

3. THE EVOLUTION OF BABYLONIAN SORCERY

According to Babylonian belief, demons almost always have the form of strange or monstrous animals. God and priests fight against them. Formulas and rites, exorcisms and invocations, talismans and amulets constitute an enormous arsenal of defence, arranged in various categories according to need. The exorcizer-priest of the Sumerians knows all the demons and is conversant with the formulas necessary to conquer and expel each one of them from the human body. The ancient conception of the origin of contagious diseases is, fundamentally, identical with the discoveries of the most recent scientific research. According to the ancient priests and to present-day physicians, illness results from infection—that is, from the penetration of the body by an invisible being, which must be

Anubis watching the tombs of the kings (Valley of Thebes, Egypt)

Egyptian amulets. The "divine eyes" that protect against the evil eye,
the "signs of life," the "columns," the "ritual vessels," the frog, and
the fish.

driven away or from whose action the individual must be protected. There is an undeniable analogy between the idea of
driving away the demon (or preventing him from penetrating
the body) by using, as apotropaics, exact images of the demon
himself, and the modern use of vaccines and serums.

The highest power of healing and beneficial magic was concentrated in the hands of priests, who held the same position
in the community as did the sorcerers among primitive
peoples. It is natural that this magic power, which we may call
official and systematic, and whose usage was skilfully arranged
and codified in a rigid form, should have been combated with
increasing vigour by the art of those magicians who, without
being priests and appealing to the great gods for protection,
believed that they could act directly on the evil demons, not
by hindering or preventing their actions, but by favouring
them. This magic constitutes the attempt at rebellion taking
place whenever constituted authority is established. Black
magic is often the sorcery of individuals or single groups acting against the magic of the priests and of the State. The
Babylonian wizards who exercised this magic were inimical to
existing institutions and ready to serve their personal interests
and ideas of revenge. They invoked evil demons to destroy
and damage their enemies and competitors, and, with practices
analogous and opposed to those of official sorcery, spread sickness, misery, desolation, and death. They are perhaps the first
types of the spellbinder, inimical to the official religion, from
which he tries to protect himself. The most terrible method
employed by black magic is the evil eye, which can wreak in-
calculable damage. Another practice of black magic is the
envoûtement, the custom of constructing the image of a person whom one desires to kill or to injure seriously, inflicting
on the image, symbolically, the injuries one craves to inflict
on one's enemy.

With the progress of culture and the increase in experience
and in the knowledge of astronomy and mathematics, religious
beliefs grew and evolved. A religious reform occurred during
the reign of the Sargonids. Traces of this reform are to be
found in the tablets written by order of Sargon II, *circa* 700
B.C. Astronomical knowledge, the study of the movement of

the stars, the establishment of the law of cycles which rules the planets, gave rise to a systematized doctrine of the control of the stars over human life and of the possibility of foreseeing the future from their position in the sky. These beliefs stimulated astrology and, in general, the occult sciences, which resulted from grafting careful, exact, objective observations on the branch of ancient magic. The possibility of making prophetic predictions notably increased the prestige of the official sorcerer, and the wizards, his rivals, attempted to avail themselves of the same powers for their own ends. The magic calendar was devised: the days were divided into propitious and unpropitious according to whether they were dominated by a favourable or untoward planet, the solar year was exactly calculated, the year was fractioned into months, the movement of the stars was precisely reckoned, and the conviction of the important influence of these laws over the life of humanity and the events of the earth was proved by countless examples. Every celestial phenomenon was held to have a reflection in the events of the earth, every individual to be under the influence of a planet or of a fixed star from birth to death, and his fate was believed to depend on the relation of his star to the moon, the sun, and the planets.

The observation of the flight of birds, of the entrails, and especially the liver, of animals offered as sacrificial victims, the examination of geometric figures, constructed according to different magic rules, the study of meteorological phenomena, the appearance and behaviour of certain animals such as the snake and the dog, gave rise to a variety of interpretations. Dreams, to which great importance was attached in the myth of Gilgamesh, were explained by soothsayers, and are recounted in the sacred tables.

Babylonian sorcery, in its complex development of sacerdotal magic and occult science, in its evolution, which follows the rapid cultural development of the people, exerted a notable influence over neighbouring nations, such as the Persian and the Hebrew. Later some of the fundamental concepts of Babylonian magic were absorbed by other peoples, including the Egyptians, and following the conquest of Persia by Alexander the Great, Babylonian magic penetrated into ancient Greece.

Babylonian magic, built upon a solid system, aided by the seductive poetical beauty of its formulas and by the realistic art of its figurations, became a pattern for all succeeding conceptions, and marks a noteworthy stage in the history of sorcery.

XV

Hebrew Magic and the Dawn of Monotheism

1. THE MAGIC IDEA IN ITS VARIOUS ASPECTS

MAGIC undoubtedly played a large role in the history of the people of Israel during the epoch preceding monotheistic legislation; and even though the extant historical documents, which bear the imprint of the fundamental idea of monotheism, and are therefore purified of every reference to the magic beliefs which monotheism severely prohibits, only indirectly allude to magic, and though the texts of magic or of magic medicine were lost or destroyed, the Bible itself contains irrefutable evidence disclosing how magic practices, widely spread among the first Semitic ethnic groups, were preserved among the people despite the Mosaic legislation. The study of magic in the Pentateuch has been, especially recently, the object of much research, with extremely interesting results.[1] The Bible contains—we may admit —two antithetical concepts, whose origins are ascribed to two different currents: the *Elohist*, (the name derives from the plural *Elohim*, the gods) of distinctly Sumerian origin, which asserts that in a remote epoch the belief in gods or demons was widespread; and that called the *Yahwist* (from Yahweh, the taboo-name of the One God), which affirms the monotheistic position. The Pentateuch contains frequent conflicts between these two creeds. Throughout the Bible, and especially in the part of Sumerian origin, there are frequent allusions to magic practices. Thus an important role is played by the wand, an essential instrument of magic, representing a power in itself. The prophet Elijah employs a wand to resurrect a dead person. The concepts inherent in the ritual prescriptions prohibit-

[1] Among the recent outstanding studies on Hebrew magic may I refer to the works of T. Reik: *Der eigene und der fremde Gott* and *Religions-Psychologie*, I; and of Erich Fromm: *Das Christus Dogma*.

ing contact with the Ark of the Covenant and punishing with death anybody who touches it, even unintentionally, as in the case of Uzzah, who wished to steady the Ark as it was being moved, are magic. Thousands of Jews died in the territory of Judah for having dared to look upon the Ark of the Covenant on its return. A blessing may be transferred from one individual to another (Genesis xxvii) like a vital force, which cannot be revoked, as is shown by the account of the deception practised by Jacob on his dying father, Isaac. Goldberg, in his book *Die Wirklichkeit der Hebräer*, states that in the ancient belief a blessing represented a magic formula, having an immediate and certain result. A blessing transmitted through the contact of the hand or through an embrace represented the efflux of a vital force. Realization of the importance of contact exists among all peoples and in all ages, and may bring about opposite effects, such as healing or striking down and killing.

According to Goldberg, the name *El Schadaj* given to God is an example of ambivalence, the etymological root of this word containing both the meaning of fecundity (*schadajim*, breasts) and of destruction (*schadad*, to destroy).

Abraham's dream (Genesis xv) is an interesting example of a derivation from ancient magic beliefs. In this dream Abraham saw the sacrificial animals cut up into various pieces, and he saw the cloud and the fire play between these parts. Evidently this dream evinces a recollection of the ancient idea of the communion between animals and the deity protecting the human race.

The Biblical descriptions of the miracles, *othot* (sing. *oth*) and *mophetim* (sing. *mophet*) given by Moses, are no less interesting from the viewpoint of magic. *Oth* is, in Biblical language, a sign of a particular character: it is the sign made by God on the forehead of Cain, it is the blood used in marking the doors of the houses when the Jews left Egypt, it is the sabbath for its importance and the significance and action which it exerts. The first miracles performed by Aaron are such signs: the rod is transformed into a serpent and then becomes a rod again, the hand grows leprous and is restored to soundness. The permanent miracle, like the death of the firstborn, is, on the other hand, indicated by the name *mophet*.

Pharaoh's sorcerers also are able to perform some miracles, and therefore Pharaoh believes that the God of the Hebrews is no more powerful than that of the Egyptians. In the contest for power between the God of Israel, represented by Moses and Aaron, and the god of the Egyptians, represented by Pharaoh's sorcerers, the King gives up only when he perceives that Moses can accomplish miracles that his own magicians are unable to duplicate.

2. THE BLOOD-RITE, THE EVOCATION OF THE NAME

The blood-sacrifice, repeatedly mentioned in the Bible as an essential practice of the cult, stems directly from ancient magic practices. The sacrifice of animals, the only one pleasing to the Lord, as is revealed by the description of the sacrifice of Cain and Abel (Genesis iv, 3–7), most likely derives from human sacrifice and in particular from the killing of the first-born in prehistoric times. Blood, the centre of life, the abode of the soul, and fat, which according to a primitive conception already mentioned is one of the most important seats of the vital force, are the principal elements in the sacrifice (*korban*) offered to God. Blood is the vehicle of the soul and is of divine origin (Leviticus xvii, 11), and the people of Israel are therefore forbidden to take the blood of animals as nourishment.

The substitution of an animal for a human victim is clearly represented in the account of the sacrifice of Isaac. Doubtless circumcision, which has all the characteristics of magic (the sacrifice of blood and the mutilation of the generative organ) and which stems, perhaps, from an ancient custom of the peoples of central Africa and of Egypt, was originally a magic and initiatory custom—a sacrifice of human blood and of the organ that, in the magic conception, symbolizes the centre of life, the organ of reproduction. Perhaps at a certain epoch, even for Israel, as for some primitive peoples, circumcision was a prenuptial rite.

The fact that according to Jewish law all male children must be circumcised eight days after birth is likely to prove the initiatory character that Jewish religion possessed from the beginning. This character is revealed, moreover, by the isolation in the desert, the prescription of special food, the exact division of the tribes, and above all by the repeated statements of Biblical texts, according to which the Jews are the chosen people. There is an essential difference between the Egyptian magic-religious system and the Jewish belief: among the Jews knowledge is no longer limited to a narrow number of adepts, but the whole people constitute a single body of initiates, all of whom are bound to observe the rules binding the group.

Other facts related in the Bible may be interpreted by keeping in mind this hidden persistence of magic: the episode of the golden calf, for instance, that of the serpents of bronze, and many others. Objects used in the cult, which play an integrant part therein, have the character of talismans and amulets. Such objects are the *tephillim* which are bound to arm and forehead with thongs of leather, the *mezuzah* which is placed on the doors of houses and has an apotropaic (evil-averting) power. The value of these objects derives from the fact that the name of the one God is written on them and that this name, according to the conception described above, is invested with supreme power.

The written word has a defensive and magic might in itself. Writing is pregnant with magic force and may therefore exert an influence which is partly apotropaic and partly propitiatory. In the time of Maimonides, the Jews of Egypt inscribed the Ninety-first Psalm on a plaque of gold or silver, which they hung around the necks of their children. This custom was condemned by Maimonides.

The importance of the name, of the manner in which it is written and pronounced, of the signs composing it, is borne out by numberless passages in the sacred texts and by the practices connected with them. Foremost among these is the severe law that forbids the utterance of the tetragrammatic name — that is, the name of God composed of four letters. This name might be pronounced but once a year by the high priest, in the temple at Jerusalem, before the Ark containing the Holy Covenant — that is, the text of the Law — surrounded by the severe prescriptions of the taboo. *Kadosch*, like *sacer*, signifies "untouchable," "devoted to the deity." This ambivalent term corresponds to the Arabic *muharran* from which derives the Hebrew *herem*. The root of *kadosch* signifies devoted, consecrated, and thus untouchable. Later *herem* assumes the meaning of "excommunicated": both the "untouchable" and the "excommunicated" being excluded from the community of believers. In India the pariah is untouchable, as is the high priest.

Magic is prohibited, according to the Mosaic law, not because of its inefficacy, but merely because it serves foreign gods. Many passages in the sacred books disclose that magic practices are held to be efficacious; for example, the description of the Witch of Endor, and the list of penalties inflicted on soothsayers. One passage declares that no wizard, magician, or sorcerer may evoke the spirit of Python, and no Jew may cause his son or his daughter to pass through the fire of Moloch. A section of the Second Book of Kings (xvi) reproves King Ahaziah for having sent messengers to consult Baalzebub, the god of the Philistines. Jeremiah (Jeremiah xxvii) orders the Hebrews to submit to the King of Babylon without consulting their prophets, sorcerers, or soothsayers. The prophet Nahum (iii, 4) inveighs against Babylon, whore and mistress of sorcery, who traffics in nations through her magic. And finally Malachi utters a prophecy (iii, 5) against enchanters.

Slowly through the centuries the memory of totemism and of human sacrifice becomes obscured, though traces remain in the sacrifice of Isaac, in the worship of the golden calf, and also perhaps in the episode of the brazen serpents. By a gradual process all kinds of images, rightly considered by the legislator as suggestive sources of magic practices, were prohibited; and the totemic gods were removed. (The most dangerous of these, because of its affinity with the totem of the race, appears to have been the *Seir* [Leviticus xvii] the goat-god fought by Jacob and, according to Goldberg, the protector of Esau; its memory is preserved in the rite of the scapegoat [Leviticus xvi, 10].) As a result a purification of Hebrew rites set in: Judaism became oriented toward the worship of a single God, who did not tolerate any other gods, and could not be imaged. The religious idea sharply detached itself from the magic and demonistic one. The origin of monotheism may not be ascribed to mistrust of magic, as some writers maintain. Religion is related to the development of critical reasoning and to man's attempt to escape from the magic circle, through the acceptance of a supreme moral law. But the text, the words, the letters of the Law, the tables of the Covenant, the Ark become sacred and taboo.

In the most flourishing epoch of the Kingdom of Israel the ancient magic idea almost vanished, or at least the traces of its survival are extremely scarce. Babylonian slavery, and the state of despair engendered by long suffering, caused the essentially magic Babylonian idea to reappear and greatly to influence the popular mind. In this period (458 B.C.) profound religious and political action, expressed in the work of the prophet Ezra, once more imposed the Biblical doctrine on the Hebrews, commanding strict obedience of the prescriptions, severely forbidding marriage between them and other peoples, and enjoining the dissolution of impure marriages, attempting the biological and ritual purification of Judaism.

Later the magic idea revives again, and definite vestiges of it are to be found in the Talmud, which portrays the intellectual life of the Jews. The Talmud contains anecdotes and ancient legends, the dicta of teachers, which seem to be faithfully reported, and the speeches and discussions, judgments and thoughts of the sages of Israel, which were probably collected in the fifth century B.C. There is in the Talmud a revival of the idea that malignant demons, both male (*scedim*) and female (*lilith*), may be the cause of sickness; thus, according to some teachers, angina is caused by an evil spirit who seizes the child in the throat, while asthmatic attacks are brought about by another hostile demon. Magic words, the fact of passing through certain places, the glance of a third person, may induce serious illnesses and even death. On the other hand, cures may be effected by uttering magic formulas or applying pieces of parchment with Biblical inscriptions to the body. The Talmud mentions the fact that a priest may effect a cure by placing his hands on the patient's head. The book, however, contains many descriptions of other medical and surgical treatments that are altogether rational.

3. THE CABALA

Although magic persisted in popular medicine and in the beliefs of the people, it followed, later, another path owing to individuals who devoted their work to the study and the interpretation of sacred books and who searched them for recondite mysterious meanings. In Judaism popular magic bears the essential traits of primitive sorcery; in the mind of scholars magic becomes mystic and speculative, delves into profound and difficult combinations, devises interpretations connected with numbers and letters, and on these interpretations constructs an entire system of great historical importance. This is not to be wondered at, since just as the mentality of the Hindus finds its expression in the essentially imaginative tendency of the people, which determines the orientation of its mind, the Chaldean mentality is animated and directed by a mathematical propensity, and the Egyptian shows the influence of an intelligence which leads to speculative philosophy, analogously the new Jewish magic arises from the speculative and critical cast of mind of a reasoning and mystic people, whose history bears the indelible marks of the two great streams of Assyro-Babylonian and Egyptian thought.

Legend, unlike a version of it asserting that the Cabala derives from the fallen angels (some commentators inferred this from Genesis vi, 1, 4, and from the narratives of the Book of Enoch), attributes a divine origin to the Cabala, according to the Babylonian Talmud. The legend claims that from Sinai God imparted to Moses, besides the law that became the fundamental text of the people, a spoken law as well, which was to be communicated to the initiated alone. Although it was only later that these versions of the origin of the Cabala assumed such precise form for the purpose of corroborating the claim that the inception of the Cabalistic system goes back to remote times, it is certain that for many centuries there existed oral traditions which were later collected in two books, the *Sefer Jezirah* (that is, the book of the creation or origin) and the *Zohar* (that is, the book of light and splendour). The *Sefer Jezirah* was written no earlier than the seventh or eighth century of our era, probably in Mesopotamia. The *Zohar* became known in the thirteenth century, and was compiled, probably on the basis of old sources, by Moses ben Shem Tob of León (1250–1305), a Jewish scholar of Spain. The grounds for some traditions and ideas contained in these two books go back to the *Mishnah*, which was probably written in the second century of our era.

The aim of Cabalistic speculation consists mainly in the search for the secret and symbolical meaning of the words of the Old Testament, as well as in the explanation of the creation of the world and in the knowledge of the mysterious throne of God. The *Zohar* states: "Every word of the Law has a profound significance and contains a mystery: the words of the Law are but its garments: woe to him who mistakes the garments for the Law itself. The wise set no more store by the Law, but observe the body that it covers. The servants of the High King, who lives on the mountain of Sinai, concern themselves, instead, with the spirit which is the foundation of the Laws." The system explaining the words and signs, raised to the dignity of a religious philosophy, often contrasting with pure sacred doctrine, is obviously influenced by the people with whom the Hebrews came in contact, particularly by the Babylonians, and often strives to reconcile the ideas of other religions with those of Judaism. These doctrines were the closely guarded monopoly of a small circle of initiates. A passage of the *Mishnah* reads: "It is forbidden to explain the history of creation to two persons, and the story of the heavenly chariot shall not be told to even one person unless he is a wise man who can understand it by himself." The circle of the initiates bearing the name of *Mekubalim* was always extremely restricted; the *Zohar* mentions meetings that could be attended by no more than seven persons, each of whom had to swear not to reveal its mysteries.

The Cabalistic method consists primarily in seeking the explanation of words, either by dotting the consonants in different manners (in Hebrew the vowels are marked by dots), thus obtaining different words, or by transforming words into numbers. Since in Hebrew writing every number corresponds to a letter, every word has a numerical meaning, and summing up the number obtained from a word one may find identical numerals for words of different meaning, which, according to the Cabalistic concept, may be interchanged. This system is called *Gematria*. For example, the word *ah(a)d* (unity) and the word *acb(a)h* (love) are each equivalent to the number 13; therefore one may take the place of the other. The numerical value of the words in the First Book of Moses (Genesis xviii, 2) describing the coming of the angels corresponds to 701, a number which may also be obtained by adding up the letters indicating the names of Michael, Gabriel, and Raphael. Thus the Cabalists claim that the names of the three angels are contained in the letters of the annunciation.

Another system is indicated by the word *Nutriqum* (Greek, *notarikòn*). This consists in considering every letter of a word as the initial letter of another word, so that every word produces an entire sentence. For example, the first word in the Bible is *bereschid* ("in the beginning"). The Cabalists, employing every letter as the beginning of one word, explain: "In the beginning God saw the acceptance of Israel in the Torah." This sentence contains a prophecy of the issuing of the Law. Another aspect of this Cabalistic system is the inverse procedure—that is, the formation of words from the first or from the last letters of the single words composing a verbal group, as we do today in forming the abbreviations NRA, AMG, etc. Thus from the phrase of Deuteronomy (xxx, 12): "Who shall go up for us to heaven" the word *Mila* (circumcision) is formed from the first letters of these words, and Yahveh, the tetragrammatic and unspeakable name of God, from the final ones. This proves that it was God Himself who suggested circumcision as a sign for the chosen people.

The third method, called *Temura*, consists in interchanging various letters according to a sort of cryptographic table, in which every letter corresponds to another. An analogous system is that called "of the nine spaces." The letters of the alphabet are distributed in nine spaces and may be replaced by points or numbers written in the same space. This system gives rise to a set of permutations and to countless combinations upon which new interpretations are based.

One of the main laws of the Cabala is that of the ten spheres of the *sephiroth*, which are not considered as numbers only, but as the essences of things. The first *sephira'*, or sphere, which has the number 1, represents the One God, the essence of the deity; the second, the number 2, is the Word. The word is a breath, nevertheless it interprets the thought of man; breath and thought are two things, yet they are one because they are indivisible. Twenty-two letters (11 times 2) form and express thought; there are thus twenty-two "paths of wisdom" divided into three groups: the 3 major paths, the 7 double, and the 12 single. There are three elements (fire, water, and earth), three seasons, three important parts of the human body (head, thorax, abdomen). The seven double paths are the intestines, which may serve both a good and an evil purpose; the seven planets, which may exert a favourable or an adverse influence; the seven days and seven nights of the week, which may be good or bad; the seven gates of wisdom, which are open to good or evil. The twelve single paths are the months of the year, the constellations, and the twelve activities of man, which are, according to the Cabalistic text, sight, hearing, smelling, touching, speaking, eating, generation, movement, anger, joy, thought, and sleep.

The *Zohar* is devoted primarily to nature and to the relations between God and man. God is described as the secret of secrets, the great Unknown. The light of His brow illumines four hundred thousand worlds; He creates thirteen thousand myriads of worlds a day; with His head He causes the dew to awake the dead to new life; His face is three hundred and seventy times ten thousand worlds long. God has not always existed in this form, but has followed a process of evolution described in the first part of the *Zohar*. In the beginning God was *èn soph* (one and infinite), and later He assumed the successive forms of the ten *sephiroth* or spheres. The first *sephira'* is the *kether*, or crown, the foundation of all power, the crown of crowns, called also *ehieh* ("I am"); and all other *sephiroth* develop from this one. The second *sephira'* is the *hochmah*, wisdom, emanating from God's crown; the third is intelligence. These three *sephiroth* form the supreme trinity from which man was created, and engender the fourth, *chesed* (piety or death), and so forth. The meaning of the doctrine of the *sephiroth*, the Cabalistic tree, is easy to understand. The *sephiroth* symbolize the qualities attributed to God, which together represent the ideal figure of man. Thus man also is godlike in his ten spheres, and possesses three souls constituting the supreme trinity. Other souls and forms depend from these.

Such is the fundamental idea of the Cabala, though interpretations of it vary greatly in different periods. The magic of the Middle Ages borrowed many of its notions from the Cabala. It was founded on numerical and geometric constructions and on symbolical meanings assigned to letters and numbers, each of which, more or less directly related to the meaning attached to it, had a particular importance in prophecy and evocation. Cabalistic mysticism and all its developments are founded on these calculations and combinations. As a result of various mystical, speculative, and analytical currents, Cabalistic mysticism offers an infinite field to those who believe that they can delve into the mystery of things by means of the supposedly symbolic significance of words and of signs. In reality Cabalistic mysticism goes beyond pure religion; it is a speculative, fantastic, and mystic superstructure of religion, and in later times magicians and practitioners of the occult sciences have resorted to its words, formulas, and symbols (the pentagram or pentacle, Solomon's shoulder-blade, etc.) as devices for evoking supernatural beings or warding off evil.

Hebrew magic originates in the period that we may call prehistoric and continues up to the year 700 B.C. Hebrew religion was established by the prophets, in a strictly ethical and monotheistic sense. They asserted the principle that sacrifices are useless if God is not worshipped by pure-handed men. This is one of the ways in which magic is effectively counteracted by the moral law. Symbolic sacrifice before the altar, representing the symbol *par excellence*, is perhaps next in importance to ethical religion. The advent of the kingdom of justice is proclaimed as the essence of the ideals of the Messiah. Who deserves to be the leader of the group? He who is without sin, who practises justice and never slanders others, who does not injure his neighbour or accept gifts at the expense of the weak. Isaiah, turning to the judges of Sodom and to the people of Gomorrah, exclaims: "What care I for your sacrifices when you commit sin?"

Magic survived during the age when the prophets spoke out their championship of monotheism, and religion definitely asserted its ethical systematization, in the popular beliefs concerning protection from sickness and battle against evil demons, but never assumed an antisocial or destructive character. The tendency of Jewish magic is speculative and metaphysical and is expressed in formal manifestations rather than in ways of thought. During the Babylonian exile and later in the Middle Ages the need to escape from continuous threats and persecutions, from the sense of inferiority engendered by forced isolation, no longer finds an outlet in rebellious or destructive adventures, but is sublimated in Messianic hope. Such a hope causes the believers to revert to their absolute and fanatical adherence to the ancient beliefs. The suggestion of the individualized God in the Biblical utterance "I am thy God" is reaffirmed in the practices of the Chassidim, which have, clearly, a magic character. Absolute trust in the written word and in the interpretations of the text persists; the belief in amulets and symbols is reborn. Talismans take on importance as apotropaic instruments; that is, they are used to keep away evil spirits when bound to forehead or arm. The mezuzah in the doorway of a house is the symbol indicating that it is protected. The miracle-working rabbis of the Israelite communities of eastern Russia possess an eminent prestige, lead the faithful, give advice in all the events of life. A vast collective suggestion is established in the schools, in the community, and in the family, and is nurtured by ancient traditions and customs and kept alive by the severe laws of Czarist Russia. These laws prohibit all contact between Jews and Gentiles and preclude all possibility of an independent life. In such a closed circle, in such groups systematically organized under the influence of faith, never penetrated by the light of criticism, where the authority of the master is absolute and the student of holy texts is considered sacred and universally respected, the suggestive and magic action of the *book symbol* is superior to that of the ethical law.

XVI

Magic and Mysteries of Ancient Greece

I. HOMERIC MAGIC

IN the history of pre-Hellenic civilization, which flourished in the Ægean Islands, the most luminous pages are undoubtedly those describing the life of Crete, probably the first centre of the spiritual life of the Mediterranean. The extant monuments of Cretan religion attest the belief in magic. In the age of the matriarchate (the domination of the mother), before the protection of Hellas was entrusted to the armed virgin goddess, born on Olympus' summit, the mother goddess, symbol of mysterious femininity, bearer of the mystic serpent, still ruled over Crete. Admirable works of an art that reached a high degree of perfection around the third millennium B.C. show that the serpent, the universal symbol of the supernatural in primitive epochs, formed the centre of religious worship. Geometric designs of manifestly symbolic character, structures of the type of magic portrayals, such as the famous labyrinth, prove that in the advanced civilization of Crete the idea of magic still lived and flourished; probably, as we infer from the portrayals, this was also due to the influence of currents reaching Crete from Phœnicia, Babylonia, and Egypt, as there was frequent and important commerce between these countries. The symbol of the cross played a great part. Cretan medicine, to which reference is often made in Egyptian medical texts, quoting formulas of the Kefti, or "inhabitants of the islands," was magical, as we gather from the strange depictions of sick people in Minoan terracottas. The magical medicine of a later age is closely connected with that of Crete.

The Homeric texts contain frequent allusions to magic practices which remained in use for a long time, particularly in the most remote regions, such as Arcady and Thessaly. Masks and rhythmic dances, as well as the cult of heroes, in which the souls of the dead were identified and worshipped, played an important role in these practices. Sacrifices were offered to the dead on domestic altars; their names and protection were invoked. The cult of the dead, closely connected with widespread practices of divination, continued, together with magic rites, well into the highest period of Hellenic civilization, and centred in the festival of the Anthesteria, celebrated in Athens in winter-time. At this festival food and drinks were offered to the dead, and they were summoned to appear.

In the Homeric epic, manifestations of the magic cult are frequent, even in the period when Greek mythology was almost completely systematized. Good and evil demons, such as that mentioned in the Canto V of the *Odyssey*, play an important role, but their wrath may be conquered or placated in the same way as that of Poseidon, who, in revenge for the blinding of Polyphemus by Ulysses, wreaks his rage on the latter. Magic rites are described when Menelaus overcomes Proteus (*Odyssey*, IV), who assumes the forms of various animals in order to escape his enemy. A ritual implication is present in the act of Helen (*Odyssey*, IV) when she drops into wine a substance banishing all memory of bitterness, the use of which she has learned from Polidamnia in Egypt. The ships of the Phæacians, which can navigate the seas without pilots and rudders, are magic (*Odyssey*, VIII).

In Greek medicine magic has an important function in the temples of Æsculapius, where it is founded on "incubation" —that is, the sleep during which suggestion occurs—and also on rites and applications undoubtedly having a rational origin.

2. THE ORACLES

In Greece the rites of divination were thoroughly systematized. The Delphic oracle of Apollo, and that of Zeus at Dodona in Epirus, were the centres of a well-organized worship. Priestesses gave their replies during ecstasies induced by exactly prescribed performances, during which they were believed to receive the direct messages of the deity. The

Pythian priestess, seated on the sacred tripod placed over a cleft in the earth emitting steam, fell into a hypnotic or hypnoidal state. The priestess of Zeus at Dodona, before uttering her prophecy was said to drink water from an inebriating spring that ran near by. These are both examples of a religious trance, artificially induced by substances causing hallucinations.

The oracle at Delphi possessed, between the eighth and the sixth centuries B.C., an extraordinary authority which constituted a political influence of the first rank (the tribunal of the Amphictyons, the supreme court of Greece, was held at Delphi). At the beginning the oracle gave its responses only once a year; later with greater frequency, but only on certain days of the year. Before consulting the oracle, it was necessary for the postulant to make a sacrifice, and only if an examination of the entrails of the victim proved the sacrifice to be satisfactory was he allowed into the sanctuary to submit his oral or written questions to the Pythian priestess. As I have said, she was seated on the tripod in a trance, with a laurel leaf in her mouth and a laurel branch in her hand. Her replies were couched in a symbolical and vague form. The head priest translated the oracle into verse, interpreting the meaning of the words, which were generally incomprehensible to the profane. The prestige of the oracle of Delphi declined after the Macedonian conquest; and the oracle ceased functioning altogether after the edict of A.D. 313.

The oldest official oracle was probably that of Zeus at Dodona. The rite consisted, mainly, in grasping the voice of Zeus, which was heard in the rustling of leaves stirred by the breeze and in the gurgling of water flowing from the sacred spring. The oracle of Dodona was in high favour for almost two thousand years, down to the times of the Roman occupation.

The rites celebrated in the Temple of Zeus Ammon, where the Egyptian practice of the interpretation of symbols and signs was added to the Greek ceremony, were analogous or closely similar. It is remarkable that an important feature of these rites was the trance induced in the priestess, not only by intoxicating substances, but also, according to Maxwell, by rhythmic sounds (the rustling of leaves, the murmur of water, the clang of bronze cymbals).

In ancient Greece divination consisted also in the interpretation of celestial phenomena or of omens, such as those derived from the flight of birds or from the scrutiny of the entrails of animals. In the darkness of night Diomedes and Ulysses (*Iliad*, X), seeking a sign from the gods, perceive the vulture sent by Pallas Athena and observe that it is flying to the right, a sign of good luck. Necromancy, or prophecy drawn from the evocation of the dead, is described by Homer. Ulysses sails across the ocean to Hades and pours into the ditch dug with his sword the sacred libation of honey, milk, wine, water, and flour for the dead, whom he evokes. He then promises them that he will offer a sacrifice when he arrives in Ithaca. He slays a goat, and the band of dead souls emerges from the depths of Erebus. Ulysses, to elicit a reply from them, requests each one to drink the blood from the ditch, an act that recalls the sacrifice of blood to the dead and the gods.

Magic and religion bear an interesting mutual relation in Greece. Belief in Zeus Lyceius is bound to the ancient magic belief in the werewolf. The importance attributed, in the worship of Apollo, to serpents, laurel trees, and other plants leads, according to Rendel Harris, to the assumption of the existence of a close connection between the magic idea of the power of animals and of plants and the genesis of religious ideas. Certain passages of Aristophanes' plays contain references to the magic origin of masks.

3. THE MYSTERIES

In Greece, magic became spiritualized in the mysteries. The Eleusinian mysteries, which are directly related to the ancient Egyptian ones, were an object of such profound veneration in Athens that they were considered sacred as late as the days of Imperial Rome. Suetonius states that Nero, when in Athens, did not dare to participate in them, since individuals guilty of crimes were severely prohibited from requesting initiation. The Eleusinian mysteries possessed an official character.

The rites centred in the myth of Demeter and were linked to the legend of Persephone, whom Pluto abducted and carried to Hades and later restored to her mother. Demeter, the goddess of the earth, the Ceres of the Romans, was held by the initiated to be the supreme intelligence, the ruling mother of the cosmos, combining in herself all vital forces. The priests of the goddess were called Sons of the Moon and acted as mediators between the earth and the sky. Masters of the esoteric doctrine, they endowed the mysteries with a lively and multicoloured form, raising them from a small local cult to the importance of a national festival.

When Athens became the political centre of Greece, the Eleusinian mysteries assumed a particular importance. They were probably initiatory ceremonies, which, with the passing of time, lost their magic significance, retaining only the symbolic meaning of the rites. The lesser Mysteries, which took place in February at Agræ, a small town near Athens, were performed with a severe and detailed ceremony; the candidates were accepted after long examinations by the priest of Eleusis, the hierocerynx, the interpreter, the intermediary, who led the novices into the temple before the priestesses of Persephone, the hierophantids in white peplums, crowned with narcissus, and singing Persephone's hymn. After long rites, accompanied by dances and prayers, the neophytes assembled on the last day in a secret place to view the mystery of the rape of Persephone.

The Greater Mysteries were celebrated in Eleusis every five years, in September, and lasted nine days. The *mystai* ("silent ones," from whom the name *mysteries* derives), the initiates of the first class, were introduced to the great mysteries and assumed the name of *epoptai;* on the eighth day each initiate was given the *cysta mystica,* the sacred sealed basket containing mysterious objects. The orgies were celebrated on the last day, when Dionysos' statue, crowned with myrtle, was carried in a great procession from Athens to Eleusis. This rite symbolized the rebirth, the return of the renovating spirit, mediating between terrestrial and spiritual things. The ceremonies which followed are interesting in that they prove the magic foundation of all these rites. The *mystai,* gathered together in a large hall, spent the night in the temple, and descended to a subterranean labyrinth, where they drank narcotic beverages inducing hallucinations. Immediately after this, secret prescriptions and mysterious practices definitely consecrated the *epoptai*, and the mysteries were ended.

Descriptions by ancient writers, eulogies of poets such as Pindar, who calls happy the individual who, after practising this rite, tastes the perfection of life, and the words of Cicero, stating that the mysteries of Eleusis were the best Athenian institution, prove that in these mysteries, as in those of Osiris, Dionysos, and Orpheus, the primitive magic idea, the tendency to project desire and to objectify it into a spell, was later transformed into mysticism and assumed a purely symbolical character; that is, the character of a rite in which ecstasy was the main factor and of which the stern prohibition against divulging the religious secret perhaps constituted the strongest attraction. Aristotle's explanation of the aim of the Eleusinian rites conforms with what I have said: the initiates are not obliged to learn, but to know, and are placed in a mood of particularly keen sensitivity.

4. THE EVOLUTION OF MAGIC IN THE ALEXANDRIAN PERIOD

The development of primitive magic was dual. On one hand it was transformed into mysticism—a common occurrence in ancient days. On the other hand, at the time of the flowering of philosophy and scientific reasoning, belief in magic was fiercely attacked by all the followers of a new way of thought, tending to destroy the foundations of magic and superstition. Pythagoras and Empedocles were among the first to deny that the dead dwell in Hades and to admit, instead, probably under the influence of Egyptian thought, the migration of the soul. In the books of the *Corpus Hippocraticum*, in which all the medical knowledge of the golden period of Greece is gathered, there are no traces of magic medicine, and the practices of sorcery are not conspicuous in the opinions of the famous men to whom Athens owes the glory of her greatest epoch.

The Greek mentality, which for the first time in history confronts with serene spirit and objective judgment all the most serious and profound problems, understands or intuitively grasps the laws of the cosmos, examines the most hidden mysteries of life and being, discusses the immortality of the soul, seeking for proofs of it, and creates the complex ideology of the democratic state, combats belief in magic; and in reality, though less openly, fundamentally modifies the religious idea as well. The superstructure of Hellenic culture, evincing great refinement in all its manifestations, rebels against every principle of dogmatic authority in the government of the State as well as in the domain of ideas; it does not admit the existence of magic or of supernatural powers, while it recognizes the possibility of the existence of unknown forces that the human mind is unable to perceive. This is perhaps the first defeat of magic in history. It is caused, on the one hand, by the development of reasoning, the necessity for criticism, leaving no room for witchcraft or recognizing its pathological character, and, on the other hand, by the establishment of a political order in which the supreme power is entrusted to law, and legislative power is wielded by men who prove their superiority, not through their knowledge of secret practices or the art of evoking the dead, but through their courage in war and in peace, their intelligence, and their art. A kind of collective suggestion is undoubtedly present in this period also, but it is the suggestion exercised by great orators, whose words spellbind the crowds, or that of the poet who arouses their enthusiasms, or of the tragic writer who moves them deeply by describing the past, re-evoking the famous dead and their achievements. It is a suggestion exercised for a particular moral and social purpose, directly connected with the laws of the State, and awakening in the unconscious those ancestral memories or instincts which may turn the individual toward the desired aim. The ancient craving to preserve one's individuality after death evolves into the thirst for glory and immortality of fame and accomplishments; desire to keep adverse forces in check assumes the appearance of an ethical force overcoming the evil instincts of the individual and creating the harmony necessary to his physical and moral life. Astronomical knowledge, revealing the laws that govern, in an unchangeable rhythm, the movement of the stars, leads to a newer and broader understanding of the life of the cosmos and that of man, indissolubly bound with it. In the biological thinking of Aristotle, the greatest biologist of all times, the new law of metamorphosis appears for the first time in a purely scientific form. Thus, in the always restricted circle of thinkers, philosophers, poets, and physicians, belief in magic wanes, though it still persists among the clans of remote valleys and islands, who piously preserve the notions and rites of their ancestors.

The Persian Wars, forcing Greece into violent contact with the East, introduced new currents, which strengthened the magic idea, especially in regions, such as Thessaly, where the Persian influence was strongest and most lasting. In Thessaly, a region far removed from progressive cities, magic ideas have constantly persisted among the mountain folk. They still believe in the existence of sorcerers who, by means of rites and unguents, have the power to transform men into animals and plants. These magicians are said to travel through the air by night in search of amorous adventures. According to Lehmann, this belief is the first example of similar notions about the nocturnal flights of witches, which became prevalent during the Middle Ages. The goddess of light, Hecate, originally thought of as a benevolent, protective deity, became, with the renewal of magic under Oriental influence, the goddess of witches and sorcery. Greek writers describe in detail the practices, ceremonies, and exorcisms of this cult. Hecate was evoked by night as the enemy of light and the goddess of graves, animals were sacrificed to her, and festivals were celebrated in her honour. She was believed to be accompanied by lamias, witches who celebrated the most fantastic orgies and lived on the blood and vital forces of the men with whom they came in contact.

The great civil wars that devastated Greece, the epidemics that decimated her inhabitants, and the conquest by Philip of Macedonia, who destroyed Greek liberty and disrupted civil life, contributed enormously to the spread of magic. This is one of the most significant instances of a phenomenon repeatedly mentioned. Just as, when an individual has been weakened by a serious illness, his state of prostration creates a mood that makes him, because of the weakening of his critical faculties, highly susceptible to suggestion, inducing visual and auditory hallucinations, so nations that have suffered from long wars and grave epidemics are apt to return to their ancestral beliefs, reverting to the archaic subconscious and becoming susceptible to collective suggestion. Thus Greece, impoverished by war, saw the most glorious monuments of her civilization destroyed, her flourishing cities reduced to a miserable existence under the rule of ambitious soldiers and officials, her famous schools, the pride of the country, closed. Having lost their faith in the strength of the State and in the power of reason and of art, the Greeks turned to magic superstitions. The occupation of Egypt by the Macedonians brought about more frequent contacts with the Egyptians and their beliefs. On the other hand, Chaldean magic, numerical and astrological, arose on the basis of the essentially philosophical and astronomical idea of the power of numbers, which stemmed from the great Pythagorean school. Chaldeans and sorcerers invaded Hellas, and the Chaldean gods ranked in Greek mythology as evil demons who had to be evoked or exorcized by formulas spoken in a barbaric tongue, whose meaning was unknown, but whose might was believed in. Sorcerers evoked the luminous figure of Hecate in dark rooms and asked her for assistance or prophecies through exorcisms, rites, and formulas. Furthermore, countless demons and supernatural beings replaced the ancient Olympian gods and formed the nucleus of an essentially magic polytheism.

With the transfer of the centre of Greek civilization to Alexandria, where Hellenic philosophy found its continuators and Greek art appeared in new forms of beauty, magic again became symbolical and mystical under the influence of that milieu, in which ancient traditions throve, constantly fed by currents from central Africa, bearing ancient unforgotten primitive ideas to fertile soil. Alexandrian magic produced a set of mystic practices and complex initiatory ceremonies, directly connected with the ancient worship of Isis and Osiris, embodying the outward forms but not the ethical ideas that in the last flowering of the Egyptian Empire attained a superior philosophical viewpoint.

In the period of Alexandria's decline the magic cult grew to full flower and gathered, in numberless manifestations, all the currents of Eastern magic, laying the foundations for the hermetic and occult sciences deriving from the union of scientific procedures, applied to the basic ideas of magic, with principles of initiatory and mysterious systems.

XVII

Trends of Official Magic in Ancient Italy

I. ETRUSCAN MAGIC

ALTHOUGH historical research has ascertained but vague indications of the ethnic origins of the first inhabitants of the Italian peninsula, and has not proved either that the Etruscans derived from the Orient or that they were transplanted from Libya or from some region of Asia, the little that is known concerning their beliefs shows close analogy with the Assyro-Babylonians.

The mythological conception of the Etruscans is embodied in the idea of the *genius*, who, according to Horace (*Epistles* II, 187), accompanies every individual and rules his natal star. Female aphrodisiac demons protecting childbirth, as well as the serpent connected with the chthonic or infernal demons, are depicted on polished bronze mirrors. The axe represents the power of death, as does the scythe in Christian symbolism. During the period beginning with the taking of Veii (fourth century B.C.) funeral monuments are decorated with horrible images of demons, expressions of the superstitions pervading the Etruria of this century, which are a strong contrast to the composed serenity of the Greek funeral decorations. Another proof of the importance of ancestor-worship among the Etruscans is the frequent portrayal of the banquet where, as in the tomb of the Veli at Sette Camini near Orvieto, the spirits of the family are gathered together, attended by the gods of Avernus seated upon a high throne. There are in these portrayals three-bodied monsters, horrible demons, such as the winged one armed with a hammer and possessing a vulture's beak, and the ferocious Tuchulcha, with horse's ears, and threatening snakes on his head. Other figures of winged monsters, such as the Chimera of Arezzo, and

[198]

of snake-footed monsters are painted on the Tarquinian tomb of the Typhon. All these depictions, of which I have mentioned only the most important among those described by Ducati, show the role played by monstrous demons in ancient Italic mythology, in which phallus-worship was widely practised.

Divination, mainly through the examination of animal entrails, and especially of the liver (*extispicium*), had a great importance among the Etruscans. It appears that the word *aruspex* derives from the ancient Chaldean *har*, meaning liver. This practice probably originated in Chaldea; ancient Chaldean clay livers bearing cuneiform inscriptions, and models of livers with Hittite words, have been found at Boghazkeui, in the ancient capital of the Hittite Empire. Doubtless the bronze of Piacenza, a true *templum* of the third century B.C., in the form of a sheep's liver divided into squares, each containing the entire or abbreviated name of a deity, stems from these earlier models. The bronze of Piacenza appears to have been an instrument of instruction in the art of divination, and every square corresponds to a region of heaven inhabited by the deity whose name it bears. In the liver, as in the heavenly temple, there was a *pars familiaris*, which was propitious, and a *pars hostilis*, which was unfavourable; the incision dividing the parts was called the *fissum* or *limes;* the protuberances on sheep's or cows' livers and the slightest anatomical alterations had a particular importance in the taking of the auspice.

Etruscan worship undoubtedly centred in demoniacal magic, in which frightful and obscene sexual acts played an important role. Grünwedel, in *Tuska* (Leipzig, 1922), reconstructs the history of these practices. Their obscenity was one of the motives prompting the Romans, at the period when the ethical and moral conscience of the people was formed, to condemn them severely. The Egyptian legend of the sun, which during the night crosses the nether world, to be reborn each morning in the sky, appears in the form of an extraordinarily complex sexual idea. Grünwedel, interpreting many of the Etruscan decorations on mirrors and vases, claims that the ritual sacrifice of youths was the foundation of Etruscan worship. One of the epistles of Horace (II, ii, 180) reveals that

Etruscan bas-reliefs were much sought after by collectors of erotica.

Other magic and deprecatory rites were frequently practised by the Etruscans, as is attested by the leaden tablets (*devotiones*), by the lens-shaped lead now in the Museum of Florence, and by the rhythmical magic formula for the cure of sore feet, translated by Varro from the book of the Etruscan Sasena:

> *Terra pestem teneto*
> *Salus hic maneto*

("Let the earth retain the illness, and leave me good health.")

There are many Etruscan ex-votos representing parts of the human body, which were hung in temples in order to express the gratitude of the healed. Magic medicine was highly developed in ancient Etruria. The *Theogony* of Hesiod refers to the legend that the sons of the sorceress Circe, of Homeric fame, became Etruscan princes.

At a later period Etruscan art and religion were both deeply influenced by Greek currents of thought. Many magic beliefs were taken over by the Romans. One of these was the belief in the books of the Cumæan Sibyl, which were considered to be magical codes. Ancient Italy worshipped the Cumæan Sibyl, imported from Greek colonies of Asia Minor. According to the legend, nine of the Sibyl's books were offered to Tarquin the Proud, who refused them because of their great price. The owner then burned three of these books, and then three more, and the King finally had to pay the same price for the remaining three that had been originally asked for the nine books. According to the legend, the prophecies were written on palm leaves; the books were jealously kept in the Temple of Jupiter on the Capitol, and fifteen soothsayers were entrusted with studying and interpreting the predictions, which were especially requested in time of public calamities. Cicero claims that the books contained obscure prophecies for all times and circumstances. The first collection of sibylline books was burned when the Temple of Jupiter Capitolinus was destroyed by a thunderbolt. By order of the

Senate, after researches had been conducted by special commissioners in Greece, a new collection was made and placed in the rebuilt temple. In A.D. 410, on the order of Stilicho, the books were burned.

The origin of these prophetic books is highly uncertain, as is that of the figure of the sibyls, daughters of Apollo or of Poseidon. In the belief of the ancients, the sibyls had some connections with Cassandra, the daughter of Priam, whose misadventures are recounted in Homer's *Iliad*, and with Manto, daughter of Tiresias, who dwelt in a cave on Mount Ida. In the fourth century B.C. there is mention of only one sibyl; in the epoch in which Greece lost her independence and after the Roman conquest, the sibyls multiplied, and apparently the sibylline responses originated mostly in the Hebrew circles of Alexandria.

2. MAGIC RITES AND PRACTICES IN ROME

An essentially magic rite was the *mundus*. It consisted in digging, as did Romulus when he founded Rome, a small circular ditch into which was thrown a bit of earth brought from the *terra patrum*, the native land of each of the persons present. The *mundus* was the road to the *inferi*, the communication with the dead. At the moment of digging the ditch the founder of the city called upon the spirits of his forebears to populate the subterranean regions and to live with the inhabitants. Simultaneously dead and living entered the city. A vestige of this rite still remains in the practice of burying documents and money in the foundations of new buildings. The *mundus* remained open at certain hours on special days: (*mundus patet*) —on the unpropitious days when the spirits of the dead could visit the living, and people were officially required to leave the doors of all houses open so that the ancestors might enter and seat themselves at the family table (Varro: *Saturæ*, I, xvi, 18; Festus: 154–557). In ancient pictures of Etruscan graves, such as that of Corneto mentioned by Grenier, the *mundus* is depicted as a ditch from which a wolf-headed human figure, who clutches the living, emerges. The trenches that are still to be seen in India near temples, into which the blood of sacrifices and precious metals are poured, bear a close analogy to the *mundus*. In ancient ages it was the custom to throw amulets and money into ditches dug for the foundations of buildings.

These magic rites, performed at the time of ploughing the furrow, conferred a sacred character upon the city. The meaning of the Latin *sacer* is analogous to that of the *taboo* of the primitives. Houses, hearths, walls, and doors are sacred; that is, they are objects of both worship and fear. The purple pattern on the *toga prætexta* has magic significance. Ritual formulas, usually consisting of unintelligible words with ancient Etruscan roots, are magical, possess and give unbounded power. Less importance was attributed to Roman gods than was given to their gods by the early Greeks. Beneficent gods, such as the *Lares*, never threatening or vindictive, belong to the ancient Mediterranean pantheon, in which all the deities are peaceful and close to men in their feelings and lives. Access to foreign gods was easy, and, according to the historians, Rome in the beginning had more gods than citizens. At the same time magic continued to flourish: threshold (*forculus*), hinge (*cardo*), door (*janua*), later deified in Janus Bifrons, all play a great part in Roman magic. The magic idea of sowing (*sata*) is deified in Saturn. In the rite of Diana Nemorensis, the goddess of the Lake of Nemi, the priest must be killed in ritual execution when someone more powerful than he demonstrates the perennial character of the magic force. (Frazer has made a close study of this rite.)

The magic of numbers was very important in Rome; according to an old adage, "*mundum regunt numeri*." And the tradition of the importance of the symbolical circle and triangle had been asserted by the Pythagorean school. In order to prove how universally accepted in Rome was the idea of the magic circle, it is sufficient to mention a story, related by Livy (xlii, 15) and Polybius. During the war waged by King Antioch IV Epiphanes against Egypt in 168 B.C., Caius Popilius, the Roman Ambassador, presented King Antioch with orders from the Senate to withdraw. As Antioch hesitated, Popilius, a brusque and energetic man, drew a circle around the King with his stick, enjoining him to reply before stepping out of it. Antioch, after protesting, complied.

In the early Roman period, forests were considered magic and sacred. Every tree represented a deity, and any person cutting one was severely punished by law. In the solemn ceremonies of the *Fratres Arvales,* celebrated in sacred woods, the first fruits of the season were offered yearly to the gods as an entreaty for an abundant harvest. Occult magic power and symbolical significance were attributed to trees. The oak symbolized robustness; the white willow, sacred to the Egyptian Isis, chastity; the ash, from whose wood Achilles' spear was carved, was dedicated to Mars; the elm signified repose; the bay tree was the messenger of joy and peace and crowned poets' brows, the temples of the gods, the palaces of the Cæsars; the cypress was sacred to the dead. A widespread and profound tree-worship accompanied this agricultural people, faithful and devoted to the earth, which was the comforter of their sorrows, the source of their joys. The Romans considered trees to be the beneficent witnesses and magic protectors of their lives and of their well-being.

From the earliest times Roman history was interwoven with magic beliefs and practices. The legend of Romulus and Remus and the she-wolf, other examples of which are to be found in the Orient, is reminiscent of an ancient magic myth reflecting the ancient idea of the relation between men and animals. Magic rites (*lupercalia*) were practised to drive away wolves. Flint (*silex*) symbolized a deity, who later assumed the name of Jupiter Lapis. A memory of ancient human sacrifices is preserved in the ceremony of the *Argeæ,* during which puppets, representing human bodies, were thrown into the sea.

Purification by water and fire (*lustratio*) is a clearly magic practice conducive, like practices of Oriental bathing, to purity of body and of soul.

Certain magic ideas are hard to explain. Such was the belief that the horse on the right of the victorious quadriga should be killed with a javelin-blow and that its head and tail should be cut off, the possession of the latter being disputed by persons of the *suburra* and of the Via Sacra, while the head was rushed to the altars where the Vestal Virgins collected its blood.

3. DIVINATION — THE MYSTERIES

The Roman gods play no role in public affairs, but it is a civic and not a moral duty to honour them. Their authority derives from the power of the State, but does not inspire it. Great leaders and emperors may assume a place in temples and public worship. Magic, or the magic part of the *religio*, alone is truly intangible. Magic in all its forms is predominant. The legend of Tullus Hostilius, struck by lightning as a punishment for his crimes, and the provision of the law of the Twelve Tables forbidding magic actions aimed at the removal of the harvest from an alien field to one's own, show that the first legislators were concerned with the necessity of restricting hostile magic practices.

From the outset divination played a conspicuous part in Rome; in accordance with the Roman mentality, it was early systematized and became a State function. The interpretation of the flight of birds, originating in Etruscan belief, is particularly important. A complicated technique for interpreting the meaning of the direction of flight and the position of birds was devised. In Rome the augurs, marking on the earth with their wands the circle within which the *aruspicium* took place, in interpreting it were public officials, performing civic duties. But even outside of the official omens, the propitious or unpropitious flight was interpreted, according to fixed and accepted laws, by every observer. Augury thus assumed the characteristics of a perfectly systematized magic practice.

Other forms of prophecy consisted in casting lots, wooden tablets with letters carved on them, into a box from which, after a preliminary ceremony, they were extracted by a child pure in body and soul. The most celebrated oracle was that of Præneste, protected by the goddess Fortuna Primigenia (Fortune the First-Born). Later, future events were predicted by haphazardly opening a book, particularly Virgil, and interpreting the first verse on the page. This practice, still in use today, was founded on the belief in supernatural assistance guiding the hand of the seeker.

Pliny writes at length on magic, which he believes was founded in Persia by Zoroaster. He claims that magic was in-

*Bull totem. Gold plastic, Sumerian art, found at Ur, Meso-
potamia, by the Woolley Expedition (British Museum,
London)*

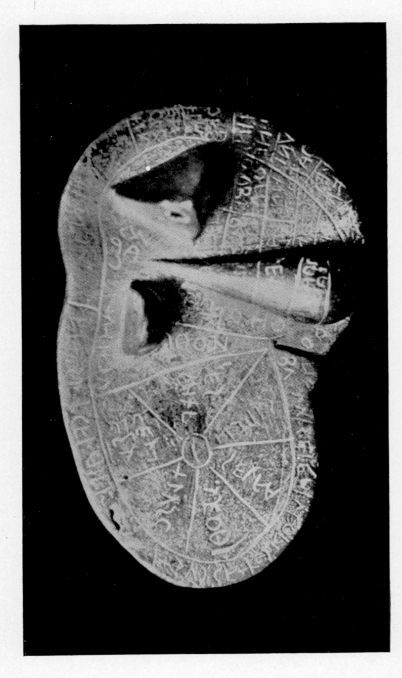

Etruscan liver in bronze, used for divination, probably of Babylonian origin (Museum of Piacenza, Italy)

troduced among the Greeks by Ostanes, who accompanied Xerxes on his expeditions, and that Democritos contributed to the popularity of the magic art by his works. Among the ancient magicians Pliny names Moses, Jannes, and Lotapes; he mentions the sorcerers of Cyprus, the druids, soothsayers, and healers, and finally the Scythians who engaged in magic. It is not surprising, he writes, that the sorcerers enjoyed great authority, because magic unites the three arts exerting the greatest influence on human thought: medicine, religion, and divination. According to Pliny, magic originated in medicine and developed along with it; however, he judges magicians to be mad or shameless liars and concludes that sorcery is profitless and futile even though it may contain some grain of truth, due more to the knowledge of poisons than to magic (XXX, 6). Many other passages clearly show that in Rome, under the Empire, magic practices for the cure of sickness were commonly employed, and that great numbers of healers, astrologers, charlatans, and sellers of amulets, talismans, poisons, and magic plants plied a flourishing trade. Pliny discusses at length the magic powers of animals, and especially the dragon, the serpent, and the basilisk, and of plants such as the rute, the peony, the mistletoe, and others which must be gathered with particular rites. He enumerates the magic virtues of precious stones, of minerals, parts of the human body, saliva, and certain humours. He makes interesting reference to the magic transfer of sickness from men to animals, such as dogs, frogs, mules, or donkeys. Pliny lists the most various amulets, and ascribes importance to numbers in therapeutic practices.

During the decadence of the Roman Empire, under the conditions predominating after wars and epidemics, these practices, owing to the penetration of Oriental beliefs and to Egyptian and Persian influence, were common throughout the Roman world, and accompanied the great wave of mysticism that swept the first and second centuries after Christ, until Christianity gained a victorious foothold.

Latin literature of the first and second centuries of our era evinces this tendency toward mysticism, and points to a progressive transformation of magic. It is said that the books of Egyptian alchemists were burned on the order of Diocletian.

Plutarch, born about A.D. 50, is a firm believer in the oracles and divination, and states that demons are mediators between men and gods. He recounts that the astrologer Tarratius, the friend of Varro, being requested to cast Romulus' horoscope, replied that Romulus was conceived in the first year of the second Olympiad, on the twenty-third day of the Egyptian month Choiak, at the third hour, during an eclipse of the sun, and to this information added a set of prognostications. Astrologers at that time were accorded the utmost faith, and belief in the magic virtues of plants and of animals was widespread. The *Metamorphoses* or *Golden Ass* of Apuleius (who lived in the second century after Christ), a physician and naturalist, philosopher and writer, is one of the most fantastic poems of classic literature. Witches possess the power of transforming their enemies into animals, of carrying them many leagues away, of killing or mutilating them, of putting them to sleep; they know the future and rule over sexual life; they can bring the dead to life, are generally old and ugly, and in their practices employ human blood, hair, and fingernails; they know all the arts of spellbinding, the might of invocation and of words, and they interpret omens. The *Apologia* of Apuleius contains his defence against the accusation of magic. He distinguishes between beneficent magic, indicated simply by the word *magic,* and malevolent magic, which he condemns. Apuleius defends the study of natural history, and considers demons as intermediaries. A naturalist, undoubtedly initiated into the secrets of the occult arts, whom St. Augustine describes as the classic author in that field, Apuleius has left us one of the most noteworthy documents bearing on the history of the new orientation of magic toward religion.

This mystic orientation is especially emphasized in the works of Apollonius of Tyana, whose life was recounted by Philostratus (*circa* 217). Apollonius, who lived in the first century after Christ, was famous as a great sorcerer; Philostratus defends him against the charge of sorcery, made against him by Euphrates, a rival philosopher. It is interesting to note that Philostratus speaks at length of the relations between Apollonius and the magicians of Babylon and Susa and with the Indian Brahmans, whose wonders he relates; he describes the levitation practised by the Brahmans, as well as astrological and magic medicine.

According to Philostratus, Apollonius possessed power to cure the sick and revive the dead, ruled over demons, and accomplished miracles. Throughout the Middle Ages, owing to the faith placed in the biography written by Philostratus, Apollonius of Tyana was considered as the wisest and mightiest of the great magicians.

All the literature on alchemy, and, above all, the works attributed to Hermes Trismegistus, the fragments that together form the *Corpus Hermeticum*, were read and studied at the end of the Empire, and formed the secret canon of the initiates into the occult arts. In this epoch, under the ethical and social influence of Christianity, there appears in prose writers and poets a tendency to orient magic toward mysticism. The magic idea is sublimated. In an age in which the fundamental ideas underlying the ancient religion and the political laws were losing their hold, magic drifts into an uncertain twilight atmosphere, to emerge in a new form after the clarification of human conscience brought about by Christianity.

Rapidly summarizing this short exposition of some of the most important points in the history of magic in the Latin world, it should be emphasized that Etruscan, Italic, and later Greek and Oriental magic exercised a deep influence on the evolution of magic in Rome. In this field also, however, the orderly and unifying Latin tendency is evident, cementing these different ideas and practices, transforming them into social functions, and subordinating them to the interests of the State. Magic, essentially individual or tribal in its primitive tendencies, becomes in the Græco-Roman era a social and political factor. It is subordinated to the idea of a powerful State, supported by unassailable laws and protected against all forces that might threaten its power. Magic was dominant when small clans, open to attack and accessible to the suggestion of their neighbours, lived in a constant state of fear, apprehension, and concern. It was admitted by intelligent legislators and keen observers of mass mentality in the epoch of the strong and wise Republic, when Rome was militarily and legislatively a conquering and ruling city. Magic served the aims of the State under the Empire, which subdued the whole of the known world, and gathered in the Imperial city, with stern critical discernment, ideas and beliefs of the conquered peoples, whose fate lay in its power. The magic idea regained its hold after the fall of the Empire, in an epoch of serious political and social decay, when the strength of laws disappeared with the might of Rome, and people sought, in suffering and misery, the comfort of mysterious and unknown things and attempted to escape from their tragic plight into a new adventure of the mind.

XVIII

Magic and Mysticism

I. DECAY OF MAGIC

THE ancient epoch, ruled by the idea of the magic circle and the laws of the clan and tribe, when religions and states were not yet strongly organized in a definite form, witnessed the apogee of the power of tribal magic. The organization of the closed caste, thanks to which sorcerers wielded civil and political power, and sometimes all power, is both the culmination and the beginning of the decay of primitive magic, and this for two reasons. Magicians, having obtained complete authority over the warriors—the tribal chieftains—thereby concentrating mastery in the hands of a closed caste, became a hindrance to the evolution of the State. With the formation of the State the sorcerer's rule had to be broken. The State, founded on rational bases codified in laws intended to ensure the rights of the rulers and of the people, subordinates magic to its laws, and controls the magician, or condemns him.

Another cause of the decay of magic was its crystallization in a set of formulas, rites, and symbols which utterly prevented further growth and adjustment of magic itself. Like any other expression of the activity of the mind, magic when immobilized in unchanging forms imposed by force was doomed to sterility and decay. Wishes and their objectives change with the conditions of life. Owing to a very well-known occurrence in the history of human thought, corresponding to the origin we attribute to the magic idea, magic is reborn in new forms although they are begotten by the same basic instincts and passions of men in all periods. Thus a new structure, more or less analogous to the ancient one, arises and develops until, creating new laws, it assumes new crowning forms and once more falls into decay.

Classical antiquity—the best-known ancient historical period—marks the end of the tribal magic world. In the Greece of Pericles and in the Rome of the Empire, when warrior and legislator ruled the State, and State power was based on conquest and laws, the decay of ancient magic as an organized political and social factor was already evident. By the formation of a monotheistic theocratic system, solidly built and backed by moral prestige and physical might, sorcerers and magic practices were confronted with another and mightier opponent. With the systematization of the religious idea, magic practices had to be done away with for the added reason that they represented a danger for the conscience of the believer.

2. RELIGION AND MAGIC IN THE PHILOSOPHY OF PLOTINUS

When, thanks to the early Egyptian attempts at philosophical speculation, and the Hebrew legislation, man reached the monotheistic conception, the abolition of magic became for the first time imperative. With the codification of the idea of one God as the source of good and evil, magic rites were ruled out, sorcerers were condemned, and no new laws recognized their powers. Nevertheless, as the monotheistic idea demands profound faith, understanding of a superior ideal, for which ancient beliefs were sacrificed, in times of danger or of severe physical, economic, or moral stress peoples reverted to the simple and obvious primitive ideas and ancestral beliefs.

Hellenic civilization had attacked both the magic conception and the religious idea from another angle: with serene spiritual tranquillity the Hellenic mentality viewed nature as a perfect harmony supported by a logic whose main essence is rhythm. The Greek philosopher judged the universe from the point of view of the actor on the stage, not from that of the spectator in the pit.

This clash between the Hellenic and the Oriental viewpoint is parallel to the struggle between the Persians and the Greeks, for instance, and later to the destruction by Philip of Macedon of Hellenic freedom and the philosophic and intellectual outlook of Greece. A blending of these two conceptions took place in ancient Alexandria. Alexandrian culture was influenced both by Oriental mysticism and by critical and speculative Hellenic thought. The characteristics of Alexandrian art, philosophy, religion, and medicine were, on the one hand, a perfect grace, exquisite beauty, critical speculation, and, on the other, a wandering in the abstract and symbolic, an escape from concrete speculation, and a fondness for abstractions and symbols, largely of Oriental derivation.

The Roman standpoint that the idea of the group or the tribe should yield to the wide and firmly founded idea of the State was essentially anti-magic. It left no place for an individualistic or antisocial system. If at certain times during the epoch of Roman greatness magic, particularly in the form of petty speculations on popular superstitions, spread in the countryside, this was due to the fact that newly conquered peoples took their own forms of worship to Rome, where they merged with Roman civilization. But at no time did these beliefs assume essential importance in the lives of the masses.

When the Roman Empire fell, not so much because of its corrupt morals and its political disintegration as of the distress and economic dislocations brought about by great epidemics and the disintegration of social life, the people once again became susceptible to magic, mystical, and supernatural influences. Plunged into profound depression by the loss of life, the destruction of possessions, and the crumbling of the whole structure of the Empire, a reversion to mysticism occurred. Suffering people, who had passed through tremendous calamities, eagerly sought a new faith, a new aim, and the will to live. In this period, the second or third century of our era, Christianity rapidly spread. Christianity, as a religion of peace and of kindness, endowed with a lofty ethical conception, placed above the idea of the State, which had proved a snare and a delusion, a much vaster idea, that of Humanity. According to the Messianic conception of the Prophets, which represented an attempt to escape from misery and corruption, and proclaimed the necessity for justice and equality, it announced that all men are brothers. It lifted up the humble, the men most seriously affected by past misfortunes and above all by their inability to regain faith in the ancient gods, and gave them the consolation of something beyond suffering, of a life after death, the hope of an escape from misery.

In an epoch of collective depression and excessive sensitivity Christianity created a new atmosphere for the injured and grieving; it revived, in a new form and with a suggestion drawing its strength from faith, the ancient and unforgotten belief in a life beyond and made of it an article of faith.

The entire Christian intellectual movement of the first centuries bears, in its forms and ideas, the impress of Judaism and later of Hellenism. During the decay of the Roman Empire, Alexandria became the intellectual world-centre. In the schools and libraries of Alexandria, the meeting-place of philosophers and mathematicians, debates between followers of all religions and sects took place. Under the influence of Hellenism, all the traditions of the Orient were discussed and blended. It was at this time that Neoplatonism was founded by Plotinus (A.D. 204–270?). Neoplatonism is the doctrine of a philosophical school which, going back to the sources of Greek theosophy, appears initially to be directed against Christianity, but in reality constitutes its philosophical basis.

Plotinus may, perhaps, be considered as the first mystic. He advocated fasting as a means of subduing the flesh, and was the first to posit the problem of the soul's ascent to God, and the Godhood's descent to the earth. The founder of the philosophy of contemplation, the speculative explorer of mystic infinity, Plotinus in his thought and still more in his feelings, shows a kinship with ancient pre-Christian magic and mystery-worship. Spiritually Plotinus is a descendant of ancient sorcerers, seekers of the supernatural, and asserters of the profound mystery of being. In the hidden chambers of the Temple of Isis the priests believed that they could discover by their ceremonial rites the secret of the relations between individual existence and cosmic life. Plotinus, in an epoch and a society ruled by Hellenistic philosophy, deeply under the influence of the Orient, combines ancient magic traditions with a new mysticism of Christianity. Life, according to Plotinus, is but a drama in which the action and the scene frequently change, and just as on the stage the actor who has supposedly been killed reappears in another role, thus death has no other significance than that of a bodily change or the laying by of earthly garments. To depart from the mortal body is equivalent to leaving the stage temporarily. In the events and hardships of life it is not the inward man, the soul, but his external self only that speaks his lines on the stage of life; and in this magnificent and terrible drama God is the playwright, man the actor. Plotinus creates the doctrine of the contemplation of God, which he calls *Theoria* and draws from an intuitive analytical introspection: his doctrine is analogous to a magic conception, as it is founded on an emotional reality, far removed from criticism and reasoning. Plotinus is undoubtedly one of the most gifted of the philosophers of all times, and in his *Logoi*, the first document of religious mysticism, his Christain mystical tendencies are disclosed.

3. THE GNOSTICS

This entire tendency, founded on mysticism and on the fundamental belief that visions and sensations of the world beyond may create a real system, gives rise to the doctrine of Gnosticism. According to the Gnostics, the world represents a set of processes of generation in all spheres, from the highest to the lowest; primitive ideas symbolizing the existing truths, and joining together in the *hieros gamos*, sacred or mystical union. There is in this epoch a close nexus between the doctrine of this sect and Christianity, hence the first Fathers of the Church violently fought against the Gnostics, and the latter, though professing to be Christians, celebrated secret rites and initiatory ceremonies. The heresy of the Manichæans was the most popular and serious of the doctrines that troubled the Church in the first centuries. The Manichæans, affirming the existence of a lofty consolatory spirit, Mani, whom his followers identified with the Paraclete of the Gospel, repudiated the Old Testament and prescribed a set of extremely severe practices.

Gnosticism is connected with pre-Christian, Oriental, Babylonian, Egyptian, and perhaps Persian currents, and above all expresses a deep penetration of the Christian idea in an atmosphere of mysticism. It reflects the ideas expressed in the Book of Enoch, famous in the early centuries of Christianity. Gnostic writers were strongly influenced by primitive doctrines: by the virtue of numbers, and by the teachings of the Ophites, a sect of Gnostics who gave great importance to the myth of the serpent.

Simon Magus was considered as one of the fathers of Gnostic doctrine; he claimed that all power was in the hands of God, who appeared in Samaria as the Father, in Judea as the Son, and to other nations as the Holy Ghost. The sect of Simonites, who were exorcists and sorcerers, derive from Simon Magus. According to Irenæus and Epiphanius, Marcus the Gnostic was believed to be one of the masters of magic. Magic numbers and words have the value of symbols and the power of spells, reflecting the music of the astral bodies. Gnostic literature, with its astrological prescriptions and references to Egyptian traditions, with its faith in astrology, in the virtue of precious stones, and in spells, which was widely and carefully studied in the Middle Ages, appears at about the same time as Christian apocryphal literature, which contains frequent allusions to magical events described by Apuleius and Apollonius—for instance, the practices performed (*Ev. infantiæ arabicum,* Chap. xv) by Christ or by Mary against the magicians who tried in vain to injure Jesus. Clearly magic practices were attributed to Christ in the Pseudo-Matthew, in the Gospel of Nicodemus, and in the Epistles of Barnabas, apocryphal books of that period.

After centuries of struggle, which centred first in literary discussions, to become more violent in regard to the dangerous deviations of the sects, it seemed that these sects were doomed to disappear. In reality, instead, the magic and mystical idea persisted in various forms, and hence in numberless deformations among individuals and groups, making the Church's action increasingly necessary. Christianity, the universal religion, assumed a position differing essentially from the attitude of tolerance and adjustment of almost all preceding national or group religions. The religious policy of Christianity, tending to a solid organization in a rigid hierarchical system, condemned and suppressed contrary beliefs, forbidding the worship of gods which, up to that time, had been accepted or tacitly tolerated. At the same time the Christian religion's incompatibility with all others, codified in immutable canonical laws, brought about a reaction: the secret survival of the religions of conquered peoples, in the form of magic. The defeat of a people proves (according to the Bible) the inferiority of its gods. Yet there.arise rebels and conspirators against the victorious gods, seeking refuge from their persecutors in inaccessible retreats and secret practices. The worship of pagan gods and demons continues, and it is this conception that represents Lucifer as the rebellious and fallen angel.

Other beliefs which were deeply rooted in the sentiments of the people were absorbed and ·slowly transformed by the new religion. This is characteristic of the vital force of Christianity: foreign ideas are deeply changed after their absorption. Thus the ancient spring and harvest festivals appeared as new rites, the sacred healers took over the functions originally attributed to single deities or beneficent demons, and relics assumed the power of ancient talismans; images of ancient pagan gods were transformed into sacred images of the Christian faith. After the increasingly energetic suppression of ideas declared heretical because they could not be absorbed and were considered inimical to the fundamental idea of Christianity, the structure of the universal religion was definitely erected.

4. RETURN TO MAGIC BELIEFS

In the first centuries of Christianity the existence of demons was not officially admitted, though it was believed that the pagan gods could act upon believers by depriving them of true faith. The sacred books, however, made only infrequent and vague mention of malignant demons or of the existence of hell. Toward the end of the third century, Lactantius stated that "the demons are attempting to destroy the Kingdom of God, and by means of false miracles and lying oracles are assuming the appearance of real gods." This new form of magic, the art of demons, thus appeared in the books of the Church Fathers, and philosophers and ecclesiastics constructed an entire complex system based on the cults that were widespread at that time. In Christianity's battle against the ancient mysteries, such as those of Isis and of Mitra, and against Neoplatonism, Gnosticism, and the different heresies, down to the most dangerous, Manichæism, the gods, symbols, and rites of these mysteries and sects were considered diabolical. St. Paul, in his Epistle to the Corinthians, had clearly expressed the belief that he who sacrifices to heathen gods sacrifices to demons. Deacon Marcus, in his Life of St. Porphyry, Bishop of Gaza (*circa* 400), described the battle against paganism and asserted the existence of the demon Aphrodite.

The figure of St. Augustine (354–430) stands out among the Fathers of the Church in the early centuries. St. Augustine's decisive and clarifying work determined the attitude of the Church toward scientific thought for many centuries. He made an exhaustive study of magic and defended Christ against the accusation that the people's conversion was accomplished by magic. This proves that as late as the fifth century it was common belief that the Christians employed magic. Later the Christians accused the Jews and Mohammedans of similar practices. St. Augustine distinguishes *goetia*, diabolical magic, from *teurgia*, the magic used in purifying the soul and preparing it for God. However, he condemns both, and attributes the success of both black and white magic to demons. He unhesitatingly admits the truth of the Holy Scriptures when they speak of Pharaoh's sorcerers and of the existence of magic and of demons, who, he grants, are capable of accomplishing wonders. He acknowledges the fact that sorcerers rule over the inferior spirits and can exorcize them, and, though guilty of horrible crimes, can perform miracles of which Christians, and even saints, are incapable. St. Augustine explains such superior power of magicians by the fact that God wishes Christians to be humble and perform acts of justice alone.

In *The City of God* and the *Divination of Demons* St. Augustine described the might of malignant demons, whom he holds capable of causing transformations and miracles with the permission of God alone. He was the fiercest opponent of heresy; he condemned all magic practices, attacked astrologers, and advised the faithful against the study of astronomy, which easily leads to pernicious errors.

It is easy to understand how in an epoch in which tormenting compunction assailed the human conscience and preparation for death was considered an essential way of life, defence against evil demons became increasingly necessary. In the struggle to save their souls the faithful were constantly exposed to the temptations and persecutions of demons, and they could only win this terrible battle by employing the weapons of the Church. The faithful, naturally, used not only weapons that, like meditation, asceticism, and prayer, were available to true believers alone, pure and strong of soul, but also those means which allure ignorant or superstitious persons. Ancient magic practices of exorcism, apotropaic means, invocations, and amulets reappeared in new forms.

In this epoch the belief in the virtue of amulets and in manifestations of divine grace, expressed in magical forms, was rife. The image was raised to a religious symbol, to a helpful tool; veneration for relics assumed such proportions that often wars broke out between cities over the possession of even the smallest portion of a saint's body, and the Pope was forced to intervene to prevent macabre treatment of the bodies of persons dying in the odour of sanctity. The preparation of the relics of St. Thomas Aquinas by the monks of Fossa Nuova, mentioned in the *Acts of the Saints* (I, 725) is an interesting page in this history of passionate belief. According to Erasmus, it was believed sufficient to look upon the image of a saint in order to win protection; thus a glance at the statue of St. Christopher ensured protection for a trip.

The history of Louis XI reveals the King's fanatical faith in relics. He believed that the most sacred of vows was that made on the cross of St. Laud of Angers. He gathered monks, saints, and relics in Paris from all parts of the world, spending large sums of money. A chronicler of his time says that Louis XI bought grace at the highest price that had ever been paid.

Magic rites and customs of the north European peoples who had accepted Christianity were adopted. One such form of bewitchment was the *seid*, practised to the accompaniment of song and music. Ordeals as appeals to the judgment of God, trials by iron and fire mentioned in the most ancient legends, and the trial by water, a magic practice of northern peoples in ancient days, became a part of the magic of the Middle Ages. The magical use of holy water to ward off evils, the employment of relics of saints for medical cures, and a series of similar practices appear clear in their significance to everyone who, as Lewis Mumford says in his admirable book *The Condition of Man,* interprets every aspect of this culture as a neurotic dream phenomenon.

Parallel with these beliefs, medicine again became mystical and magical. Contrary to the Hippocratic idea that illness is but a disturbance of the normal rhythm of life, the return to the primitive and instinctive concept of the demoniac origin of sickness immediately gave a new trend or brought about a return to therapy which consisted in the placing on of hands, the repetition of formulas, and so forth. Relics were believed to possess magical powers against the most varied illnesses. Bishop Gregory of Tours, in *The Miracles of St. Martin,* describes a set of cures, one of which was accomplished by touching the curtain hung before the tomb of the saint.

5. THE REIGN OF TERROR

The need for systematic protection, for a stable and definite plan establishing the way of life, and for acting and thinking according to set regulations derives from an innate tendency of the human mind. This tendency is probably engendered by the living example of the inflexible laws governing all manifestations of nature, the movement of stars, the life of plants, the repetition of physiological phenomena at determined times, among men and animals, and by the mathematical law of harmony, which made its first appearance among the Greek mathematicians and philosophers in the works of Pythagoras, and is manifest in the sculptures of Phidias and Praxiteles as well as in the writings of Hippocrates. The biological law of harmony is a necessity of life. When in the life of the individual harmony is disturbed by extraneous forces, accidents, and illnesses, the organism tends to rebuild it with its own forces. In society as well periods of destruction and disorder are followed by attempts at creating a new order. Likewise any inferiority of one organ or of a system is compensated for by the hyperfunctioning of another. Also in society the inferiority of one group is compensated for by a vicarious development of other groups. The organism itself attempts to find a remedy, to substitute temporarily or permanently for the diseased part.

The disintegrating society of the Middle Ages was dominated by a conviction of guilt and the necessity for finding a means of salvation or a remedy for the misfortunes that destroy individuals and society. Mediæval man witnessed ferocious struggles between feudalism and slave labour, between countries and cities, between communes and princes, between Papacy and Empire, systems and factors that had been considered absolutely stable. He was threatened by famines, wars, epidemics, and all kinds of accidents; he sought an escape from his misery by believing in all kinds of help; he accepted both truth and legend, the real and the unreal, emotion and logic, instinct and reason, and believed in both God and the Devil.

All activities were absorbed by war and defence; manual work was enslaved, complicated, and difficult, and the things that today are easy to accomplish or obtain required exhausting physical labour. Work therefore assumed the importance of an act expressing not only, and primarily, the need for earning, but the passion, pride, and sensibility of the person performing it. This explains the origin of institutions of defence, created with marvellous patience, such as the guilds or corporations. Money and wealth are much less important in a period of limited needs, and those who lived without working could hardly manage to subsist.

In this chaotic world in which no salvation could be found in the State or in societal life, Christianity was the only living actuality, and ideas and faith constituted the centre of life. It was not necessary to reason, but to believe; all problems of ideas were actual facts. What must one know? asks St. Augustine. God and the soul—nothing more. The Middle Ages awaited the salvation by faith, faith in Christianity as a practical religion, an exterior manifestation rather than a moral law; faith in all spiritual and magical practices, since these appeared to be a means of salvation or escape. All things were held possible and all ideas real.

Fear was the sovereign ruler of this epoch. The people believed that the Antichrist could dominate the world and the reign of evil precede universal judgment. An eloquent picture of this spiritual situation is presented in the art of the period; paintings, drawings, poems, and sacred representations describing the so-called dances of death and the triumph of death are of conspicuous importance. Belief in demons and in magic rituals was manifested in individuals and in groups. Humanity was pervaded with the terror of the approaching end. Political and social conditions justified this panic.

6. ASCETIC MYSTICISM

Thus a whole new adventure of the mind was prepared, originating in the higher and deeper mystical conception which in turn constitutes a necessary foundation of it. Religious ascetic mysticism was born; the religious system necessarily accepted magic conceptions and practices; individual and collective suggestion was exerted on a large scale by preachers, martyrs, and prophets, in great religious assemblies as well as in monastic orders and the intimate gatherings of the faithful. Groups of believers leading, in common, an ascetic life of prayer and sacrifice, were particularly swayed. In the believers' opinion, the ascetic life represented man's communing with God, and the victory of the spirit over the flesh, which had to be tamed by fasting, maceration, and the renouncement of all pleasures.

The evident necessity of suppressing the critical faculties of the ego and of giving entire dominance to emotional powers, in order to accept and plunge into the supernatural, logically gives rise to prescriptions dictating the subdual of carnal instincts, which are considered as impediments to spiritual life. Spiritual life is manifested through a high psychic sensitivity —consisting, as it does, in the ability to hear distant voices, to perceive mysterious fragrances, to grasp images appearing in visions—and the abolition or at least the decrease of physical sensitivity. It is, evidently, a procedure identical with that of the magical trance, accompanied by excitation of the emotional faculties and suppression of the critical ones.

The archaic unconscious, tending toward myths and mystic interpretations of everyday occurrences, thus comes into play again as a prime and predominant factor. All the phenomena of primitive bewitchment manifest themselves once again in the beliefs of the people, induced by another set of ideas and by different suggestions. Visions and hallucinations, amnesia and ecstasies, perceptions of perfumes and of light, and, finally, ecstatic flight, passage through fire, and other manifestations may be interpreted, though not completely explained without resorting to the intervention of the supernatural, as phenomena arising from the breaking through of the unconscious, and they undoubtedly manifest certain of its characteristics.

One of the most interesting forms of religious mysticism, from the viewpoint of magic, for its close analogy with the spell induced by self-hypnosis, is that (mentioned by Stoll) of a monastic sect whose members, about the year 1300, gathered together in the cloisters of Mount Athos, taking the name of *Hesychasti*—that is, "those who are at peace." Their prescribed ceremonies were extremely interesting: they bowed their heads on their breasts and, reciting endless prayers in monotonous tones, fixed their gaze upon their navels, thereby inducing visions of luminous magical figures, among which they distinguished sacred images. Feeling themselves surrounded by a divine light, the *Hesychasti* slowly achieved a state of ecstasy.

All the procedures that, according to the mystics, tend to prepare for ecstasy or for direct communication with the deity consist in physical or psychic practices for creating a special emotional state. According to the most authoritative ascetics, these practices may be divided into three categories: First, the practices that Ribet calls purgative—that is, the struggle against temptation, and the attempt to subdue the passions. Second, the contemplation of truth, the enlightened path; leading to the third, the state of absorption, the *raptus*, ecstasy. This means of attaining spiritual perfection requires, according to the most authoritative Christian mystics, a special vocation rarely accorded even to the faithful. According to this doctrine, it is essential to abandon all interest in material life and to concentrate on a single, supernatural idea. This doctrine is generally held by all those who may be called legislators of asceticism, not only in Christianity but also in Yoga—which consists essentially in progressive detachment from exterior life and gradual concentration on a single idea—as well as in the prescriptions of Buddhism and all mystic religions in general, such as Hebrew Chassidism and the beliefs of some Moslem sects. If we think that in these practices the intermediary, whether priest, leader, image, or voice, plays an essential role, we will immediately see the analogy—in fact, the identity —of these facts from the objective viewpoint of the psychologist. These practices consist in the arousing of a special emotional attitude, which manifests itself more easily in individuals of a special sensitivity, in the abolition of external control, in the suppression of criticism, and in the concentration on a single idea, which at times assumes a monomaniacal character and creates around itself an entire world of ideas, prepared by desire and induced by suggestion.

Mystic ecstasy, not considering the facts inducing it that may have escaped scientific checking, was frequently determined and explained without recourse to the supernatural. Thomas Aquinas, in the *Summa Theologica*, gives the name of miracle only to what is *præter ordinem totius naturæ creatæ* (beyond the order of the whole of created nature), stating that there are real miracles, contrary to natural laws, and that God alone can perform them, but that there are other occurrences that appear miraculous only because we are ignorant of the natural laws producing them. Thus, even according to Thomas Aquinas, one may judge alleged miracles by searching for and discovering the natural laws that may be their cause.

Maxwell states rightly that the Church admits that not all candidates to the mystic life achieve the grace of supernatural gifts, and thus affirms the congenital or acquired disposition of the individuals who may receive these gifts.

The need for an intermediary, a spiritual director, a master, to support the man preparing himself for the mystic life, to direct his efforts and help him to concentrate his ideas, is evidently analogous to the need for initiatory procedures. Passive concentration, accompanied by the weakening or abolishing of reasoning, and the "mystic" silence, constitute the preparation for the final state, which has the characteristics of mystical intoxication, of exaltation, or of sleep accompanied by complete unconsciousness.

I shall not examine in the light of medical criticism and explain here the well-known facts that are a part of the history of individual ecstasy, nor shall I discuss the ways in which these psychic phenomena are transformed into, or give rise to, manifest physical facts. This problem has been widely studied by modern psychiatry, and it has been proved that even fact, such as marks produced on the body (stigmata), to mention the best-known phenomenon, may be easily explained.

7. ILLUSIONS, HALLUCINATIONS, AND PSEUDO-HALLUCINATIONS

From what I have just said it appears evident that individuals who, owing to special psychical conditions, can easily induce a mood analogous to enchantment or can dissociate their ideas —who are generally in a condition in which hallucinations, deliriums, and similar states can be manifested with facility— are inclined to proceed rapidly or unexpectedly, guided by self-suggestion alone, or as a result of apparently simple external facts, toward these manifestations. It is therefore easy to explain how, when individual criticism is abolished, subconscious instincts and ideas spring up, or obscene and perverse tendencies (demoniacal temptations) appear; and the necessity for the active and continuous suggestion of a conscious or unconscious intermediary, who can guide the individual toward a set goal appears evident.

The history of the mystics, of their temptations, trials, sufferings, and doubts, discloses the picture of these anguishing contrasts and reveals that, under the guidance of the strong will of a leader, they may turn to divine exaltation, or, under the influence of other intermediaries or facts or the powerful eruption of uncontrolled instincts, they may be led to diabolical ideas and manifestations.

An objective examination of these facts results in a reconsideration, along general lines, of the best-known phenomena. Visions and hallucinations are sometimes spontaneous, and at other times the result of simple intuition, which may be based on a keen judgment of the object. These phenomena result from the state of spell, which in its turn may depend more or less on pathological factors or on external physical or psychical agents. The state of spell may be induced by physical and psychical practices, always under the suggestive action of the intermediary.

Hallucinations are ideational experiences conceived as perceptions of the senses. These perceptions do not differ from those of normal individuals, though they lack a real cause. Illusions, on the other hand, are erroneous perceptions of present data.

According to Bumke, illusions or pseudo-hallucinations may be a part of normal mental life. The difference between perceptions and representations is notable: perceptions are sensorially clear, corporeal, while representations are mental repetitions of frequently vague and incomplete perceptions. Sometimes, however, representations are extraordinarily vivid, as in the case of persons who visually remember series of numbers. In these cases suggestion can exercise an extraordinary influence, not only on hysterical but also on perfectly normal individuals. Seashore made an interesting experiment in this matter. A pearl was hung on a thread at the end of a long, completely dark corridor. The subjects of the experiment were made to walk slowly along the corridor and to announce immediately their first sight of the pearl's glow. The experiment was performed twenty times, and though five of these times the pearl had been removed from the corridor, two thirds of the subjects claimed to see it at the moment when they thought it should be visible.

In order to understand how suggestions and states of anguish may lead to a mistaken perception of one's surroundings, we must remember that every representation is composed of both a sequence of normal sensations, and intellectual action, a judgment upon which the recognition depends. This complex judgment may be altered in various ways: it may be due to habit, as when a person mistakenly believes a printed word with which he is familiar to be correct, not noticing the typographical errors it contains; or it may be due to an illusion determined by a pathological condition, as occurs when pictures or music appear changed to a person suffering with fever.

The relation between normal illusions and fantastic representations may appear in another way. Sometimes vivid imagination adds extraneous components to actual facts, thereby creating new figures. Jasper calls these illusions *pareidolias*. Leonardo mentions this phenomenon, saying that while thinking of landscapes he would sometimes imagine that he was seeing rivers, valleys, and lakes.

Hypnagogic images of a hallucinatory character are similar to hallucinations, and frequently occur to very tired persons in the drowsy state before they drop off to sleep. These hallucinations are independent of the patient's will.

Real hallucinations, on the other hand, occur without any external cause. However, they are very rare, and arise generally from excitation of the sensory centres. Some of these hallucinations are characterized by their extraordinary persuasive power, which is far greater than that of actual perceptions. They express, with few exceptions, the wishes and fears of a sick person.

Visual hallucinations occur, generally, when the mind is in a disturbed condition. Cocaine induces slight visions, while hashish, opium, and alcohol produce magnificent, brilliant pictures.

The most frequent hallucinations are auditory, and are in the form of either noises or voices or melodies. They may be of either external or internal facts (ticking of clocks, beating of the pulse, etc.). True hallucinations also occur in which voices are heard not only from without, but also within the head of the sick person, in his body, his feet, or his clothes. These are almost always antagonistic voices, insulting, reproving, or giving orders. Patients often complain of hearing their own thoughts. It is easy to understand the individual or collective suggestive power of such hallucinations, which manifest themselves in persons who, because they are deeply convinced of the factual verity of these appearances, express themselves with an exceptional suggestive power.

The Church has invariably checked all cases of this nature

and, from the theological viewpoint, has distinguished between supernatural, preternatural, and natural events. A real miracle may be attributed to God alone, and theologicians have devoted careful study to the determination of miracles, examining closely the way in which such manifestations have occurred. The Church has admitted divine intervention only when the facts were co-ordinated with the highest religious principles, and has thus condemned all forms of mysticism extraneous to dogma. A theocratic and political structure, the Church has necessarily classified miraculous occurrences so that either directly or indirectly the description or suggestion of mystical facts has strengthened religious sentiments.

Thus part of what may be called the magic idea re-entered the orbit of a universal religion, which wisely disciplined with its authority its facts and procedures. The majority of the manifestations that in other periods would have been considered either magical or miraculous are now easily classified as symptoms of specific temporary or permanent mental disorders (hysteria, paranoia, schizophrenia, etc.).

PART THREE

DECADENCE AND REVIVAL OF MAGIC

XIX

Enter the Devil and the Witch

1. ORIGINS OF DEVIL-WORSHIP

WITCHCRAFT, which, according to Jean Bodin, is the art that knowingly attempts to obtain desired ends with diabolical means, originated in the earliest days of humanity. It resulted from the demonological idea according to which demons, the possible cause of the most important happenings of life, could be conquered by secret arts and means, and their hostile power thereby hindered or their help obtained against distress, sickness, or death. The medicine-man of primitive tribes bent his efforts in this twofold direction; unseen powers might be either beneficent or maleficent, demons, or protectors, enemies or friends. With the passing of time, beneficent magic slowly became detached from diabolical magic and inclined toward religion. Beneficent magic entered as one of their formative elements into the new religions that, by accepting certain beliefs of ancient peoples, absorbed their practices and gave them the character of mystical actions, subject to the power of the deity.

Diabolical magic and witchcraft are opposed to dogmatic religion in so far as this holds the concept of one supreme deity, whereas diabolic magic is founded on the hypothesis of two opposing principles, constantly at war for primacy. (This is the fundamental idea of many Oriental religions such as that of the Avesta.) It stands by to extol the enemy of God and turn to him for help. All the diabolical cults derive from this idea, which is as old as the world.

The ancient demoniacal traditions which persist in different forms and under various environmental conditions and were present in the dualistic idea of the Manichæans gave rise to the belief in the existence of the Devil, the enemy of God, capable of endowing his worshippers with the strength to combat divine power. An entire system was slowly formed around this myth, which gradually took a more and more definite shape. The Council held in 547 officially admitted the existence of hell, and the fear of the Devil's power was intensified by the weapons employed by the Church to fight spreading belief in it. In this conception, the Devil is the opponent of God, and hell, where he reigns and where souls suffer after death, is the opposite of heaven. This dualistic idea, originating in human nature and in the beliefs of the earliest religions, this almost instinctive conception of antagonistic and adverse forces, gives rise, little by little, to a new systematized cult, that of diabolical or black magic.

Initially, taking their departure from the idea of an opposition of forces, the practices consisted in deforming prayers by repeating them backwards or by changing their words, and in consecrating contemptible and obscene objects, as occurs in certain forms of psychosis. In this new system the whole of ancient symbolism was, I might say, revived in reverse. The reversed pentagram became the emblem of the worshippers of the Devil. Voodoo, a strange and interesting manifestation of devil-worship, is associated with obscene practices and, at times, in a hybrid combination with the worship of the deity. Voodooism is still in use among the natives of Haiti, according to scholars who have amply studied this cult there at close range. In Voodoo, owing to the motif of two forces pitted one against the other, the rites are celebrated by persons attired in both black and white garments, and are led by priestesses. One of the features of this cult, and of its derivatives, is the Blood Mass, which was attended by cruel secret rites, and, at certain periods, had many followers.

The existence of the Devil, as distinguished from lower demons, is asserted in the Acts of the Fourth Lateran Council (1215), stating that God created the Devil and other demons by nature good, but they became, of their own will, evil. This shows the close relationship between diabolical beings and fallen angels. The Apocalypse of St. John (xii, 7–9) relates that the dragon killed by St. Michael was none other than the Devil, the world-seducing Satan. The first Fathers of the Church believed that the existence of Satan was proved by the words of Isaiah (xiv, 12–15) referring to an angel fallen from heaven. The belief that the sin committed by the fallen angels was the attempt to become independent of, and equal to, God was slowly formed. St. Thomas claims that it would be impossible for the Devil to conceive this overweening design "because he cannot even desire to be equal to God since he knows that such a thing is impossible."

The worship of the Devil spread, under the guise of rebellion against God, in many ancient sects, and there gradually arose a rite of prayers to Satan, invoked because of his power to perform miracles, to read the future, and to reward his followers.

2. WITCHCRAFT

In order to attain its ends, diabolical magic avails itself of every means, practising all forms of worship, and especially those most definitely opposed to the prescribed and officially enforced religious ideas. The phallic cult, originating in the symbolical worship of the male organ and of its portrayals and in the recognition of the existence of a superior being endowed with the characteristics of both sexes, was adopted, with variations according to time and place, by all who practised witchcraft. Obscene rites, opposed to religious and moral laws, are an important element of witchcraft. Later, under the predominance of ethical ideas and the establishment of moral laws, this cult is disguised under symbolical forms. Just as in primitive religions communion with the totem or the protecting demon, by means of food or blood, was one of the basic practices, so, due to the same idea that led to the general popularity of phallic worship, carnal communion with the Devil was the foundation of these rites. These practices are manifestly antagonistic to spiritual communion with the deity, which is the ultimate objective of monotheistic religion, and hence witchcraft is based on carnal communion and relations.

Other diabolical magic practices derive from those of ancient sympathetic magic, according to which, if one wishes to harm an object or a person, it is sufficient to exert a magic action over a similar object or person. All practices aimed at killing an enemy—for example, burning a wax heart, perforating with a pin an image constructed in his likeness, or destroying objects belonging to him—stem from this belief. These rites are accompanied by complex symbolical ceremonies in which the effect of the magic spell and of suggestion on persons seeking help from the witch is highly important.

A further popular belief was faith in the testimony of the deity in favor of the innocent. Such a faith gave rise to the ordeals by iron, fire, and water, and to the trials known as judgments of God (the duel is an example of this belief still extant today). The idea that the innocent may be defeated and the guilty triumph by diabolical arts is closely connected with belief in the judgment of God; hence those who fear divine judgment and wish to avert its consequences in any possible way turn to witchcraft.

In contrast with the moral and civil law, developing from the religious concept, the diabolical art of witchcraft represents a revolt against constituted law and order, a recourse to the deities worshipped by one's ancestors, a reversion to ancient practices which retain their significance, founded as they are on superstition, on the attempt at survival with the help of the Devil, and on the desire to rule over the order of events and to make oneself master of the life and death of one's enemies.

In reality, witchcraft persists, among primitive peoples, almost unchanged in its practices throughout the centuries. When the religious idea appears, grows, and becomes organized and powerful in a more highly developed society and more civilized epoch, the practices of witchcraft become more and more wrapped in mystery, and it becomes definitely separated from white magic, with which it shared a common origin. Being underlaid by a conglomerate of legends and primitive beliefs, it becomes the powerful weapon of revenge and political ambitions, of corruption and of base, antisocial, and anarchic passions, and is therefore strongly opposed by all legislative systems. Hebrew laws already prohibited contact between believers and practitioners of witchcraft. In 172 B.C., under the triumvirate of Octavius, Antony, and Lepidus, astrologers and witches were banished. According to Suetonius, Mæcenas insisted that Augustus punish them severely. Suetonius writes also that over two thousand books of magic in Greek and Latin were discovered in Rome and burned in the streets. In the reign of Tiberius—according to Tacitus—Lucius Pituanius, a famous sorcerer, was thrown from the Tarpeian rock, and Publius Martius was beaten and killed on the Esquiline. Under Claudius, the Senate issued another decree of banishment of sorcerers; and the laws promulgated by Vitellius, Vespasian, and other emperors were equally severe. It is therefore evident that in Rome, even though official magic existed, augurs were honoured, and soothsayers played an important role in politics, diabolical magic was vigorously attacked. De Causon and Summers assert that it is erroneous to claim that witchcraft came into being in the Middle Ages, under the influence of the Church. In reality just the opposite took place. The Catholic Church in the first centuries did not admit the existence of persons having truck with the Devil or capable of practising diabolical arts: it condemned heretics, and bitterly assailed the Manichæans, ordering their extermination, but did not admit the existence of witchcraft. St. Martin, Bishop of Tours, protested to the Emperor when Priscillian, Bishop of Avila, was condemned to death for witchcraft. Many examples prove that, in the first centuries, the Church acted severely against heretics, but did not admit the crime of witchcraft. In 785 the Holy Synod of Paderborn decreed: "Whoever, being fooled by the Devil, maintains, in accordance with pagan beliefs, that witches exist and causes them to be burned at the stake, shall be punished with death." This decree was confirmed by Charlemagne in the so-called episcopal Canon of Anciran, ordering the bishops to exclude from the Christian community all believers in diabolical magic and in the night flights of witches.

3. THE CHURCH AGAINST DIABOLICAL MAGIC

A cause of the change in the Church's stand against witchcraft and the admission of its existence was the spread throughout Europe, between 1000 and 1200, of heretical sects, particularly the Manichæans. Secret societies, practising grotesque and often indecent rites, sprang up everywhere, and soon a vast organization, aimed not only at combating the authority of the Church, but also at subverting its laws and ridiculing its institutions, was established. In 1179 the Lateran Council appealed to the secular powers to fight the spread of heresy, and at once began its campaign against heretics. The episcopal courts, forerunning the Inquisition, were definitely established by a brief of Gregory IX in 1235. The ecclesiastical authorities abandoned the established principle of the non-existence of demons and witches. Owing to the constant attestations of trustworthy persons, and above all to the necessity imposed by the continuous battle against the enemies of religion, the Church had to reject its former contention of the impossibility of obtaining results by diabolical arts.

Mediæval witchcraft arose, in the form generally described by persons convicted by the tribunals of the Inquisition, from the ancient, still persisting traditions of diabolical magic. Heresy in the thirteenth century became identified with witchcraft. It was no longer a question of theology or of discussions of principles (as had been the case with the first heretics), but it assumed the character of a struggle against the activity of well-organized hostile groups. The writers of that period, in fact, asserted that both heretics and witches worshipped Satan and practised opprobrious rites. In these rites, as numerous documents bearing on trials of that period show, there was a grotesque combination of sacred words and diabolical formulas.

I cannot discuss here the different heresies that flourished about the year 1000 or examine the widely discussed question as to whether, and to what degree, these sects succeeded in setting up new doctrines, and their relations to ancient beliefs. However, an important fact must be pointed out: toward the middle of the thirteenth century St. Thomas Aquinas (1227–74) asserted the existence of witches and by implication that of demons.

Because of the lucidity of his ideas and the clarity of his judgment St. Thomas Aquinas undoubtedly appears, even to modern historical criticism, as one of the most outstanding among the men who have coped with philosophical and moral problems. Aquinas, according to the biography of Thomas of Cantimpré, had a stormy youth; he was a Dominican friar in Bologna, then a student in Paris; was called to the Papal Court, and fled from there to Cologne, becoming a pupil of Albertus

Magnus. According to other biographers, he lived in Paris for three years, went from there to Naples, where he refused the Archbishopric of Naples, and returned to Paris.

Unquestionably St. Thomas was a profoundly erudite theologian and convincing teacher. A commentator on Aristotle, he had a deep knowledge of the texts, was well versed in patristic literature, and was familiar with the most frequently discussed problems of his day. During his stay in Paris he devoted himself to research on irrigation and mechanics and to the study of zoology and botany, and he may be considered as a precursor in the field of scientific research.

St. Thomas Aquinas' attitude toward witchcraft, therefore, must have had great weight because of his authority. He claims that magic exists and is the work, not of witches, but of the Devil. He denies that the divinatory power of magicians who are able to discover hidden objects, to render men invisible, or to move inanimate things is imaginary, and affirms that it has been established by trustworthy witnesses. He believes in the existence of witches, and declares, on the authority of the saints, the Catholic faith, and witnesses, that witchcraft is an actual phenomenon, capable of impeding carnal union and preventing the consummation of matrimony. The affirmations of St. Thomas, in contrast to those of many of his predecessors asserting that witchcraft exists solely in the imagination and fear of man, thus definitely strengthening the belief of the faithful in the existence of witches and formed the basis for all action exerted against them.

The Synod of Toledo in 1229, with the approval of Pope Gregory IX, decreed that the bishops of southern France should designate a priest in every parish to judge, with the assistance of a certain number of laymen, the orthodoxy of the parishioners and denounce heretics. Such an institution rapidly spread to other countries: in 1229 the Count of Toulouse introduced this spiritual jurisdiction into his domain, and in 1235 Gregory IX entrusted the Dominicans with this task. In 1251 the power of the Inquisition was extended throughout Italy, with the exception of the Kingdom of Naples. The first witch trial took place in 1264. The Inquisition flourished toward the end of the fifteenth century in Spain. In 1540 Paul III established the Holy Office in Rome, and the Inquisition, drawing its power and rules from the Vatican, was introduced into almost every Christian state.

The battle initially fought against heresy was thus combined with a campaign against diabolical magic. In the beginning the two accusations were identical: every heresy was diabolical, and everyone convicted of practising magic was a heretic. Later a distinction was made between the two crimes, and, apparently, they were joined for the sole purpose of influencing the judgment of the tribunal.

In Spain, where the Inquisition claimed the greatest number of victims (it is asserted that Torquemada, the great Inquisitor, subjected more than a hundred thousand persons to inquisitorial procedures), it was directed mainly against Moors and Jews. Often, with the establishment of the autos-da-fé, hundreds of infidels were burned at the stake in a single day, offering to the ecclesiastical authorities, the court, and the people a frightful spectacle believed to be a solemn manifestation of faith. In Germany and France witches were burned in great numbers. In 1596 the Bishop of Geneva caused more than six hundred persons to be burned in less than six weeks, and other inquisitors sent several thousand victims to their death. In this epoch the mysterious and perfect organization of the supreme penal power was employed with such severity and cold passion that all Europe was a prey to terror. The inquisitors held the lives, liberty, and belongings of all citizens in their hands. Secret denunciations were not only permitted but demanded. Sentences were the order of the day, and the Dominican friar, in his white tunic and black cap, appeared as the implacable avenger, the fearful administrator of a remote, inexorable justice. It is therefore easy to understand how, despite the grave measures and severe penalties, heresy appeared to be increasingly widespread, the number of persons condemned was constantly augmented, because under the suggestion of passions and fanaticism, every act, gesture, and word that did not conform exactly to rules or appeared suspicious when repeated by denouncers gave rise to long trials, which rarely resulted in the establishment of the victim's innocence.

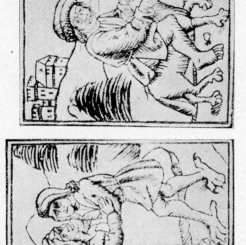

Witch riding on a goat (from Molitor: De lamiis et phitonicis mulieribus, Constance, 1489)

Witch in love with Satan

Witches transformed into animals

Belial and demons at the door of the hell

*Satan requiring from his victims strict observance of pacts
(from Guaccius*: Compendium maleficorum, *Mediolani,
1626)*

4. THE DAWN OF SCIENTIFIC RESEARCH

It is interesting to observe that these facts occurred simultaneously with the spread of Arabian ideas in the Christian West and with the beginning of experimental study in the field of the natural sciences. Ideas slowly progressed from mystical and magical belief toward a process of clarification, and during this process, especially in the field of practical medicine, scientific thought took shape. The School of Salerno is an example of this historical process. It originated in the medicine taught by Benedictines in their convents, and undoubtedly in the beginning it was a school for clerics; later it became a lay institution of practical medicine. The monk Constantinus Africanus introduced the medical ideas of the Arabs and translated many of their texts. The medicine of the School of Salerno became detached from magic and mysticism and took the path of clinical and experimental science.

At the same time, or perhaps a little after the flourishing of the Salerno School, toward the thirteenth century, the entire scientific movement took its inception. This, though strongly influenced by scholastic tradition, it steadily advanced toward experimental science. Petrus Hispanus, probably of Portuguese origin, the author of the *Thesaurus pauperum*, one of the most popular medical texts at the close of the Middle Ages, which was considered as a sort of encyclopædic manual of medical knowledge, took a stand against sorcerers and demons, prescribed exorcisms and ritual practices, but at the same time believed that the *via experimenti*, scientifically conducted, with doctrines and logic, was necessary.

The most interesting figure of mediæval science in opposition to magic is undoubtedly Albertus Magnus (1193–1280?), the companion and teacher of St. Thomas Aquinas. Born in Lauingen, Swabia, the son of the Count of Bollstädt, he studied at Padua and in 1222 entered the Dominican order. He was a provincial of the order in Germany and later Bishop of Ratisbon. He went to Rome in 1256, then to Cologne; taught in Paris, and attended the Council of Lyon in 1274. During his lifetime he was considered the greatest theologian of his age. His best books, however, are those dealing with natural science. A famous botanist, he was the first to carry out the researches initiated by Aristotle. Passion for nature, thirst for knowledge, and need for personal experiment reawoke with him. In his *De Animalibus* he writes that knowledge cannot be attained by demonstrations alone: experience is the best teacher. He had the courage to oppose some of Aristotle's assertions and to state the necessity for critical study. In regard to magic, Albertus Magnus was convinced that demons possessed the power to perform works of necromancy; he believed, however, that the majority of the miracles ascribed to magicians were in reality natural phenomena. He distinguished between beneficent and harmful magic, admitted the magic virtues of plants and stones, but affirmed that he was unable to discuss the subject, as these virtues cannot be proved by physical laws. He dealt at length with the interpretation of dreams. All his works reveal Albertus Magnus' passion for research in the laws of nature and his ardent effort to explain by natural laws all seemingly magical phenomena. It is therefore amazing that he should have been popularly considered a sorcerer and accused of magic practices. But in those days this was the natural consequence of the conflict between different ideas and of the violent battle fought by ecclesiastical authority in defence of dogma. The scientist who sought to delve into natural laws through research was considered as no less dangerous than the teacher of magic. Thus, for example, Arnold of Villanova, physician and philosopher, the friend of Clement V, author of the *Tetragrammaton*, which deals with the meaning of the sacred name and with the mysteries of the Trinity, was convicted of heresy. He appealed to Boniface VIII, whom he had once treated and to whom he had given a book containing predictions of events up to the coming of the Antichrist. His life was restless and stormy: he travelled in Spain and France and was in Avignon with Clement V in 1305. The Inquisitor of Valencia forbade the reading of his books, and five years after his death he was declared a heretic.

Arnold did not approve of magic, excluded it from the practice of medicine, believed sorcerers to be guilty of cheating, and thought that most of the results of magic practices were purely imaginary. However, he pointed out rites and practices for combating magic, such, for example, as the fumigation of the nuptial chamber with the pulverized teeth of a corpse, in order to prevent the action of adverse sorcerers. In spite of this and of his stand against magic, and notwithstanding the fact that he championed the experimental method, Arnold was persecuted and sentenced by the Inquisition.

5. THE BLACK DEATH AS THE ORIGIN OF MASS-SUGGESTIONS AND PSYCHIC EPIDEMICS

In the fourteenth century the most frightful disaster ever to overtake humanity, destroying millions of human lives and arresting the progress of social life, occurred with the outbreak of the epidemic known as Black Death.

In 1333 the bubonic plague spread from Asia across India and Syria along the major communication routes. At the end of 1346 central Asia, Egypt, and almost all of southern Europe had been invaded by the disease, which struck with terrifying violence, especially in Sicily, southern Italy, and France. In 1349 the plague reached England by way of Holland, and invaded Poland. In 1351 Russia was devastated. In 1348, 120,-000 persons died in Florence, and almost as many in Venice and London. Richard Fitzralph, Chancellor of Oxford, wrote that in that one year the students at the university were reduced in number from 30,000 to 6,000. In 1353—that is, twenty years after its appearance—the plague ceased to be pandemic, but returned periodically to Europe in the following years. From 1357 to 1364 southern France, Flanders, and central Italy were once more devastated by the disease, which is believed to have struck down no less than twenty-five million Europeans, a third of the population at that time.

Epidemiologists and historians have discussed at length the possible causes of this frightful destruction of human life, which resulted in the interruption of the social, civil, intellectual, and political life of Europe. A study of the history of epidemics reveals that they often appear with great violence, only to vanish without any apparent reason. Now we are able to identify the germ that is the immediate cause of this disease, but cannot assert why identical pathogenic agents bring about widespread and disastrous plagues in certain epochs, and appear with diminished virulence in others.

Humanity in the fourteenth century undoubtedly lived through a period of profound depression. Blame for the epidemic was laid to a conjunction of the stars, to the corruption of morals, and first and above all to hostile demons who were said to carry the disease into houses, to individuals who were believed to spread the plague with diabolical ointments, and often to the Jews. This was one of the many manifestations of the popular tendency to blame persons living outside or on the margins of organized society for disasters. Thousands of Jews were massacred in Europe, and their belongings confiscated, especially in France, where the rumour spread that they had poisoned the wells. The mild protection of Church and of rulers was unable to save them. The spread of anti-Semitism had all the characteristics of psychic contagion determined by mass-suggestion.

Another outstanding example of psychic contagion was that of the Flagellants, self-scourging fanatics who banded together in groups of a hundred, travelling from city to city, preceded by men bearing banners and crosses, singing, shouting, and throwing themselves, bleeding from their many wounds, on the ground. Flagellation is practised in all types of magic and has a background of obscene practices. It was originally aimed at removing evil influences and driving away the evil demons preventing fecundation. The Egyptians, Spartans, and Romans had practised flagellation, and in the festivals of the Lupercalia women were scourged with thongs cut from the hide of the sacrificial goat, to prevent sterility.

The psychic epidemic of flagellation broke out for the first time in southern Italy in the Middle Ages, and in Germany and Bohemia around 1260. Hordes of crazed individuals traversed the cities, a prey to mystical fury, and aroused terror wherever they went. After a few years these manifestations ceased, thanks to stern punitive measures adopted by ecclesiastical authorities.

In 1349, immediately after the plague, bands of Flagellants once more appeared in southern Germany. They were organized under a leader to whom every member of the fraternity swore blind obedience. Flagellation was practised for thirty-three days, and was performed with strips of leather studded with iron nails. The populations of the towns and villages traversed by the Flagellants regarded them with terror, but often groups of the inhabitants, especially poor or criminal persons, joined the Flagellants, who incited persecutions of Jews. In Poland, in the Rhine regions, in Flanders, and elsewhere the Flagellants spread very rapidly until in 1349 Pope Clement VI issued a bull ordering the ecclesiastical authorities to take decisive and energetic steps against these heretics, many of whom ended on the gallows. Thus the epidemic finally was stopped. In 1414, however, an outburst of flagellation occurred in Germany, where the Flagellants joined other bands of hallucinated individuals who, under the name of Brothers of the Holy Cross, preached revolt against the Church of Rome and abolition of the sacraments. The Inquisition intervened with such energetic measures that in a short time most of the members of the sect were either incarcerated or burned at the stake, and flagellation disappeared from European history.

A collective psychic epidemic, the so-called dance of St. Vitus, frequently described, occurred in Germany after the plague, and swept in frequent epidemics through the Rhinelands in the fourteenth and fifteenth centuries. Groups of men and women would begin to dance and continue with violent contortions until they dropped to the ground, frothing at the mouth and suffering from violent convulsions and epileptiform seizures. The symptoms were allegedly analagous to those of the disease known as *chorea minor*. This was the only time in which the disease has occurred in epidemic form among numerous individuals whose previous health had apparently been normal and who, after the attack, became sound again. St. Vitus's dance was probably caused during the depression following the plague by the relations (of which there are many examples among primitive peoples and in certain Oriental countries) between mystical and symbolical conceptions (which often have a sexual character) and the dance.

Another psychic epidemic that broke out in Germany was

the so-called Children's Crusade of Schwäbisch Hill. Thousands upon thousands of children left their homes and departed to liberate the Holy Sepulchre. Many died during the voyage, and many more were taken to hospitals in a serious condition. In this case it is not known when the suggestion was exerted or by whom. The Children's Crusade was perhaps a result of the panic fear of the masses who saw their only hope of salvation in desperate acts of religious fanaticism.

All heresies that assumed this epidemic form and were caused by widespread fear and by the dreadful destruction of human life by the plague were vigorously fought by the Church.

Ecclesiastical authorities kept a close watch not only over individuals suspected of committing forbidden acts, and persons attacking the dogmas, but also over all who did not adhere strictly to the doctrine and aroused suspicion by their passion for research and by not showing a blind belief in and devotion to authority. Perhaps—and this is a fact that causes no amazement to the historian—it was precisely this fierce persecution, often exaggerated or based on scanty evidence, that helped to intensify the spread of witchcraft.

6. THE PACT WITH THE DEVIL

The authority of the highest Church dignitaries, the enormous amount of material collected by the Inquisition, and vast collective suggestion contributed in strengthening and evolving the idea of the witch and establishing her powers and attributes. The problem of the origin and manner of execution of the witches' pact with the Devil gave rise to numberless debates and a copious literature. The most exhaustive attention was paid to the contract signed with blood by which witches sold their souls to the Devil. Another problem that the writers of this period discussed most concerned the qualities inherent in children borne by witches after carnal contact with the Devil.

There is an apparent analogy between the powers that were attributed to witches and the crimes with which Christians were charged, according to Origen and Celsus, at the time of their first persecutions.

The history of mediæval witchcraft clearly reveals that the Devil was held to be the witches' ally. Even the doctors of the Catholic Church credit the Devil with the power to rebel against God and to thwart His plans. Francesco Maria Guazzo, quoted by Sinistrari (*De Demonalitate*), stated that witches are wont to sign pacts with the Devil or with sorcerers or evil men representing him, pledging themselves, in the presence of witnesses, to give him their unstinted allegiance. In return the Devil promises them honours, riches, and carnal delights. This pledge is almost always in the form of a legal document, and such documents have frequently been examined by judges. The library of Upsala contains the contract by which Daniel Salthenius, a professor at Königsberg, sold his soul to Satan. The custom of signing the contract in the blood of the individual binding himself to the Devil derives from ancient magic of primitive peoples, originating in the importance attached, in every epoch, to blood as a factor of life. The contract could be made for a lifetime or for a limited number of years, and, according to the most renowned authorities, could be annulled by the obligee if he confessed his sins and performed the necessary acts of penitence. Many cases of repentant and converted wizards are known. One of the most famous of these was that of the blessed Gil of Santarem, who in his youth signed a pact with the Devil and for seven years engaged in magical and diabolical practices, until he repented, burned his books, donned the habit of St. Dominic, and led a life of prayer and penitence. He died in 1205 and was beatified in 1748.

Very often the pact with the Devil was sealed with the diabolical stigma, considered the most important identification sign of the worshippers of Satan. The stigma consisted of a deep mark on the skin; according to the descriptions of inquisitors and physicians, it was a small red spot, similar to an insect bite. At times it took the shape of a depression in the flesh or of an ulcer; at others it bore the shape of the foot of a frog or mouse. According to Sinistrari, the Franciscan monk, this diabolical seal resembled the claw of the Devil, and was borne by witches and wizards on the most hidden parts of the body, under the eyelid, in the armpit, or on the genitals. Two physicians who, in 1611, examined Luigi Gauffridi, a priest of Accoules near Marseille, suspected of heresy and witchcraft, describe with great exactitude his three absolutely recognizable diabolic marks, which were pain-proof and, according to the experts, not caused by a disease of the skin. It is an established fact that the presence of anæsthetic zones is characteristic of a pathological condition of the nervous system.

The main cause of witchcraft, *causa efficiens primaria*, is the Devil himself. All individuals who lack absolute faith in religion and are the prey of their passions are exposed to the temptations of the Devil. The first sign that a person has entered a diabolical alliance is, according to writers, that he lives contrary to the doctrines of the Church, disavows its precepts, rebels against the authority of priests, and invokes the enemies of God. A final pact with the Devil or his representative endows the signer with powers that are minutely described in canonical texts and in trial evidences containing the confessions of the guilty and the statements of witnesses.

7. THE SABBATH

Orders were believed to be imparted either directly by the Devil or at gatherings where obscene rites or grotesque counterfeits of religious ceremonies were practised. These witches' gatherings were one of the most important manifestations of witchcraft. The word Sabbath as applied to these gatherings has no connection with the Biblical sabbath or with the number seven, but, according to Summers, probably derives from Sabatius, a Phrygian goddess, sometimes identified with Zeus or with Dionysos, the protector of orgies and obscene practices. The meetings were held at set dates. In most of western Europe they took place on April 30, but often were celebrated at other times as well. June 23, the Day of St. John the Baptist, and December 21, the Day of St. Thomas, were festal dates for witches. During the Inquisition of 1610 at Logroño in Castile, the witches confessed that the Sabbath meetings took place on the days of solemn Catholic festivals, and this same confession is alleged to have been made by other persons accused of witchcraft. Some writers say that the great Sabbath, which is celebrated by a meeting

Witches attending the preparation of magic beverages
(from Molitor: De lamiis et phitonicis mulieribus, *Constance, 1489)*

Adoration of the bisexual demon Baphamet. Engraving by Ellain after a painting by Borel, 1658.

of all the witches of an entire region, must be distinguished from the minor Sabbath, a meeting of the witches of one village or city alone, held in an abandoned chapel or isolated house. There is a vast literature concerning the dates, localities, and rites of these meetings.

The meetings usually began at midnight. The witch of Keith, Agnes Sampson, who was tried in 1590, confessed that the Devil ordered her to attend the Sabbath at midnight, and that the rites were personally directed by him. Such confessions are to be found by the hundreds in the accounts of the trials of the Inquisition and in the voluminous books of jurists and ecclesiastics who devoted themselves to the study of witchcraft.

According to Baronius (*Annales ecclesiastici*), the substratum of the Sabbath and all like practices consisted in sexual acts. The practices of the Sabbath were directly linked with ancient Roman celebrations in honour of Venus, and with the mysteries of Bacchus, which took place in a forest near the Tiber. Analogous practices were widespread in all periods, among all peoples—in the Roman Lupercalia, for instance, held in honour of the god Pan, in the Liberalia festival, in the ceremonies whereby the Hindus consecrated temples and columns to the lingam, portrayed in the form of a phallus, and much earlier in primitive rites, the memory of which is perpetuated by the monoliths. One of the most characteristic figures employed to symbolize sexual union in a mysterious form is the bisexual androgyne or hermaphroditic figure that appears in many ancient mythologies.

In much later periods sexual rites—with the characteristics of devil-worship—continued to be practised or were revived in various countries. The famous Black Mass celebrated in France in the seventeenth century belonged to these rites.

8. DIABOLICAL POSSESSION AND EXORCISM

The idea of diabolical possession is closely bound with the history of witchcraft. It originated in the ancient belief that every sickness, particularly those resulting in a change of personality, such as hysteria, epilepsy, and other forms of mental disease, is caused by a demon. A devil was believed to have taken possession of the sufferer's body. This idea is attested by Egyptian monuments and the legends of the ancient Celts, Greek tragedies and the books of the Fathers of the Church. Persons possessed by the devil were supposed to be unable to talk, and it was thought that the devil spoke in their stead. Analogous cases are described by all the evangelists. The Gospel of St. Mark relates the case of a young man possessed of an evil spirit who was cured by Jesus. According to St. Luke, Jesus clearly distinguished between diabolical possessions and natural illnesses (xiii, 32): "Because I drive forth demons and cure illnesses." According to St. Matthew (x,1), Jesus gave his disciples the power to drive out malignant spirits, to cure every kind of sickness, and, according to St. Mark, entrusted the apostles with driving out demons in the name of God. Gradually an entire doctrine of exorcisms, accompanied by the proper ritual and by exact prescriptions as to practices and rites to be performed, was developed. The *Rituale Romanum* describes in detail the prayers to be said at these rites (*Exorcismus in Satanam et angelos apostaticos*, Rome, 1903, *Horæ diurnæ*).

One of the most interesting cases of diabolical possession is recounted by St. Gregory the Great in his famous dialogues. A Roman nun, while passing through the convent garden, picked and ate some lettuce, forgetting to pronounce the benediction, and was immediately possessed by the devil. The priest was called, and as he began the exorcism, the devil was heard to complain: "What have I done? I was sitting on the lettuce and this woman picked and swallowed me!" The priest soon succeeded in driving the devil from the body of the nun.

The literature on exorcism is enormous; it may be said that every ecclesiastic ritual contains exorcisms. One of the most complete collections was published by Maximilian d'Tymatten, Bishop of Anvers, in 1678.

In the history of art, scenes of exorcism are important. This theme was often painted by great artists, such as Rubens (the famous triptych in the Vienna Museum), Breughel (the engravings of the exorcism of St. James), Callot, and many others.

From the ecclesiastical viewpoint, the problem of diabolical possession was studied in a number of works containing important evidence. Such evidence includes even papers, duly signed, in which various demons assumed obligations and made promises. Father Surin, of the Order of Jesus, was invited by Cardinal Richelieu to the Ursuline convent of Laudun to exorcize the devils who had lodged in the bodies of the nuns. Father Surin began a fight that lasted for many years and was reported in detail. In 1629 Father J. B. Gaus drove forth the demon Asmodeus from the body of a nun, forcing him to sign a declaration (now in the Bibliothèque Nationale in Paris), which was countersigned by the Bishop of Poitiers and other ecclesiastics witnessing the event. In this autographed statement the demon promises that his companions will also leave the body of the nun. However, despite Asmodeus' promises, the expulsion of the demons proceeded too slowly, and consequently, on March 7, 1634, Father Surin took up his difficult task. Three months later another demon came forth and added his signature to the same declaration, and a week later the demon Nestali was in his turn expelled. In 1635 Father Surin wrote to a Jesuit friend in Reims that he was in constant conversation with the devils, one of them being always near him. The devils who possessed the Mother Abbess were called Leviathan, Balan, Isacaron, and Behemoth. At times the father himself was possessed. It is interesting to observe that under the influence of these demons the most ignorant inmates of the convent at times spoke perfect Latin. Finally all the demons, one after another, were expelled. One demon marked a red cross on the Abbess, another imprinted the name of Mary on her hand in Roman characters. The last demon left the patient in 1637, whereupon the convent of Laudun reverted to peace.

I choose this case, out of the hundreds told in the literature of this period, from the narrative of Grillot de Givry, because it contains particularly interesting details on writing, direct and indirect suggestion, and objects brought in or transferred. This case, I think, whose history is accurately described day by day, throws much light on the problem of diabolical possession and shows how phenomena considered supernatural may be accounted for if they are examined from the viewpoint of our present knowledge, which regards them as caused by suggestion. It is particularly noteworthy that the most complex phenomena usually take place in a closed milieu, such as a monastery or a college, whose inhabitants are almost entirely isolated from the outside world. The cases of diabolical possession which have been frequently and exactly recorded by the great Church Fathers such as St. Justin the Martyr, St. Athanasius, St. Cyril, and others, show that the idea of diabolical possession never ceased to exist. Fairly recently some interesting cases have been described. The latest one occurred in 1925 when a young woman living in Keighley declared that she had been possessed and tormented by an evil spirit for over a year. The young woman, kept under close observation in London by various psychiatrists, revealed mediumistic qualities, was hypnotised and exposed to suggestion, exhibited serious phenomena, and was finally cured when the evil spirit left her body after psychic treatment.

The case of the two Burner brothers is one of the most famous and perhaps the most interesting in the history of diabolical possession. This story is told by Father Paul Sutter in a book printed in London in 1922, with the permission of the ecclesiastical authorities. Theobald and Joseph Burner, born in Illfurt, Alsatia, of a family of peasants, at the age of eight showed symptoms of a mysterious disease. In 1864 the physician of Altkirch and other physicians called into consultation declared that they were unable to diagnose the disease. In September 1865 the brothers suffered from convulsions which, after violent and uncontrolled motions, frequently gave way to rigidity attended by absolute unconsciousness for several hours. Often following these fits the two youths, who for more than a day were unable to utter a word, abandoned themselves to frightful and obscene speech. At times they allegedly spoke rapidly and correctly Latin, French, English, and even Spanish and Italian dialects, of which it is certain they had never had the occasion to hear even a word. This phenomenon is considered characteristic of diabolical possession. The two young men were exorcized and, according to the author, became perfectly well and lived a peaceful life, one dying at sixteen and the other at twenty-five years of age.

The role played by suggestion in witchcraft trials is evident in hundreds of cases. I quote one that seems to me particularly worthy of attention. In the year 1500 in Lindheim (Upper Hesse) six women under trial by the Inquisitor confessed to having dug up the corpse of a child and having used it in preparing the famous evil ointment. The tribunal sentenced them to death at the stake. However, the family of one of the condemned women succeeded in having the police authorities examine the spot. The grave was opened and the body of the child was discovered perfectly intact. The case was given a retrial, but the sentence was once again passed and executed, the Inquisitor supporting the contention, accepted by the judges, that the body of the child was found intact thanks to diabolical intervention and that the confession of the six women before the tribunal had more weight than the judgment of the senses infected by infernal mystification.

Another case that throws light on the problem of diabolical possession is that related by the Dominican father Nider (1380–1438). He says that he heard from another priest of a woman who claimed that she attended the Sabbath regularly in the company of the Devil. The two Dominicans asked the woman to allow them to be present at her departure for the Sabbath. She consented, permitted them to invite other witnesses. At the day and hour fixed, the woman lay down in a kneading-trough and, uttering diabolical invocations, rubbed her body with an ointment. After a while she plunged into profound sleep, speaking of Venus and the Devil and violently thrashing about with her hands and feet. She finally fell to the ground, wounding her head. When she awoke, the priest asked her where she had been and she replied that she had been with the Devil and seen the meeting of witches and devils. After talking to her for a long time the Dominican friar finally persuaded the woman that she was possessed by the Devil.

The witches' ointment, frequently mentioned in the Inquisition trials, was repeatedly analysed by physicians. The chief physician of Pope Julius III discovered that such ointment was composed of extracts of hemlock, mandrake, henbane, and belladonna. He rubbed the ointment on the body of a woman and noticed that she fell into a deep sleep which lasted thirty-six hours, and was interrupted by frequent hallucinations. It is evident that these ointments, as well as the beverages and poisonous substances that are an important part of the magic cupboard, are the main agents of bewitchment, and may explain hallucinations of all kinds.

Undoubtedly, one of the factors that threw into a trance psychopathic individuals or persons possessing qualities that today are commonly called mediumistic, and perhaps are due to excessive sensitivity, was the threat of serious punishments and their frightful consequences. Witch trials were held for four centuries, and thousands of women (some writers quote much larger figures) were convicted of sorcery and put to death. A study of the terrible *Malleus maleficarum* (*Witches' Hammer*) by Jacobus Strenger, published in 1487, the most authoritative text of the persecutions of witches undertaken by ecclesiastical authorities, and of the trials, which consisted mainly in charges and confessions, often obtained by means of torture (only slight importance was given to proof), convinces one that all this long episode, which certainly did not come to a close with the official ending of the trials, is the product of vast collective suggestion, involving accusers and victims. These trials were the frightful consequence of fallacious interpretations of phenomena containing no supernatural elements. Simple, calm, and impartial observation would have resulted in a just evaluation of the facts.

It may be asked how these women (and why almost exclusively women) yielded to this psychosis which often cost them their lives. Evidently the delusion of possessing supernatural powers, dominating the world, and acquiring extraordinary riches, added to the more immediate and efficacious hallucination of carnal relations with the Devil and of sexual orgies, had an overpowering effect upon hysterical women. Moreover, the fact that carnal relations with the Devil and sexual orgies were officially recognized by the people at large and by court decisions was thought to be a proof of their actual existence and favoured suggestion.

Witchcraft is a tragically destructive and antisocial phenomenon, which becomes collective but rarely, and is eradicated
not by burnings at the stake or threats, but only by the establishment of a rational scientific criticism that overcomes the
influence of superstition and suggestion.

9. THE REBIRTH OF CRITICISM

In the period in which witches' pyres were burning and
authoritative men such as John Tritheim, Abbot of Sponheim,
maintained, in his *Antipalus maleficarum,* the general opinion
that sorcerers and witches could wreak immeasurable damage,
and when Martin Luther himself warned against the danger
of witches, some courageous spirits began to affirm that
witches in reality were only persons suffering from mental
disorders.

John Weyer, or Wier (1515–88), born at Grave in Brabant,
a physician and man of letters, known under the Latin name
of Wierus, published in 1563 his famous *De præstigiis dæ-
monum et incantationibus ac veneficiis* (*On the miracles of
Demons, or Incantations and Poisoning*), which ran through
many editions in a few years. In this book Weyer courageously stated that witches cannot be compared to heretics,
but are melancholy old women, not in command of their
senses, discouraged and timid, whose minds are so confused
that they believe they do things which are, in reality, impossible. Weyer maintained that the confessions wrung from
witches by torture were a horrible mistake, and denied the
possibility of the transformation of men into animals, and of
witches' flights. Incubi or nightmares, according to this courageous physician, are phenomena caused by apprehension and
anguish: filtres, magic practices, and witchcraft can, at most,
lead to madness, but never to success. Diabolical arts and
their bogies should frighten nobody, said Weyer, and the
schemings of witches, on which he lavished his ridicule, are of
no importance.

Weyer's second book, *De lamiis* (*On Witches*), completes
his *De præstigiis* and sums up its conclusions. Weyer quotes
from, discusses, and comments on ecclesiastic textbooks. He
explains at length the notions concerning the power of imagi-

nation and describes many cases. He is not yet a free thinker or an inspired innovator; he sincerely believes in the Devil and in magic arts, and describes Satan's strategies. He is a perspicacious observer, however, unmasking cheaters and charlatans. In the case of a woman who claimed to vomit strips of cloth that the Devil placed daily in her stomach, Weyer pointed out the complete absence of gastric contents on the material, asserted that the woman was an impostor, and soon succeeded in proving that she kept the cloth hidden in her mouth, spitting it out with simulated efforts. A beggar, Barbara, claimed that she had lived for many years without food and bodily functions. The senate of her native town gave her a certificate testifying to her supernatural powers. Weyer took her to live in his house, kept her under observation, and soon discovered that her abstinence was only a trick, and that her sister brought her nourishment which she gave to her in secret. Weyer's opinion was that sorcerers really existed, but that there were likewise a great many persons, and especially women, who were mentally ill, and instead of being accomplices of the Devil were the victims of hallucinations and dreams causing them to believe that they had committed crimes. The truly magnificent achievement of this courageous physician was that he submitted witches to clinical examination, observed them from the viewpoint of the pathologists, and stated that they were irresponsible. As early as the mid-sixteenth century he demanded outright acquittal for the accused defendants, and when this was not possible, asked that they should at least not be tortured and put to death. He wrote: "If you believe that witches deserve punishment, rest assured that their malady is a more than sufficient penalty, which leaves them no peace either day or night." He rebelled against barbarity, described as executioners the judges who persecuted these wretches, and with amazing courage rose up to defend them as a just and impartial judge.

The work of Weyer had immediate and remarkable success. In a few years it ran through five editions, and was translated into German, and the most famous physicians and theologians of the period wrote to him, giving him their support. Vehement protests were made by inquisitors and theologians. One of the latter, Father Bartolomeo da Spina, the author of a polemical book against Weyer, states: "Recently Satan went to a Sabbath attired as a great prince, and told the assembled witches that they need not worry since, thanks to Weyer and his followers, the affairs of the Devil were brilliantly progressing." No less violent were the criticisms of Jean Bodin, Minister of Henry III and learned scholar, who, basing his contentions on texts, violently attacked Weyer, accusing him of irreligiousness and heresy, ignorance and indecency, and tenaciously defending his belief in the dangerousness of witches and the necessity of condemning them. However, despite the antagonism to Weyer's courageous stand, his work had a profound influence on public opinion, and although witch trials continued to be held almost everywhere, the truths that the physician of Grave was the first to champion began to make their way among intelligent and honest groups of people.

Another brave adversary of the belief in witchcraft was Reginald Scott (1538–99). In 1584 he published the famous *Discovery of Witchcraft*. In this book, which is admirable for the modernity of its ideas, speaking of witch trials, he says: "These women are but diseased wretches suffering from melancholy, and their words, actions, reasoning, and gestures show that sickness has affected their brains and impaired their powers of judgment. You must know that the effects of sickness on men, and still more on women, are almost unbelievable. Some of these persons imagine, confess, and maintain that they are witches and are capable of performing extraordinary miracles through the arts of witchcraft: others, due to the same mental disorder, imagine strange and impossible things which they claim to have witnessed."

Slowly, as we shall see, such ideas propounded by isolated physicians who dared to stem the current made headway and led to definite results.

Modern psychiatry gives us the means of judging these facts, so important in the history of mankind, from an objective viewpoint, which is vastly different from that of the inquisitors, but not identical with that which regarded the trials as systematic crimes. Such facts brought about, on the one hand, an increase in blind faith and fantastic superstition, and, on the other, a secretly creeping sense of rebellion. The work of the tribunals of the Inquisition did not destroy witchcraft. It was not until the end of the sixteenth century, when the culture and civilization of the Renaissance spread from Italy throughout Europe, and criticism regained its station, that the decay of witchcraft and diabolical magic set in. It was only then that their devotees crept to cover in the most hidden places, and were attacked and conquered, not by persecutions and judicial massacre, but by the light of new ideas illuminating, in a heroic moment, the paths of civilization.

XX

The Occult Sciences

A. ASTROLOGY

I. THE ORIGINS OF ASTROLOGY

THE so-called occult sciences are not and never were sciences, since they are founded neither on analysis nor on synthesis, experiment nor critical reasoning, or, to state it more adequately, since they make use of only a part, and only up to a certain point, of the methods of research and study that we call scientific. The name "occult sciences," however, is not entirely unjustified, as it may represent the first contacts of scientific thought with the magic complex. The basis of the occult sciences is a heterogeneous complex of superstitions, ideas anchored in the unconscious, and magic traditions deriving especially from Egypt and Chaldea. On this foundation, dominated by the idea of magic and by all the characteristics accompanying it, a new structure is erected, scientific in appearance because of its use of mathematical calculations and of experiments, its study of the stars and its investigation of chemical elements.

We must, first of all, take into account an essential fact: that the fundamental laws of positive science, discovered through experiments, were first noticed or admitted only by a small minority. Recollection of the centuries-long struggles that preceded the final acceptance of positive, scientifically substantiated facts, such as for instance the heliocentric system, blood circulation, the location of intellectual faculties in the brain, the septic origin of puerperal fever, reveals the difficulty of rendering evident truths acceptable, not to the masses only, but to cultivated individuals as well, intellectually capable of understanding. Logic has long been overpowered by traditions, by superstitions linked with unconscious sensations or emotions; experiment has triumphed with difficulty over unshakable faith in ancient errors, and factual evidence

[255]

has for centuries been powerless to invalidate conclusions drawn from dogmatic statements, hypotheses, or analogies.

Astrology and alchemy, magic sciences *par excellence*, may be regarded as the earliest attempts, uncertain yet systematically arranged, to apply the results of exact studies in order to obtain magical success—that is, in order to objectify desires that cannot be fulfilled by natural means. Astrology makes a precise study of the position and interrelation of the stars: it examines their course with admirable accuracy, logically judging that the relations between the macrocosm and the microcosm may give us definite assurance as to the influence of stars over terrestrial life. It perceived by intuition certain facts that science had barely demonstrated, correctly interpreted some of the phenomena of physiological life, but employed this entire systematic structure in the service of divination, for the purpose of casting horoscopes of persons and of events. Alchemy took cognizance of, and successfully investigated, the connection between metals and stars; it drew conclusions that were important to medicine and opened new horizons for the study of the cosmos. It organized a system of experiments and research, but used it primarily to achieve the fruition of magic wishes. It searched for the philosophers' stone and for a method of transforming metals into gold. After centuries of travail, astrology, under the guidance of exact science, became astronomy, solving, or attempting to solve, the deepest problems of the cosmos. Alchemy became chemistry, turning to the investigation of the fundamental facts of life, seeking for its origins and attempting to explain it. The occult elements of astrology and alchemy—that is, divination and the solution of alchemistic problems—remained purely magical.

2. THE CONCEPT OF ASTRAL INFLUENCE

Astrology is, apparently, of Egyptian or Assyro-Babylonian origin. A calendar containing a list of propitious and unpropitious days dates back to 1300 B.C., and tables indicating the course of the stars have been found in tombs of that period.

In classical Greece astrology was extremely popular and many works were written on the subject. In the epoch of

Alexandrian culture astrology slowly became connected with objective observation. Ptolemy (150 B.C.) created the doctrine of the cosmos and of the movements of the stars, which had dogmatic validity down to Copernicus. Knowledge of the sun and moon and the position of the stars in relation to each other and to the earth constitutes the theoretical basis of astrology. Fundamental information regarding this subject is contained in Ptolemy's *Tetrabiblos* or *Quadripartitus,* which for centuries was held to be the classic text of astrology.

Ptolemy's point of departure is the opinion, common to his times, that both the elements and the humours are divided into hot and cold, moist and dry. The sun is pre-eminently hot and cold, the moon is moist and causes vapours to rise and things to decompose; Saturn, being farthest from the sun, is cold and dry; Jupiter is humid and hot; Mars possesses the heat of dry ardent fire; Venus, being near the sun, is equally hot, but emanates moistness; Mercury is dry and sometimes humid. These ideas underlie the prognostications and horoscopes concerning the influences of the planets. Jupiter, Venus, and the moon are benign; Saturn and Mars, having completely opposite qualities, are malign. The sun and Mercury are between these two groups and may have different influences according to their position.

According to Ptolemy, the stars are divided into male and female: Venus and the moon are female because moistness predominates in them and therefore fecundity. Saturn, Jupiter, and Mars are male. Mercury, possessing the qualities of both groups, is of an indeterminate sex. Analogously, the same qualities possessed by the planets are to be found in varying quantities in elements, regions, seasons, organs of the human body, food, and so forth.

The influence of the planets is not absolute, but depends on their position in the sky. The course of the stars, and the fact that they follow approximately the same road, was known. The zodiac, an imaginary belt encircling the heavens, was divided into twelve parts, each named according to one of the constellations. Maximum importance was given to the respective positions of the heavenly bodies. The relations of the planets were considered "essential principles."

On this doctrine the theory of the planetary triangles was constructed. In such a system each of the twelve parts of the zodiac was divided into four equal triangles. Horoscopes were drawn by observing the position of the planet in the triangle, its rising and setting, and the relations between different planets at a given moment.

It is of the greatest interest in judging the origin and growth of astrology to know the grounds of astral influence as given by Ptolemy. Such grounds seem to be in partial agreement with the modern doctrine concerning the principles of constitutional disposition. Ptolemy affirms that the physical and moral natures of people depend to a large extent on the position of the region in which they live in relation to the sun; he notes that persons living in southern regions are sunburnt, their hair is black, and their blood hot as a consequence of the long duration of summer. People, on the other hand, who live in northern countries have white skin, fair hair, and cold natures. The qualities of people likewise depend on the various relations of the stars. Jupiter and Mars rule the northeast—that is, Europe—but the reciprocal position of the constellations exercises a particular influence. The cold, pugnacious Germans and the Gauls are under the rule of Mars and Capricorn, the Italians under that of the sun and the Lion, and so on.

The great Latin writers Vitruvius, Plutarch, and Apuleius held astrological beliefs. Later, astrology was attacked by philosophers. Cicero repudiates it and criticizes horoscopes, asking how it is possible that all the men who were killed in the battle of Cannæ could have been born at the same instant or under the same constellations, and how it happens that individuals born in the same place and at the same moment have completely different characters, temperaments, and destinies. He declares that he is firmly opposed to belief in horoscopes and divination. One of the most violent adversaries of astrology was Lucian, who derided sorcerers, who in his time enjoyed great popularity in Rome. There were, nevertheless, outstanding men such as Celsus who still admitted the influence of the stars.

The writings known as pseudo-Clementine, attributed to

Clement of Alexandria, contain a number of passages in which astrology is considered as a mathematical science. Magic is recognized as an art exercised by demons or by the souls of the dead through human agents.

Celsus (A.D. 178?), an eclectic Platonist and opponent of Christianity, charging the Christians with the practice of witchcraft and with the worship of magicians, affirmed that the Jews also were addicted to sorcery. Origen, defending the Christians, denied Celsus' charge and gave a living picture of the ruling opinions of the Church in regard to magic. He admitted that sorcerers are helped by evil spirits who preside over witchcraft, attributed great power to spells, discussed the personality of the devil Balaam, granted the force of evocation of names, and clearly opposed horoscopy because it annuls freedom of will. He affirmed, however, that the stars are reasoning beings which can foresee the future, and that they seem to foretell wars, disasters, and important political events.

Neo-Platonism, which is generally thought to have been founded by Plotinus in the third century of our era, appeared in the beginning extraneous and hostile to magical and astrological ideas, but later came close to astrology. Some writers ascribed to the stars an influence on crimes and discussed the friendly or inimical relations between planets and living beings. A dominant idea of Christian writers in the Middle Ages in regard to astrology was that the power of stars is analogous to that of the wind which blows upon ships: it may shake the body in which the soul makes its voyage on earth, but the soul itself is free. Thus believers attempted to reconcile the existence of free will with the idea of the occult influence of celestial bodies.

One of the first books to have great ascendancy on the culture of the Middle Ages is attributed in turn to Hermes Trismegistus and to the patriarch Enoch. This treatise is probably a collection of writings compiled from various ancient Hebrew or Aramaic fragments. It had the authority of a canonical text and St. Augustine in the *City of God* (xv, 23) admitted, on the faith of the apostles, that the book of Enoch contains divine writings, not excluding the possibility, however, that some of the texts may be apocryphal. This book contains a true personification of the stars, to which tremendous importance is attributed in so far as their control over human life is concerned.

The astrological theory predominated in Gnosticism, which originated in Chaldean astrology and was influenced by Persian and Egyptian beliefs. The so-called Gnostic gems are, according to King (*The Gnostics and Their Remains*, London 1887), astrological talismans often possessing magical or medical virtues. A frequent symbol, of Egyptian origin, is the *agathodaimon*, a portrayal of the Egyptian lion-headed snake, wearing a seven- or twelve-rayed crown, representing the planets or the signs of the zodiac.

Among the astrological sects that of the Manichæans, or disciples of Mani, in whose writings astrology plays an important role, deserves mention.

3. THE CHURCH'S OPPOSITION TO ASTROLOGY

Discussion of the importance of the stars and the momentous role they play in human events dominated the literature of the first centuries of the Christian era, permeated all arguments and comments concerning the history of creation, and influenced the philosophic conception of a future life. The problem of reconciling these ideas with the tenets of Christianity became increasingly urgent. St. Augustine clearly voiced the opposition of Christianity to all magical arts connected with witchcraft. He strongly condemned crimes committed by sorcerers, and asserted that the actions which these individuals were credited with performing derived from deplorable rites of demons disguised under the name of angels. In regard to astrology, which St. Augustine studied in his youth, he sustained (*De Doctrina christiana*, ii, 21) the falsity of astrology and horoscopy, and maintained that the world is governed by divine will alone. Nevertheless, he admitted that Christ was born under the influence of the stars and did not settle the problem of their action.

Oriental science exerted notable influence over Occidental culture around A.D. 1000, and was dominated by essentially magic concepts. An Arabic author, Alkindi, in his *Astrologia*,

Torture of a sorcerer. German print, about 1550.

Autograph signed by the demon Asmodeus on May 19, 1629. (Bibliothèque Nationale, Paris M Fr 7618 f 20) translated by Gerard of Cremona, attempts to give a scientific explanation of astrological theories and makes a number of prophecies regarding the conjunctions of the stars. Among other important Arabian astrologers may be mentioned Albumazar, frequently quoted by Pietro d'Abano, and Thebit, often referred to as an authority by Roger Bacon, Albertus Magnus, Pietro d'Abano, and Cecco d'Ascoli. According to Thebit, the perfection of the mysteries depends on astrological knowledge; images that may be burned or wounded must be constructed by taking into account the position of the stars.

In the ninth and tenth centuries astrology and divination, joined with the observation of the moon and the stars, assumed increasing importance throughout central Europe. The belief in unpropitious days, frequently called Egyptian, became a fundamental principle on the strength of which medical texts prohibited certain treatments, such as blood-letting, on certain days.

I shall not mention here the numerous books on astrology of the Middle Ages, filled with descriptions and with astrological combinations, the pseudo-astrological texts, and the volumes dealing with the virtues of precious stones.

Thomas Aquinas admitted the great importance of the astrological theory and maintained the nobility and incorruptibility of the heavenly bodies, governed by supreme wisdom, and ruling over all earthly events, but not over the human soul. Aquinas defined fate as the power exerted by the stars in their movements and reciprocal relations.

The attitude of Roger Bacon, one of the great precursors of experimental science, deserves to be pointed out. Bacon's faith in experiment, his affirmations of the existence of flying dragons, his attitude toward magic, which he believed contained something of truth, his attempt to draw a line between science and magic, and his position in regard to astrology are characteristic of his method. Bacon believed that a physician who was not versed in astrology could not cure a sick person, and contended that the stars exercised a great influence over life, health, and sickness. He claimed that Mercury, the planet of wisdom and eloquence, oracles and prophecy, ruled over

Christianity. Bacon shared the belief of astrologers that Islam-ism would last a number of years—693—equal to the number of the beasts of the Apocalypse.

The question of whether Bacon was condemned and jailed because of his astrological writings is problematic; this, how-ever, appears unlikely, since, as we saw, astrological doctrines were generally accepted. Undoubtedly Bacon had a clear vi-sion of the necessity for a profound study of nature, for a separation of science from magic. He affirms (*Opus tertium*, Chap. ix) that only philosophers who carefully study the forces of nature are able to reach an adequate appraisal of the illusions of magic and the miracles of Christianity. He states that certain forms of fascination which are thought to be magical should be looked upon as diseases and are contagious.

In this epoch the idea of scientific research spread rapidly in various parts of Europe; medical and biological studies in-creased. Various texts by authors of this period, such as Gug-lielmo da Saliceto in his commentaries on Honein ben Izach, and the books of Giovanni Paolino on snakes, and many oth-ers, explicitly refer to experiments. Thorndike, who has made a close study of these texts, emphasizes their importance. The *Liber Astronomicus* of Guido Bonatti (Dante: *Inferno*, XX, 118) is the most important astrological work of the fourteenth century. Bonatti bases his study on the authority of Ptolemy and Hermes and, to a still greater extent, on Arabian astrol-ogy. The *Liber Astronomicus* was tremendously successful, was often plagiarized, and later was frequently reprinted. Guido Bonatti, who died about 1300, was, presumably, a pro-fessor at Bologna. He was the astrologer of Guido da Monte-feltro, "captain of the people" of Forlì. He stated that astron-omy and astrology were one and the same thing, but clearly professed his belief in the influence of stars and the importance of horoscopes. Muratori, the Italian scholar, writes: "Guido made a wax image of a ship for a poor druggist, ordering him to keep it hidden and predicting great luck and riches for him as long as the image remained in his possession, but warned him that he would be overcome by misfortune should he lose it. The first part of the prediction came true, but the druggist, in fear, confessed everything to a priest, who ordered him to destroy the magic image. The druggist did so, whereupon he fell into misfortune."

The most authoritative astrologer of the period was Arnold of Villanova, physician, philosopher, famous statesman, and naturalist, who proscribed the use of magic in medicine, opposed the popular superstition regarding witches, but believed in the existence of sorcerers and in the efficacy of remedies against them. He supported the doctrine of astrological medicine, closely connected blood-letting with the phases of the moon, and gave a description (*De parte operativa*, p. 107) of seals or images of an astrological character which, according to him, possess multiple efficacy. The figure of a lion on a precious stone drives away pain, that of a man holding a dead snake in his right hand with its tail in his left hand is an antidote against poisons. He fashioned a magic figure as a talisman for Pope Boniface VIII. Arnold described in detail the manner of preparing and engraving gems with the signs of the zodiac.

Cecco d'Ascoli, whose name was associated with Dante's, was condemned and burned at the stake in 1327, along with his book *L'Acerba* and his astrological works. Boffito has made a study of the grounds for this sentence, which probably was not due to Cecco's astrological beliefs but to his attacks on the Catholic faith and to his predictions of political events.

In this period, as Thorndike shows, the study of astrology predominated in the schools.

4. THE HOROSCOPE

There is no doubt that until the close of the seventeenth century astrology was the most important of the occult sciences, on which all others were dependent. The means employed by astrology consisted mainly in two operations: the drawing up of the horoscope, and its interpretation. The drawing up of the horoscope consisted simply in calculating the position of the heavenly bodies at the moment of the birth of the individual whose horoscope was being cast. After this was done, the length of the individual's life and his fortune could be determined. This was established according to the planets appearing in the astrological houses. Each of the twelve signs of the Zodiac is the controlling sign of its "house of life." The sign rising at the moment of birth is called ascendant. Jupiter and Venus are harbingers of good luck; when Venus is in the first house it indicates a long life. Jupiter in the first house means riches and fame. A study was then made of the reciprocal positions of the planets according to their angles. Conjunctions, quadrature (90 degrees), and opposition of the planets were considered to be unfavourable, whereas the other angles (60 and 120 degrees) were thought to be favourable. It was possible, by means of calculations, to determine the various life-fortunes of the new-born child. The stars to be found in the twelfth house mark misfortune, untoward events, and so on. The date on which these events will occur may be ascertained by means of the directions of the planets—that is, by calculating the degrees necessary to bring about a certain relation between two planets. When, however, the forecasts did not agree, there were a number of systems for the correction of the horoscopes, the most usual of which was called *"per accidentia nati"* (according to events) in which various possibilities could be combined.

Astrology may be considered as a magical science inasmuch as it tends to give objective form to man's desire for a better knowledge of his future. But in reality, like magic medicine, astrology led man to a close study and better knowledge of nature. Modern studies on the constitution of the human body, which trace back to ancient Hippocratic doctrines, and affirm the relationship between meteorological facts and the normal and pathological life of the human organism; modern research in radiations emitted by substances contained in the stars and revealed by the spectrum, the hypotheses that have been recently advanced concerning the relations between solar spots and extraordinary historical events, the publications by Swoboda and Fliess on the laws of septennial periods, all these lead us to think that the intuitive and profoundly human conception, deriving directly from man's immediate sensitivity to the action of the stars, may have a vaster and deeper foundation of truth than was realized when this primitive idea of intercosmic solidarity seemed to be forgotten.

B. ALCHEMY

1. THE ORIGINS OF ALCHEMY

Alchemistic notions stem directly from the astrological theory according to which the planets and their laws rule the universe. All facts of life are bound with countless links to astral phenomena, and in fact are but their reflection. Since earliest days man has sought for a parallelism between metals and the planets, believing that metals are formed by astral influence and that every metal corresponds to a planet. The idea that a correlation exists between gold and Sun, silver and Moon, lead and Saturn, iron and Mars, is ancient; traces of it are to be found in Hellenistic writings and in Ptolemy, Philon, and their contemporaries. Pliny states that every star has its own colour; Pindarus writes that the creative power of gold is due to the spots in the sun. The yellow-red colour attributed to the Sun, the *aureus sol* of poets, corresponds to the colour of gold; the pale light of the moon is duplicated in the colour of silver. Mars, which Pliny calls *igneus,* recalls the colour of blood and of iron and from these symbols of war draws its name. Venus' bluish tint recalls, in the belief of the ancients, the colour of the copper salts known as *cuprum* from the island of Cyprus, sacred to the goddess.

Alchemy, also called the Egyptian art, is generally believed to have originated in Egypt; the word appears for the first time in the writings of Zosimus of Panopolis (third century after Christ). It undoubtedly developed, according to Berthelot and Thorndike, from the practices of jewelers and Egyptian workmen who experimented with various alloys. The word *alchemy* probably derives from the name of Egypt, Kamt or Qemt (that is, black, referring to the Nile mud). This word was also applied to the black dust derived from certain mixtures of mercury, thought to possess marvellous properties, and other substances; it was mystically identified, according to Budge, with the body of Osiris and was considered the source of life and power. The first traces of this idea, which, like astrology, grows out of man's secret desire to know and to dominate the laws of nature and to better his fate, are undoubtedly much more ancient. Ancient Egyptian and Babylonian priests and sorcerers devoted themselves to chemical problems, and particularly to the transmutation and transformation of metals. The attempt to change base metals into gold is founded on the idea that it is possible to ascertain stellar changes, and on the dominant idea of the metamorphoses of animals. The origin of alchemy is analogous to that of the doctrine of the elements and of their mutations.

The relationship between this ancient, secret doctrine and practical experiences is hard to establish, inasmuch as attempted interpretations varied according to period, place, and individual; the mystical paths and rules differed, the aims pursued were uncertain, and descriptions and explanations were almost always wrapped in obscurity. The studies of Forke (Berlin, 1927) on the evolution of thought in Chinese culture prove that in ancient times alchemy was viewed from a philosophical standpoint. In the alchemistic conception, a supreme spiritual power, neither visible nor recognizable, directs the transformation of the elements. Thus according to ancient Chinese philosophy the principles of the world are immanent in the mixture of primitive substances and in the series of transformations which these elements, *yin* and *yang*, are about to undergo. Everywhere we find the idea of the conjunction, which we may call chemico-biological, of these elements—the idea of a universal and cosmic law of continuous transformation determined by invisible forces.

Although the theory or the philosophical idea of alchemy consists in this explanation, and although alchemy is a search for the fundamental laws, in close relationship with astrological doctrines based on the principle of the possible metamorphoses and of the reciprocal relations governing the cosmos (these metamorphoses and relations being related to those laws of sympathy and antipathy already mentioned), alchemical research was not slow in directing its efforts to the artificial preparation of gold, silver, and secret remedies, which could be effected through the combination of different metals. The fundamental idea of all great alchemists of every age was that of a hermetic science, of a profound and secret doctrine lead-

ing to the "great work" of the trasmutation of all substances
into gold.

Very soon the thought of a practical application develops,
and for this purpose men turn to the secret art of the alchemist
for the preparation of a magical water or of some other substance to prolong life. The idea of immortality to be obtained
by means of magic devices provoking, determining, or has-
tening the transformation of matter gives impetus to the secret
preparation of means serving this purpose. Chinese literature
of the third and second centuries B.C. is rich in recipes for universal remedies. In these cinnabar has an important part. For
centuries, preparations made by combining cinnabar and real-
gar, aphrodisiacs composed of iron and mercury, were considered unfailingly efficacious, and were recommended by
physicians, sorcerers, men of letters, courtesans, priests, and
astrologers who thronged princely palaces.

According to the ancient cosmic conception of the followers of Heraclitus—who supported the view that becoming is
the characteristic of being, and that nothing in nature is dura-
ble or immutable—the earth is transformed into water, air into
earth, dead into living, mud into silver, silver into gold; all
things may derive from and be transformed into gold. The
symbol of this idea of the eternal becoming of being, which
occurs under the influence of fire—the latent element of creation—is a single ring, which later came to be known as "the
Platonic ring." Fire is both God and fate, destiny and end,
cause and beginning. The principle of every evolution is the
logos, the word, measure, definition, which becomes, in the
opinion of later philosophers, the dominant intelligence, in
which all contrasts disappear. Every substance may be destroyed and created according to a secret art. This is both the
principle of natural sciences and the ruling idea of universal
vitalism. Hence alchemy, in its fundamental notions, is but the
doctrine of life renewing itself, of transelementation, and is
linked with religion and philosophy.

The "first matter" is, according to Plato, the foundation of
everything. Just as nature can transform it in various ways, it
is believed that man can likewise transform it, to the extent of

creating out of it the *homunculus* (men produced artificially) if he possesses the necessary knowledge. Mercury represents the first matter because of its mutable qualities, which in remote antiquity amazed observers. Plato attributes to the mixture of elements and metals, each one of which seeks its counterpart, the creation of all things.

Aristotle founded the universal vitalistic theory which assigns the utmost importance to the development of energy: the world is created by the mutations of substance and form. He believes in the qualitative mutation of the elements: *Corruptio unius est generatio alterius* (Corruption of the one is generation of the other). Becoming is, in its entirety, nothing but a transformation of latent energies in various patterns.

All succeeding alchemistic concepts derive from this doctrine, which postulates a *metabole*, a chemical change of the first matter, which causes its transformation. Just as marble embodies the potentiality of artistic expression, which is created through form, so the soul creates the individual out of the substance.

This doctrine of the transmutation of matter is a fundamental concept of alchemy: it asserts theoretically the possibility of achieving the ultimate purpose, which is not only the preparation of gold, the noblest substance, but also the creation of the homunculus.

2. THE EVOLUTION OF PRACTICAL ALCHEMY

In the practical field the idea of alchemy probably derives from a notion familiar to the ancient Egyptians, who thought that precious metals, gold and silver as well as copper, tin, and lead, are to be found in nature in various mixtures and, by fusion, may be combined in different alloys. As a consequence, the transformation, or rather the possibility of transforming metals—a change which, according to the ancient view, was determined by the colour and other outward aspects of metals—was taken to be a proved fact. The ancients knew that bronze was produced by mixing copper and tin, and that the alloy possessed qualities not inherent in either of the two components by itself; they knew that brass was made by mixing copper and zinc; they were aware that in the fusion

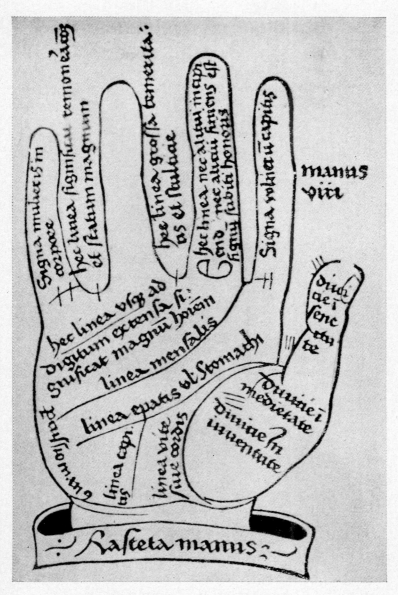

The lines of the hand (from Aristotelis Chiromantia, *Ulm, 1490)*

alraun man cclviiᴄ

The mandrake (from Hortus sanitatis, Mayence, *1486)*

of certain metals with lead some small amounts of silver became detached. It was thought, therefore, that there was an affinity between lead and silver, which resemble each other in appearance, as well as between the combination of arsenic and sulphur, which because of its likeness was called gold pigment, and gold.

Alchemy slowly began to employ all kinds of perfected techniques in order to accomplish its ultimate purpose: the production of gold. This purpose was symbolized by the *urobolos*, a serpent with its tail in its mouth, which represents the cosmos, the sun, and gold. The furnaces and other instruments of the alchemists are but means to reach the goal, and were looked upon as symbols and mystical tools.

During the Middle Ages practical, positive, utilitarian trends predominated in the evolution of alchemy, and its philosophical concept disappeared. Alchemy parted company with philosophy and turned toward mysticism. It became an interpretation of the events of life, and particularly of sexual facts, as chemical phenomena, and its practitioners thought it possible to create the "first matter." This accounts for the idea of the philosophers' stone or egg, which were viewed as universal means of obtaining masterful effects. It accounts likewise for the belief that life may be re-created by recombining all the parts of a dead being in a particular way. These beliefs go back to ancient myths. The creation of the homunculus through the preparation and decoction of all the substances of which man is composed opens numberless possibilities: alchemy becomes the royal art, dominated by the magical and mystical idea. It interprets birth and death by mystic theories, particularly by that of palingenesis, which is analogical to the Christian theory of the resurrection.

Chemical practices conformed, at first, with the traditions contained in the papyri of Leeds and of Stockholm, which Berthelot has studied, and which are connected with the prescriptions of Egyptian goldsmiths or painters for transmuting or falsifying noble metals. The combinations of various alloys to be fashioned into weapons, coins, and ornaments, the making of glass and colours such as cinnabar, indigo, and so on, the preparation of foodstuffs with various yeasts, and of beer and wine, and the dyeing of materials, represent the first steps of this art. Practical alchemy took shape in a number of prescriptions, necessarily mysterious and secret, like those of all arts.

3. ALCHEMY TURNS TO POSITIVE RESEARCH

Toward the close of the mediæval period a school of passionate researchers was gradually formed. It is hard for us today to judge whether such men were always sincere and led by faith in their experiments. In the penumbra of the mediæval mind, the magic of alchemists and fondness for their secret theories appeared in strange forms. Men of great scholarship and intellectual honesty, who sacrificed all their possessions and activities to research, anxious to penetrate the high-walled, moat-surrounded alchemistic citadel, which could be broken into only by persons endowed with rare gifts; deluded men who lived in the certainty of being able to encompass the famous philosophers' stone, guarded by an enormous dragon which would surrender it only to the overcomer of all obstacles; philosophers and mystics who approached the problem by secret words, complicated numbers, invocations and exorcisms; practical men who, being keenly aware of the marvels that chemistry could accomplish, disregarding doctrines and secrets, hoped to achieve some practically useful result; and finally charlatans and cheaters, bombastic flatterers, erudite adventurers, philosophers discussing chemistry at random, and small empiricists chattering about philosophy—these constituted the crowd of alchemists who for centuries, especially in princely courts and sickrooms, ruled the minds of men, thanks to collective suggestion.

In the view of every adept, of every initiate, the *opus magnum* secretly prepared in retorts was analogous to the creation of the cosmos: the alchemists anticipated a new mystery, a new creation which must develop in the athanor, a receptacle shaped like an egg, like the world, which is a gigantic egg, the first egg, the symbol and foundation of every initiatory undertaking. Creation is effected by means of a breath, analogous to the breath of the Lord which, according to Genesis, blows over the world. Many illustrations in the books of alchemy portray this idea. Alchemy is linked with natural magic, because in reality it claims to draw its strength from, and to be an imitation of, nature. This is the deep significance of the symbolism of alchemy, preserved in a number of depictions, which, according to Grillot de Givry (who published a precious collection of these emblematic images), have remained almost identical throughout the centuries. However, besides these fundamental portrayals, alchemistic iconography contains a little of everything: the androgyne, the sun, the moon, the dragon, and a number of two-headed magic animals, the eagle-headed griffon, the sirens, and the hermetic fountains. Strange and inexplicable formulas, causing us to doubt that even their authors understood them, refer to complicated and difficult practices and prove that hieroglyphs were an essential part of alchemy and were engraved even on the doors of churches. The statue of St. Marcel on the main façade of Notre Dame in Paris is an alchemistic hieroglyph.

What were the practices of the *opus magnum* that took place in the philosophic vase, *aludel,* placed on the furnace athanor, and itself often the same as the furnace? Writers are very vague and nebulous concerning this. First of all, the work had to begin at a moment exactly calculated by astrologers; otherwise it would have been unsuccessful. The time needed in the preparation of the philosophers' stone was, according to some writers, one year; according to others, from seven to twelve years. The first step was to combine salt, sulphur, and mercury. The result was marvellous, the stone being not only a safe device for transmuting metals, but a remedy for all illnesses.

Toward the end of the seventeenth century, alchemists of the ancient school and astrologers disappeared or become transcendentalists, lost in increasingly vague mystical speculations. Researches clarifying important difficulties and leading to unexpected discoveries opening up new paths to science were carried on in laboratories by ardent students of practical problems. Just as natural magic became detached from magic and, with truth-divining intuition, attributed to nature what had heretofore been considered magical, so that astrology, in its essential parts, slowly evolved into astronomy, in like fashion alchemy paved the way for the fundamental researches of chemistry.

The growth of alchemistic literature from 1600 to 1700 was enormous. Among others, J. B. Helmont (1578–1644) and H. Helvetius (1671–1727) championed the possibility of the transformation of metals.

Toward the close of the eighteenth century, alchemy, or rather belief in the practicability of transforming base metals into gold, disappeared. Chemistry inherited its tools and technical skill, and absorbed some of its basic ideas.

Thus, from the ancient Egyptian conception of alchemy as a science and passion leading to the discovery of the world-secret, to the affirmations contained in the books of the eighteenth-century alchemists, packed with strange formulas and complicated prescriptions, concealing the failure of the attempts made to solve with a "great work" the profound mystery, the idea of alchemy is wrought upon and transformed by time, milieu, the growth of critical thought, and scientific research. Gradually the basic conception of the mysterious composition of the universe is transmuted by experimental studies; manifestations of the desire to prolong life and cure sickness by magic elixirs and the philosophers' stone take another course. This was partially a result of the studies and keen observations of Paracelsus and his school; alchemy turns to laboratory research for the *arcanum*, the secret useful remedy. This remedy—and the point is essential—is now sought not in supernatural forces but in chemical combinations. Sympathetic magic again finds shelter in the attempts to discover analogies of form, colour, and aspects between plants and human organs on the one hand and sicknesses on the other. This idea leads to re-examination of the therapeutic virtues of plants, carefully investigates their uses, and regulates their application. The alchemist becomes a researcher, biologist, and chemist. From the mysterious laboratory, immortalized in the paintings of the great Dutch artists, there emerges, instead of the sensational announcement of the discovery of the cure-all, a new universal and vivifying idea: that of the chemical relations between living organs and the inorganic world.

The knowledge of the forces inherent in matter, which the ancients rightly considered as capable of causing the deepest transformations and rebirths, led modern science, not to the solution of the problems examined by ancient alchemists, but to a vaster and more direct study of questions that we deem basic to life.

The fundamental magic spell of life and of death, the intuition, deeply rooted in the human mind, of creation and destruction, to be evinced through chemical changes and transformations of the same substances, guided the ancient alchemists in their craving for the philosophers' stone and the modern scientists in our times in the secret laboratories that produced remedies undreamed of, and the means of total destruction of life—the atomic bomb.

Astrology and alchemy are two great adventures of the mind. Initially they are escape-efforts, attempts to evade reality with the help of mysterious and unknown forces, whose future role in the growth of human life is barely glimpsed. Astrology and alchemy assume all the characteristics of magic practices, such as suggestion exercised by persons or objects, enigmatic symbols, secrets communicated to a few chosen people through initiatory rites, mirage of extraordinary riches, guarantee of survival or of continuation of life in other beings, promise of exceptional powers. The astrologers and alchemists of antiquity and of the mediæval period were led by faith and by the hope of creating the possibility of rediscovering the secret paths to a better life. Securing the protection of the stars, achieving the philosophers' stone, discovering the fountain of youth, the metamorphosis of metals, the creation of the homunculus—that is, of human life—these were the ideal goals of astrologers and chemists.

With the revival of physics, the establishment of experiments, the predominance of reasoning over fantastic delusions, research turned to new paths; and in this as in other fields early intuitions such as the subconscious awareness of the biological law of the life-cycle, or of the unity between the laws of the cosmos, or of the mutability of immortal matter, of the conservation of energies, were once again proved right. The search for a cure-all led to the chemical discovery of remedies that in earlier days would have been regarded as magical, and to the artificial creation of life from the cell through chemical fecundation in the laboratory. To sum up, the many biological and mathematical discoveries that have given a new direction to science derive from alchemy. Subconscious suggestion originated a vast work of reconstruction and reorganization, while principles of ancient magical sciences found a new interpretation in the light of experimental science.

XXI

Natural Magic

THROUGHOUT Europe, and particularly in Italy of the fifteenth century, with the revival of learning a first attempt is made by some great scholars to inquire into the problems of the universe, by trying to explain its mysteries rationally. The Humanist, *homo doctus*, becomes the type of the new epoch, taking the place of the *homo sanctus*.

A great scholar, Giovanni II Pico della Mirandola (1463–94), waged an intelligent and lively battle against astrology, and collected his studies on Hebrew philosophy and the Cabala in his *Conclusiones cabalisticæ* (1482). Johannes Reuchlin (1455–1522), who was born in Germany but lived in Italy for many years, had numerous friends among Jewish scholars and acquired a perfect knowledge of Hebrew. Reuchlin's *De verbo mirifico* (1494) attempted a mystical reconciliation between ancient Hebrew doctrines and Christian ideas founded on the occult meaning of words. His *De arte cabalistica* (1517) was widely read throughout Europe. A third scholar worth remembering is Johannes Tritheim (born in 1462), who entered the Benedictine order at an early age and became abbot of the cloister of Sponheim. He devoted himself to the study of secret writings and to the occult meaning of words, was soon suspected of heresy, became abbot of the cloister of Würzburg in 1505, and wrote a valuable book about cryptography. Tritheim was the friend and teacher of two men who played an important role in the evolution of magic: Agrippa and Paracelsus.

2. ORIGINS AND TENDENCIES OF NATURAL MAGIC

The idea of the magic action of the word, of the perfection of alphabetical characters, of the value of symbol, which, as we saw, was fundamental to the magic of the ancients, springs up again in a new form, higher, vaster, and more complete. The value of letters, words, and symbols was derived from the shared secret, the intellectual communion, of those understanding it. Upon the basis of this idea an entire system was slowly built up at the time when culture began to spread and the return to the classic spirit became visible in Humanism, and the revival of Greek philosophy became manifest. The significance of symbol and letter, like that of the *opus magnum* of alchemists and the calculations of astrologers, is, above all, philosophical and strives for a natural explanation. Ancient magic changes with the change of ideas, with the succession of new spiritual and social events modifying the milieu: the observation of nature, which begins to attract the attention of scholars as the fundamental element of research, attains predominance. Agrippa of Nettesheim, Theophrastus Paracelsus, and G. B. della Porta are the founders or, rather, the organizers of these ideas in a system of natural magic. Restless and independent spirits overwhelmed by struggle and conflict in times of bitter religious and civil wars, thinkers both rebellious and still mystical, impassioned observers still fettered by the bonds of ancient magic beliefs, they are the towering and characteristic figures of that transitional epoch in which natural magic appears and is universally accepted.

Natural magic marks a further stage in the evolution of primitive magic toward experimental science. It detaches itself from the fundamental magic concept as well as from the religious idea, borrows its form of reasoning from philosophy, but adheres to reality in so far as its observations are concerned. Natural magic slowly develops from primitive magic, as observation proceeds and method advances according to the speed with which critical faculties subdue the emotional ones, and the human mind forsakes the notion of supernatural beings and their intervention and seeks for the explanation of nature in the forces of nature itself. Natural magic, on its way to becoming science, carries with it, for a long time, a large part of its ancestral heritage of primitive magic and with difficulty frees itself from some of its beliefs, especially from those most firmly anchored in the deepest strata of the mind. We saw how the earliest writers, champions of the magic idea

Paracelsus. Portrait by Rubens (?)

G. B. della Porta (from his book De distillatione, *Rome, 1608)*

and disseminators of occult sciences, repeatedly glimpsed the necessity of criticism and of experience. In an earlier epoch only a few single, isolated individuals faced this problem. Later more and more scholars and research workers, though assuming different attitudes in regard to magical and mystical problems, created a new current of ideas. Maxwell rightly remarks that this new orientation was earlier manifest in the domain of physical and natural problems, as they lend themselves more readily to observation and criticism.

The evolution of the psychic phenomena of witchcraft is more laborious because the problems are more complex, the causes less easy to establish, and the results less controllable. All the problems concerning the mind remain much longer under the rule of magic and mysticism, because many of them do not appear sufficiently clear. Not until our day has scientific research on the functioning of the brain and on the unconscious, determining the characteristics and origins of certain psychic states (such as hypnotism, suggestion, double personalities, dreams), raised the veil of mystery and illuminated a series of formerly occult phenomena by the light of observation and criticism.

3. AGRIPPA OF NETTESHEIM

Natural magic begins with the study of atmospheric and astral phenomena and establishes a link between the individual and the elements. It asserts that all phenomena are sympathetically co-ordinated. This doctrine of sympathy enables the practitioners of natural magic to imagine the existence of secret relations and incantational connections. The inborn secret link is asserted between things and their names, which contain the power of the things in the form of their expression. The magic strength of the word derives from its relationship with the thing it designates, and the magical properties of things originate in their forms.

Agrippa of Nettesheim (1456–1535) is the first of the great figures ushering in the new era. The history of his life is a perfect illustration of his studies and mentality. Born of an ancient noble family, he assiduously devoted himself from an early age to the study of languages and passionately collected all the literature on occult sciences, tried his hand at alchemy, and at twenty founded a society for the study of secret sciences in Paris. He lived in France, and visited England and Germany, indefatigably preaching his ideas. He was often persecuted by the ecclesiastical authorities. He wrote his *De occulta philosophia*, which made him famous, in 1510, fought with the Imperial troops against the Venetians, and was knighted on the field of battle. Later he was obliged to defend himself against the accusations of the inquisitors. At Metz, where he supported the cause of some persons who were accused of witchcraft and succeeded in saving them from the death penalty, he himself was accused of being an accomplice of the accused and was forced to flee to Lyon, where he was appointed physician to the King of France. He later became historian at the court of Margaret of Austria, and a physician in Cologne. At last he returned to Lyon, was persecuted by his enemies and misfortune, and died in 1535, famed as a sorcerer.

Among new ideas in the process of formation, and amid the conflict between ancient magic conceptions and the new way of thinking, Agrippa attempted, with a magnificent intuition of the truth, to lead magic onto the highroad of the observation of nature and to explain diabolic and supernatural phenomena as the results of natural forces. Magic occurrences appeared to him as demonstrations and applications of scientific truths; the doctrine of the "sympathy and antipathy of things," which was a fundamental part of ancient Italic philosophy, was reborn. With the decline of Galen's anatomy, of Aristotle's physics, of Ptolemy's astronomical system, ancient magic was gradually forsaken by its followers. Agrippa of Nettesheim, who was called the last of the sorcerers, but might be called the first of the naturalists, placed the idea of magic on a new basis and perceived that everything formerly attributed to magic must be assigned to nature instead.

Natural magic, according to Agrippa, is a science. He claims that a direct and reciprocal relationship exists between the highest and the lowest things, and asserts that every thing is attracted by its likes, which in turn it attracts with all its forces. These secret forces are a part of the spiritual world

where ideas exist. However, according to Agrippa, ideas cannot act over things by themselves, nor can matter be put in
motion by itself. A medium is necessary, a vital force that can
transfer the activity of the spirit to the body, and this medium
is the quintessence, the fifth essence, since it is not composed
of the four elements but exists beyond and above them. It
fulfils the same function in the world as the soul does in the
human body, and is therefore the soul of the world. It irradi-
ates from the planets, and the occult qualities of living substances such as minerals and metals stem from it. It may be
extracted from one substance and transferred to another. Because of it fire rises toward celestial fire and water flows toward the waters; living beings convert their nourishment into
the substance of their organism; and stars, precious stones,
plants, and animals exert an influence over men. Its signs are
marked on the earth, plants, and man's organs (*law of the
signatures*).

Natural magic, according to Agrippa, must, therefore, no
longer admit the performance of magic and forbidden operations with the help of the supernatural, but has to search for
the secret laws of nature and the utilization of natural forces.
Sorcerers, according to this conception, become the priests
of science.

In such a scientific belief the magic power of words, however, is important. This doctrine, which goes back to Neo-
platonic philosophy but whose beginnings may be traced to a
much remoter era, claims that words and names are but the
reflection of the creative power of "forms" in God's mind.
The same is true of writings. A speech composed of many
words has a power greater than that possessed by an isolated
word. The value of a magical spell depends on enunciation, on
the rhythm and the enthusiasm with which it is uttered, on
the emotion and conviction of the sorcerer. Agrippa mentions
the example of Orpheus, and states that incantations, uttered
with vehemence and passion and under careful observation of
the measure and number of their words, endow the enchanter
with tremendous strength due to the impetuous outburst of
his imagination, and are projected on the object of the spell,
binding and directing it in accordance with the desires and

words of the magician. The true instrument of spellbinding is a sort of breath, pure, harmonious, and alive, which embodies movement and will, is skilfully composed, endowed with deep feeling, and conceived by reason.

✓ Maxwell rightly observes that Agrippa thereby voices a perfectly modern psychological idea: the idea that the strength of the spell is dependent on the emotional intensity of the spell-caster, and that magical strength dwells in the sphere of passions, whereas reason must conceive the purpose and prepare the methods to encompass it. According to Agrippa, reason's task is to calculate the position of the stars or the numerical proportions between words and things or the mutual relations of things; the task of emotion is that of imparting its direction and force to the magical action. Thus natural magic and modern psychology are closely linked in the evaluation of the power of suggestion.

4. PARACELSUS

The law of sympathy and the doctrine of the "signatures," which, as we saw, is clearly propounded by Agrippa, was widely applied in a new fashion by a violently reforming medical genius who effected a real revolution in the scientific domain. Philip Theophrastus Aureolus Bombast von Hohenheim, Paracelsus, was born in Einsiedeln, Switzerland, in 1493. The son of a physician, he engaged at an early age in the study of alchemy, philosophy, and medicine. He studied in Basel and conceived an enthusiasm for occult sciences. Later he went to Würzburg to call on the famous abbot Tritheim, who introduced him into the mysteries of magic and on whose recommendation he entered the laboratory of a rich alchemist, Fugger, at whose hands he received his initiation into the secrets of chemistry. After travelling throughout Germany, he betook himself to Italy and attended the Medical School of the University of Ferrara, where he became a student of Leonicenus. The latter was an ardent follower of the Neoplatonism of Marsilius Ficinus and one of the first who dared to oppose the authority of Galen. Paracelsus resumed his roaming life and seems to have visited Asia and Africa as well as Europe. On his travels he mixed in curious company, gathering everywhere traditions and secret rites, maxims and superstitions, judgments and popular medicines. With great sagacity he saw and cured sufferers everywhere; he was both a physician and a wonder healer and soon rebelled against the authority of schools, rising up against the bondage of dogmatism, which until then had been borne in silence, even by renowned and talented men. His was a romantic spirit which in its defiant restlessness exaggerated in overcoming without discrimination all traditions, and gave free rein to destructive criticism. In 1524 he left Salzburg and went to Strasbourg, and later to Basel, where he obtained a lectureship, but soon he was forced to leave the city and to resume his travels through Germany. He was persecuted by his enemies and unable to find a printer for his manuscripts or a ruler who would permit their publication. In 1541 he died at Salzburg.

In the judgment of his numberless followers Paracelsus was the greatest scientist and the most outstanding occultist of his times; in that of Basel university professors he was a charlatan and a drunkard. He was constantly fought against and persecuted. But there was undoubtedly in him an inspired conception, a limpid and new idea of the necessity of shaking off the traditions that stifled academic teaching and of entrusting one's mind to experience and unprejudiced judgment alone. In the field of medicine Paracelsus was a fertile innovator, in that of natural magic he was a student and follower of Tritheim and Agrippa, and it is interesting to note that he introduced the teachings of his masters into medicine. The basic conceptions, in Paracelsus's view, fused; his medicine originated in the theory of the sympathy and antipathy of all substances. Those which act on a certain part of the body are called "*arcana*," and the task of alchemy is to search for arcana —that is, the efficient substances in metals and plants. As a consequence, it was along this path that the complex teaching of Paracelsus led, through fantastic premises, to chemical research.

It was through the agency of this extraordinary man, faithfully mirroring the stirrings and uncertainties of the epoch in which he lived, that the secrets of ancient magic were attributed to the infinite and mysterious power of nature.

5. G. B. DELLA PORTA

The third of these latter-day magicians was an Italian, G. B. della Porta, the scion of a famous family, born in Naples in 1545. His existence unfolded under very different conditions from those which determined the life vicissitudes of Agrippa and Paracelsus. The latter two lived in Germany while that country was in a terrible turmoil of religious and civil war, went through overwhelming misfortunes, and were dominated by a feeling of restlessness that drove them to roam over the world. Della Porta, instead, was born under another star. Belonging to a rich family, he was able to devote himself peacefully to his studies. He travelled through Italy, France, and Spain and came in contact with the most outstanding men of his time. From his childhood on he took a great interest in occult sciences, and his biographers state that he was hardly fifteen when he published his first book, *Magia naturalis*. The young della Porta lived with his brother Vincenzo, an enthusiastic archæologist, in a beautiful country house near Naples. This house very soon became a meeting-place for many young scholars, and della Porta founded a circle called the "Circle of the Secret Ones."

The most important of his works is doubtless the *Magia naturalis*, the first edition of which was the most widely read and famous, and appeared in Latin, Italian, French, German, Dutch, and Arabic. The second edition, in twenty volumes, was published in 1589. The first part contains an extract of the occult philosophy of Agrippa, while the rest gives much practical advice and contains various remarks on the laws of attraction and sympathy, on the different kinds of secret writings, cosmetics, perfumes, medical remedies, pyrotechnics, and chemistry, besides a description of the telescope and of the camera obscura. A whole book is devoted to alchemy, but the author declares at the outset that he is no believer in the production of gold or in the philosophers' stone, and that he thinks instead that it is important for the reader to learn formulas for melting metals and for preparing medicaments. Some pages of the eighth book of the second edition deserve

particular interest. In them della Porta evidently deals with
hypnosis and hypnotic suggestion. It seems that the members of the Neapolitan Circle that he founded engaged in
some practical experiments along this line. There are descriptions of the method to be followed in putting a man to sleep
and forcing him to carry out unquestioningly the orders given
to him, so that when he is told that he is a fish, he will go
through the motions of swimming, or when told to eat grass,
he will do so. Throughout the *Magia naturalis*, which, according to Goethe, clearly reflects the great progress of science
in the author's time, della Porta shows a perfect conviction
that all magic phenomena are dependent on natural causes.

The importance of this work is due to its enormous sugges-
tiveness. Written by a youth, it was later enlarged when he
had the greatest authority as a scientist. He was the first writer
who attempted to disclose to a large public a number of facts
that until then had been considered extremely secret, and
who dispensed with the profusion of mystical formulas, Cabalistic cryptograms, and inexplicable terms to which readers
had been accustomed by his predecessors. The Neapolitan
scientist expounds facts and ideas with great simplicity, constantly tries to gain a foothold in experience, and shows profound understanding of the phenomena of the past and a correct intuition of many new truths.

Thus, after the two restless and rebellious masters, G. B.
della Porta contributed to the transformation of magic with
his high intelligence and profound knowledge, and still more
with his wise discernment, with that orderly and serene way
of reasoning which kept him aloof from the iconoclastic exag-
gerations of Paracelsus as well as from the metaphysical speculations of Agrippa. In the history of science his work marked
an important stage, inasmuch as it determined—in a moment
of transition—new conceptual orientations; new orientations
not only of a minority of scientists but of that cultivated public which was gradually forming in sixteenth-century Italy,
of those sedulous and curious investigators of nature who
crowded the academies and played a most notable role in the
emergence of the European culture of that age.

6. LAWS OF SYMPATHY

At the dawn of the Renaissance, science forged ahead; criticism, unshackling itself from scholasticism and superstition, increasingly tended to build self-supporting systems and to dispense with supernatural explanations. Slowly ideas were clarified, natural magic was transformed into physics and chemistry; phenomena decisively attributed in the past to magic influence, as, for instance, those of rhabdomancy, were examined from the viewpoint of science. In popular legends, like that of Faust, the traditions of the great sorcerers were preserved, while in popular belief all the forms of primitive magic persisted; talismans and amulets, "sympathetic" and occult cures, evocations of the dead and relic-worship remained embedded in popular consciousness.

Natural magic attempted to discover in the laws of sympathy and affinity the causes of the phenomena of magic; and we saw that belief in these goes back to an exceedingly remote period. Owing to a particular train of thought, which in modern times led to special therapeutic methods such as homœopathy, natural magic did not hesitate to avail itself of the prime incantational device of sympathetic witchcraft: love philtres. The *poculum amatorium*, which enjoyed the widest diffusion, and the most famous example of which is the love potion of Tristram and Yseult, consisted of a beverage prepared with herbs gathered at certain hours, in secret places; some locks of hair or a small amount of physiological secretion of the person whose love was to be won were added to this beverage. Natural magic, and the medicine connected with it, therefore attempt to combine, within the framework of a single conception of causes and effects, phenomena of alchemy and astrology, as well as of primitive instincts. They group those phenomena in artificially constructed systems, reject superhuman facts, and deny the supernatural action of demons, witches, hobgoblins, fairies, etc., ascribing all phenomena of a mysterious character to secret and unknown natural causes. Their conception plainly evinces a well-defined beginning of critical perception; a concept, not always expressed, of the necessity of experiment, an understanding of the importance of the psychological factor.

The wise, cultured, and widely experienced men who attempted to give to magic such an orientation toward science lived in a milieu and epoch in which mysticism was dominant and research was completely fettered by dogmatic premises that seemed unassailable. They made an attempt to reconcile new ideas, elicited by a clearer and more profound view of the world and of existence, with facts that seemed irrefragable and were such in the general consciousness of their age. Doubtless an important evolution of magic was determined by their efforts to substitute for vague beliefs in unverifiable supernatural occurrences, which could be modified with the help of demons and their intermediaries, a conception, however queerly formulated, of the operation of natural laws. The process by which the bonds tying the thinker's individuality to ancestral traditions and to the iron laws of his environment are unloosened, one by one, is of necessity very slow. Often these bonds fall only to be replaced by new and more complicated shackles, and the old conceptions, which appeared to have been definitely overthrown, revive under new forms. But the effort to replace ancient explanations with new ones represents an important aspect of the perennial struggle between criticism and authority, between reason and feeling, the individual and the anonymous multitude. These early attempts at an explanation of natural magic (attempts that bear a close similarity to more modern ones) mark a definite departure from the primitive conception of magic.

XXII

The Renaissance of Science

THE great trend in the growth of studies toward experimental observation must not be dated, as some writers assert, from the Protestant Reformation, but originates in that complex series of intellectual, social, and political phenomena which make up the Renaissance. Fed by a thousand streams, by the return to traditions of classic antiquity, and by the movement of thought that takes a definite path toward the positive and the concrete, favoured by the flourishing state of the great maritime republics and the cities which had reached a high level of financial prosperity through trade and industrial crafts, and a high degree of freedom and civic awareness, the intellectual movement evinces a new orientation. This marks the birth of the conception of artistic individuality and of free criticism, which, taking its inspiration from the pure classical forms, reasserts the sovereign rule of beauty and the rhythmic harmony of the universe and creates the most outstanding masterpieces of art. It is likewise the revival of the fervid study of nature, which, we might say, is purified from the murky atmosphere of the Middle Ages and idealized in a conception of beauty. It is the epoch in which Leonardo blazes the trail of anatomical studies, and the study of the human frame on the dissecting-table takes foremost rank in the medical curriculum of the Italian universities. The anatomist's knife attacking the secrets of nature, the research of the physiologist who, while overthrowing the old systematic constructions, attempts to scrutinize the laws of the human organism, keep pace with the diligent studies of physicists and chemists. While the laws of beauty are sought in the gatherings of men of letters and artists, while the laws of harmony are embodied in new musical structures, and Italian piazzas and streets witness the rise of perfect works of art, investigators strive, in ever greater freedom from fallacious dogmatic presuppositions, to discover the laws of nature, and philosophers attempt to construct new systems. The new scientific criticism is born, and Leonardo's visions seem to find their incarnation in the later affirmations of Galileo. Leonardo is not only the greatest artist, but the most tortured by his inextinguishable desire for knowledge of the most profound mystery of existence. He is, one might say, the personification of the very soul of the Renaissance. This perpetual scrutinizer, this restless doubter who, after having finished his daily task as an artist and brought to an end the creative work of his imagination and genius, spends his night hours in dissecting "corpses of males and females" in order "to discover the prime cause and the intimate essence of life," is a man whom all problems torment and who tries to find answers to all of them, to solve all the questions that appear unsolved to his great spirit in travail. He epitomizes, in an exquisite form, the intellectual anguish of mankind in every age, and is driven to a desperate search for what he feels it is his duty to pursue, with an unquenchable thirst for knowledge which he tries to slake by means of new, deeper, and more painful researches.

One of the most important characteristics of this age is the rebirth of the consciousness of human dignity and of the evaluation of human personality. In addition to this, the Renaissance witnesses a revival of the thirst for glory, the craving for a more intense life, for an existence rendered more lovely in its earthly stay, prolonged, thanks to fame, beyond death. *"Omnis non moriar."* I do not choose to die entirely: I wish something of myself, the best, most noble part, to survive.

This craving for glory was but the noblest, highest sublimation of the instinct of self-preservation of the individual, beyond physical dissolution. It was a new manifestation, analogous to that fostered by classic antiquity, of the supreme law of nature, a return to the Apollonian conception of life and beauty. To preserve more than one's body, much more than one's ephemeral life (to which, however, the Renaissance assigns an importance utterly unlike that attributed to it by Christian mysticism), and to preserve for ever, engraved on the tablets of history, the name and the glory of one's actions, this is the new way of escape, the new creative adventure of the mind.

It is precisely for this reason that the men of the Renaissance possess such a high and perfect sense of the traditions of ancient times as to be able to re-create their greatness and anxiously to seek for proofs of their direct kinship with their glorious forbears. It was at the time when ancient codices were discovered, when the documents of former greatness were redisclosed by the restoration of ancient manuscripts, and when the figures of heroes and gods re-emerged from ancient ruins, that the whole nation affirmed that it was directly and by rights not only the historical heir of so much beauty, but the direct continuator of the ancient glory. Thus the ancient magical conception was transformed and had a new growth in the light of the Italian Renaissance, when individual and group consciousness was formed and became visible in the communes and the craft guilds. On the one side, the need for individual and national preservation was expressed in this thirst for glory which seized even the humblest city dweller; on the other, the tendency toward the unknown, toward mystery, manifested itself in the current bearing Italian thinkers toward experimental science.

Galileo alone would be sufficient to illustrate this whole epoch. His vision penetrated time and space, he investigated the infinitely great and remote as well as the infinitely small, and he created, in the telescope and microscope, powerful instruments of research. He affirmed that every world-law is a mathematical one, that every scientific truth must be proved; and he consecrated the truth and dignity of science with complete self-sacrifice. For him and for his age the law of scientific experiment became a necessary and incontrovertible canon. This rising light drew to the Italian universities of the seventeenth and eighteenth centuries students from all parts of the world, yearning to drink at the fountains of learning. As a consequence the idea of magic underwent a complete change in the minds of thinkers and students. The human mind is no less in search of adventure than ever before, but it follows a different path toward light and beauty. The most striking example of this tendency of the new adventure of the mind is shown by the mass-suggestion that draws seamen, explorers, warriors, merchants, workers, and criminals toward the exploration and conquest of new roads to undiscovered, fabulous countries, riches, and glory. Burckhard says that the men of the Renaissance are the explorers, sailing toward the unknown and the mysterious. That is the new objectivation of wishes for power and wealth—the escape from the world of the Middle Ages.

This exploration of new roads brings about the discovery of unknown continents, contact with new realities, and the end of many ancient beliefs.

Doubtless astrology and alchemy were still alive and dominant in the schools, since the progress of truth, which is not for all, is exceedingly slow. Nothing is harder than to combat ancient errors, and the most reliable and complete experiments are not sufficient to dispel the fogs of superstition and ignorance. The physical and experimental demonstrations of the circulation of the blood were unable for decades to destroy the conception founded on Galen's authority. Astrology still had its followers. Throughout the seventeenth and part of the eighteenth century, witches were still tried, and people still believed that wizards and sorcerers existed. But the magic of this age was purely superstition or business: it was subservient to political or religious aims, or to the pecuniary advantage of those who speculated on the credulity of the people. In medicine experimental science rapidly forged ahead; in the universities astrology was taught theoretically, but importance was no longer attached to magic practices; experimental criteria were used to study the causes of disease, and sympathetic and magical cures no longer enjoyed credit except among those who still clung to ancient superstitions. Thus in the history of human thought the scientific Renaissance stands for the transformation of the idea of magic; it marks the end of a state of oppression under a spiritual and political yoke and, first of all, of a regime of terror. Doubtless, when the Renaissance evolved, absolute rulers still dominated everywhere, and the influence of scholastic doctrines was still prevalent. Aristotelians, dogmatists, and Galenists still fiercely inveighed from lecture platforms and pulpits against the founders of the new science. The law courts may still have sentenced the most outstanding among the intellectual heretics, but they were powerless to suppress their ideas.

The Renaissance is the escape of the fiercely oppressed collective mind, the reappearance of individualism and of the sense of man's worth; it is the first solemn scientific and doctrinal affirmation of human rights, which three centuries later were consecrated in legal enactments. Developing after a long and laborious preparation in a Europe still convulsed by civil and religious wars, the Renaissance sounds the death knell of magic systems and demonstrates that at the moment in which shackles are broken and criticism is freed, a tragic adventure of the mind is at an end, and the construction of a new life order begins.

2. THE RETURN TO THE STUDY OF NATURE

The scientific Renaissance took its point of departure from the Hellenistic philosophical conception, wavered at first between Plato and Aristotle, but later founded a method of observation and of experiment according to which, admitting that mathematical laws governed the universe, scant space was left for the magic idea in its ancient primitive form. The scientific trend of the Renaissance was eminently critical and synthetic, and it therefore forsook or fought against fantastic and untrustworthy conceptions. Thus there was gradually established a rational measure of judgment, a positive school of studious investigators of truth; and magic in this epoch fell into decline. It lost the place that it had won in the Middle Ages when mystical and fantastic trends predominated.

Scientific research in chemistry won superiority over alchemy; astrology yielded almost entirely to astronomy. The problems of alchemists and astrologers shrunk in importance when compared with the new and magnificent problems with which students were confronted, and which were evidently cosmic and universal, since the idea of cosmos and universal laws revived in the Renaissance. The search for gold or for the philosophers' stone appeared a problem of doubtful importance, and one lacking a safe foundation, to the scientist who glimpsed the laws of the transformation of bodies. To investigate the influence of the stars and of their conjunctions over man's fate seemed a puny task, or an altogether vain undertaking, to a mind that grasped the conception of the laws of space. At the same time the great political and social events of the Renaissance, the formation of the consciousness of one's individuality, the assertion of a limitless freedom of thought and of criticism, co-operated in bringing about the decadence of scientific and official magic and caused it to become again, and to remain, the embodiment of individual desire. The man of the Renaissance could not afford to ignore or deny positive knowledge, and had a tendency to give objective expression to his desires by another method, in another form, and through other manifestations. This may be an explanation of the orientation of the Renaissance toward art and biological knowledge. There is a profound analogy between these trends, because in both the fascination of a supreme law of rhythm is predominant.

3. UNIVERSAL MAN

The art of the fourteenth century had been dogmatic and stylized in the rigidity of its forms. It had been an art of groups and of schools, almost always an exact transference to canvas or marble of concepts that were perfectly rounded out and sealed in a final form, from which they could not escape. In the Renaissance, when thought was being freed from the laws oppressing it, the element of rebellion no longer manifested itself in antisocial currents. It is interesting to observe that simultaneously ecstatic saints, individuals possessed by devils, and witches became increasingly rarer. Trials of heretics were not discontinued, but there were no more witch trials. That violent spasm which had sought an outlet through faith in renunciation or open rebellion seemed to calm down in renewed freedom of criticism. The Italian Renaissance was not characterized by open revolt, as was the German Reformation. The reformers in Italy were the painters who gave to the images of the Virgin, of Christ, of the saints, an expression of lofty humanity, removing from them the stiff mask of symbolism; they were the historians who studied events with keen observation and unprejudiced minds, such as Guicciardini,

Machiavelli, and Vasari; the naturalists such as Aldovrandi, who lovingly attempted to descry the history of life in plants and animals and to discover the laws of intercosmic relationship, not through exorcisms or magic practices, but through investigation and study.

The art of the Renaissance exerted a greater, subtler, and deeper fascination than that of the epochs preceding it, or rather exerted its fascination in a different manner. Rites, symbols, and formulas imaged in the stiffness of ancient art were vivified by the emotional and personal temper of the artists. Spirit reanimated what seemed to be a rigidly closed literalism; and thus beauty, rediscovered in its laws and forms, again cast its ancient fascination over the mind of the new man. Among primitive peoples, as we saw, suggestion was founded more on acts, objects, or words than on concepts; it was the suggestive rhythm, the strange figurations of fantastic beings, the verbal husk, the letter, that constituted its strength and exerted the most important magic action. The word was a sound enclosed in a rhythm, or a form likewise enclosed. A profound significance attached to the fact, which the most recent research has substantiated, that prayers, invocations, and tales were always, in primitive times, chanted. Thus it was a suggestion that recurred in the simple rhythm of primitive drawings, in the portrayals symmetrically repeated in long series, with a slow, monotonous movement of figures, in music such as can still be heard today on the great plains of India, on the Russian steppes, in the Argentine pampas, a slow, unvaried music instinct with profound yearning for something unknown and steeped in sadness. A similar principle is at the basis of all the dances of Oriental peoples, consisting as they do of a rhythmical succession of gestures whose meaning lies precisely in their repetition. I do not think there is a more characteristic picture than that which I frequently saw on the banks of the Ganges: thousands of believers bending their knees and arms, and touching their eyes and mouths, endlessly repeating these gestures in a mood of profound emotion. The spectacle of the mosques at prayer time, when, in an ample synchronous movement, thousands of men bend and rise, and kneel again, raising their arms, thus unconsciously

Bust of Cagliostro, by Houdon (Museum of Aix-en-Provence)

Valentine Greatrakes, the wonder healer (English print, about 1700)

and mechanically repeating a rite that obviously has the aim, or at least the effect, of arousing a mood of suggestion in performers as well as in the onlookers, is no less impressive.

4. THE MAGIC OF BEAUTY AND ART

Owing to the growth of thought, to the evolution of the mind, and also, perhaps, to a new virtue inherent in gesture, gesture itself assumed a formal beauty, rhythm became melody, and drawings that portrayed men or animals were not, as in the past, merely reproductions of a perception, but were also reproductions of a mental representation and, at times, of an illusion, a hope, a belief. Magic in its history may be said to tread the path followed by nature in its search for means of bringing about an incantational mood, with the identical purpose: that of exalting procreation. In the formation of the colours of birds' feathers, in their song, in the fragrances of flowers, and perhaps in a thousand other expressions unperceived by our senses, there is a progressive evolution of beauty.

Human magic assumed the characteristics of art; its incantation is new in its forms, not in the process of its formation. It originated under special conditions, inasmuch as its creator, the new magician, himself was caught, like the magicians of all times, by the spell that he created and to which he succumbed. Human magic induces a mood that may be merely one of slight excitement, but also one of a crepuscular, hypnoidal, hallucinatory, or stupefying character determined by toxic substances; its devices are words, music, or pictures, and its suggestion is particularly effective when the onlookers are predisposed. Such is the suggestion exercised by museum paintings over visitors whom study or guides have prepared for it; by stage performances over the audience, and so forth. These suggestions often paralyse criticism. Sometimes they have their basis in emotion, as, for instance, the complex and modern suggestion of motion pictures.

The magic of art! I truly think that this word, which has been used so often to express in a metaphorical and conventional sense the things just described, exactly indicates an undoubtedly true psychological phenomenon, the intensity and characteristics of which are hard to evaluate and define, but which, none the less, are objectively real. If, as I have said, magic is the objective projection of a desire and a will to encompass a result by methods known to but a few, by secret, individual, preternatural means, by compelling superhuman forces, we might well call magical the idea of the artist who invokes, craves, and achieves the miracle of creation. Thus in the expressions and thoughts of the great artists of all ages, and in the influence exerted by their works, the characteristic elements of magic may be perceived: the creation of a particular mood in which emotional faculties predominate over the critical ones, and the idea of the artist or of the magician exerting its influence by a persuasive or violent penetration of the observer's mind. I think that in order to illustrate and demonstrate the truth of this fact it is sufficient to examine closely the analogies between the mood of the artist when he creates his work and ecstatic and hallucinatory states of mind. It is enough to mention that rhythm and music, in both nature and art, and in all ages, were given a primary role whenever it was desired to bring about an incantational trance. It might be easily objected that art does not solely or predominantly arouse emotional faculties, but awakens the critical powers as well; and furthermore it might be advanced that critical faculties are indispensable to the understanding of art. Granted; in order to judge a work of art at its full value, in its forms, and in reference to the devices used by the artist, critical powers are essential, and in this sense a work of art stimulates these faculties whenever they are present. But the work of art acts on emotional individuals directly through suggestion and incantation; and in this, I conjecture, as in all other forms of magic, the impact of the spell is at its maximum only when the work of art takes complete possession of its creator. This is perhaps the primary condition required in order that a work of art may produce the effect intended; it must be perfectly sincere, utterly consonant with the thought of its creator. It is from its absolute sincerity that the strength of the influence of a work of art derives.

Another very important fact accounts for the atmosphere of the Renaissance. This is an age which, for the reasons mentioned, and primarily because the sense of freedom is reawakened and the concept of the value of the individual and of the nation is formed, witnesses an immense revival and spread of optimism. Nothing seems unattainable now, nothing beyond human powers. The man of the Renaissance, the *homo universalis*, feels that vast unexplored horizons have suddenly opened before him; he looks into the depths of his own personality and of the far-away universe; his glance penetrates the starry skies that the telescope has made accessible, and the bewildering variety of the infinitely small world that the microscope has made visible. He no longer truckles to astrologers' prophecies or to the laws of fate, or at least he no longer accepts them without question; he examines them sceptically and often rebels against them. In an age in which the Mediterranean stem appears to have produced new offshoots from the blood-soaked soil, the primitive magic conception no longer suffices to indicate the path or to check man's impulses. The reawakening of human reason, unshackling itself from traditions, prepares the rebirth of the *homo sapiens* after the rule of the *homo sanctus* and of the *homo doctus*. The collective rational social ego is about to be formed.

XXIII

Romantic Magic Ideology in the Eighteenth Century

I. THE METAPHYSICAL ORIENTATION

THE Thirty Years' War (1618–48), caused by events that apparently did not justify such a violent and vast outbreak of passions, was a social catastrophe. It destroyed hundreds of cities, wrecked civil institutions, left in its wake an enormous number of dead and wounded, physically or mentally disabled, and failed to settle the most serious conflicts between all the countries of Europe and between the various religious groups and social classes. This is perhaps the most notable fact of this dreadful war: its development and consequences were completely out of proportion to its apparent causes. In small collective adventures the aim is determined: whether the aim is political or economic, the war one of conquest or of destruction, the purpose is always visible. In the great collective adventures that overwhelm many nations and states, the aims are different and often contradictory. The motives that originally determine wars are displaced by others, often completely different. The goal of an international conflict is determined and emphasized only when the war, brought about by motives apparently insufficient to justify an international clash, assumes unexpected proportions.

The Thirty Years' War upset a world in chaos, resulting from a rapid and unorganized outburst of new ideas. In Italy and in the other Latin countries the Renaissance had been a creative springtide and had blazed, without leaving many victims, a path of scientific and artistic progress. In Germany the conflict of ideas culminated in a religious war, waged with extreme fanaticism, and the cruel and grotesque conflict ended only when misery and famine had almost totally destroyed the populations of central Europe. The whole of Europe was more or less directly sucked in by the vortex of war. The conflict was waged without a program, and none of the countries participating knew how to grasp the opportunity of terminating it. The imperialists gained a decisive victory in 1620, and more than once Wallenstein and Gustavus Adolphus could have imposed a victorious peace, but none of the leaders seemed able to stop this frightful slaughter. Each one wished to carry on to the annihilation of his enemies. Two great leaders emerged from this tragic adventure: Wallenstein, Duke of Friedland, the commander of the Imperial troops, and the Swedish King Gustavus Adolphus. Wallenstein's fascinating personality as a leader enlisted the unconditional loyalty of his followers. He was a soldier and an astrologer, a political adventurer who did not enjoy the trust of the sovereigns for whom he fought, the Emperor, and the King of Bavaria; he incarnated the idea of the personal, totalitarian dictator in Germany, thirsting for power and glory. The people believed that this leader of the Catholic troops had signed a pact with the Devil so that he could not be wounded in war; but he was assassinated on the order of the court of Vienna, which, rightly fearing the excessive growth of his power, was alarmed by his great popularity.

Gustavus Adolphus was the champion of the principles of Lutheranism and the leader of the Protestant rulers against Rome, but his primary motive was conquest. He created the myth of the strong, blond Nordic, the subduer of Europe and the heroic defender of religious freedom. In reality he was a great commander who understood, at the right moment, the importance of cavalry in the field, and carried his victory as far as the Alps, where he was killed in battle. After his death two astute and powerful statesmen, Cardinal Richelieu and Cardinal Mazarin, became the supporters of the cause, not of Catholicism, but of monarchic and conservative France, which was anxious to preserve and enlarge its political and economic power. In this frightful war, apparently waged for religious motives, Catholics fought in the ranks of Protestants, and Protestants obeyed the orders of Catholic generals. This war marked the destruction of the prevalently religious order of things which until that time had been predominant in European politics.

The consequences of this violent upset appear in the eighteenth century, which was an epoch of political revulsion against all the ruling structures, an age animated by a spirit of revolutionary idealism tending to liberate the conscience of man as well as the multitudes. This idealism spiritually originated in the trend of culture toward natural sciences and in the increasingly violent attack against scholastic dogmatism; it advocated the necessity of finding substitutes for the values whose destruction was urged, and obtained control over both political and intellectual life. The creators of these new values, in politics and economics as well as in other fields of thought, were scholars who, in the attempt to explain life problems in accordance with scientific discoveries and results, often badly interpreted, of experimental research, often indulged in metaphysical speculations.

At the beginning of the century the influence of philosophy predominated, and it was thought that all questions could be solved rationally. Philosophers moulded the new social order and exerted a notable influence over the development of science. The system of Leibnitz (1646–1716), published by his follower Christian von Wolff, which is founded on the existence of infinitely small, indivisible beings, the so-called animated and thinking monads, an essential part of all bodies and all living beings, whose souls they are, and deriving from a central monad, God, to whom they bear a relation of pre-established harmony, evinces some interesting points of contact with the conceptions of ancient beliefs.

Near the close of the century we notice, particularly in Germany, a trend toward romantic and mystical fantasies, which lead to the appearance of other systems in which the idea of magic again assumes some of its characteristic traits. Animal magnetism or mesmerism is an eighteenth-century product. Its prominent advocate was Francis Mesmer (1733–1815), who exerted an extraordinary influence over the orientation of medicine toward mysticism. It is significant that his doctoral dissertation dealt with the mystical influence of the planets on the physiology and pathology of the human body.

Magnetic medicine is closely related to sympathetic medicine. William Maxwell, an English physician who lived toward the middle of the seventeenth century, may be considered as the founder of magnetic medicine. He was the author of a treatise entitled *De medicina magnetica*, which was printed in Frankfurt in 1679. According to Maxwell, the soul is not contained within the limits of the body, but acts outside of it. Every human body emits radiations composed partly of material, partly of immaterial elements which are the vehicles transmitting the soul's action and containing the vital forces. This vital force is to be found also in all substances that have left the body, such as blood, secretions, and so on. The effects of every action exerted over a substance deriving from or belonging to the diseased body reverberate on it. A vital spirit resides in all substances belonging to the body and persists in them as long as they preserve their nature. The vital spirit of substances belonging to different individuals gives rise, when blended, to sympathy and consequently to love. Countless other doctrines derive from these. They are based on a correct and ancient conception of the reciprocal relations that bind all living beings and the microcosm to the macrocosm. They originate partly in objective observation, and trace back to primitive views regarding the extension of human personality beyond the boundaries of the body. Because of incessant search for links between the material and the spiritual world, these doctrines inevitably reassert the value and importance of symbols and give rise, as may be easily imagined, to countless fantastic systems and practical applications of all kinds, in which the initial conception of correlations is replaced by the notion of relationships founded exclusively on the similarity of names, sounds, and accidental shapes.

Mesmer's theories, according to which every living body possesses a magnetic fluid which circulates a special force animating both the living and the inorganic world, culminated in his "magnetic therapy," deriving from the imposition of hands on the patient and other "magnetic" practices. This doctrine, examined in the light of modern science, with criteria different from those which were responsible for the exaggerated enthusiasm with which it was accepted or for its rejection, which seemed to be final, appears to belong to the history of suggestive therapy and hypnotism rather than to that of mysticism, and it is therefore under this aspect that I will discusss it later. The term *animal magnetism* and its conception were unusually popular, and gave rise to a mystical trend that was important in eighteenth-century history.

Magnetizers arose everywhere in great numbers; some few of them, who were in good faith, attempted to give a scientific sanction to the new theory with the assistance of natural philosophy, which at that time particularly in Germany, was being developed. Others, forming the great host of impostors and charlatans, were quick to perceive the enormous field of action that was being opened to clever and unscrupulous men, capable of exploiting an idea that had an irresistible appeal for the credulous, the suffering, or the naïve. Serious debates were held concerning questions called problems of the spiritual fecundation of the magnetized by the magnetizers, of the polarity of sensations. Collective infatuation gave rise to an extensive literature on animal magnetism. A physician, Kieser (1778–1862), affirmed the existence of a solar brain to which the functioning of intellectual life during the day must be attributed, in contrast with the telluric ganglion, a sort of superior psychic centre regulating spiritual functions during the night. Among the followers of Mesmer were a host of philosophers and physicians. He attracted, in general, all those who saw in his theory a confirmation of that trend toward occultism and mystery which is one of the peculiar traits of the eighteenth century. The success of strange and fascinating personalities like Casanova, the Count of Saint-Germain, and the numberless great adventurers of the century is only to be explained in reference to this atmosphere.

In the last decades of the eighteenth century and at the beginning of the nineteenth, simultaneous with the growth of the romantic trend, magnetic medicine and occultism spread throughout central Europe. Homœopathy, founded by Samuel Christian Friedrich Hahnemann (1755–1843), who affirmed that diseases could be cured by inducing, through medicaments, phenomena analogous to those which caused the illness, belongs to medical systems that rely on a suggestive influence. Hahnemann prescribed hot compresses for the cure of burns, opium for somnolence, and the like. This idea is obviously analogous to that of sympathetic medicine. Another fundamental idea of Hahnemann's theory is that the greatest effects are produced by the smallest amounts of the remedy. According to this doctrine, the reduction of the dose increases its efficacy. Another system, called isopathy, was developed from Hahnemann's theory. According to isopathy, illnesses must be cured with the very products of the illness. For instance, persons suffering from tapeworms were advised to swallow proglottids, worm segments; sufferers from gonorrhoea were treated with gonorrhoeal pus; tuberculous patients with the saliva of another person suffering from the same disease, and so on. It is sufficient to mention that the conception of immunity has, in some ways, an analogous application in modern systems of treatment, and particularly in prophylaxis, although starting from an entirely different principle.

It is obvious that the arousing of special emotional states, facilitating direct suggestion, is a dominant principle and a typical feature of magnetic and other romantic systems of eighteenth-century medicine. Magnetic medicine employed evocatory practices like those of Schrapfer, who, by means of fumigations, caused his patients to fall into trance-like dreams in which they saw ghosts in material form. A reading of the descriptions of the seances presided over by Cagliostro in Paris, of those at which Mesmer magnetized his clients, and of the magic operations performed by Casanova, convinces one of the evidence of these facts. The idea of magic invariably owes its success to that direct and reciprocal relation between agent and subject of which we spoke, irrespective of whether it is manifested in the form of divinatory arts, easily believed in by minds tending toward mysticism, or is applied in therapy, when it sometimes exerts through suggestion a beneficial influence which at times results in astounding cures.

2. EMANUEL SWEDENBORG

Eighteenth-century mysticism is dominated by the figure of Emanuel Swedenborg. He was born in Stockholm in 1688 and was undoubtedly one of the most alluring personalities of

his time. The son of a very erudite bishop, he devoted himself
at an early age to the study of theology. He took courses in
natural science at the University of Uppsala, travelled in England, was a pupil of Newton's, and later played an important
role in the administration of his country. He was considered
an excellent organizer, and managed the administration of
mines, canals, and harbours. In 1745, after winning renown in
his own country, he resigned from all his positions, and engaged exclusively in the study of mysticism and occultism. It
is very hard to determine what factors were responsible for
the psychological evolution of Swedenborg, whose conceptions were undoubtedly exceedingly brilliant. We may be
justified in supposing that certain facts of his sexual life exerted
a decisive influence over this change in his studies and the
tenor of life. On the night of April 7, 1744, he had his first
vision. As he relates, he was worn out by his labours, was
having restless dreams, and was in a state of disquiet in which
he frequently heard internal voices and perceived luminous
visions. During his first vision, which had the character of a
hallucination, Swedenborg had the sensation of being touched
by the grace of God. A year later, in London, he had another
vision. A purple-clad figure appeared before him and announced that he had been chosen to explain to men the spiritual meaning of the Scriptures. That night, according to Swedenborg, his internal eyes were opened and he saw heaven and
hell and the spirits dwelling therein, recognizing many of his
acquaintances among them. Swedenborg then related that he
was continuously in touch with spirits for the rest of his life
(he died in 1772). Virgil, Luther, and Melancthon frequently
visited and conversed with him. He claimed to possess the gift
of television. Emmanuel Kant gave an interesting report on
the facts related by Swedenborg. The best-known and most
frequently mentioned case is that which occurred in September 1759. At that time Swedenborg, in Göteborg, minutely
described a fire which took place in Stockholm, pointing out
that the fire stopped three houses short of his own. Some days
later, letters reached him from Stockholm describing the fire
in precisely the manner he had related. Many facts tending to
show Swedenborg's prophetic powers are told by his biog-

raphers, but the evidence brought to substantiate such facts is so unreliable that it is hard to attribute real value to it.

Swedenborg's doctrine is revealed in his *De cœlo et eius mirabilibus, et de inferno ex auditis et visis (On Heaven and Its Wonders, and on Hell According to Things Seen and Heard)*, printed in London in 1758. He affirms the existence of a world of spirits and of a transitional state through which the soul goes after death, during which it is made ready, according to its merits and sins on earth, for heaven or hell: some souls remain there but a short time, others for many years, but never for more than thirty. All angels and demons —since angels and demons were originally men—are endowed with human form; the spirits maintain their human appearance and the functions of their earthly life. Man, in order to establish contact with spirits, must be in an intermediate state between sleeping and waking.

Toward the close of the eighteenth century, belief in occultism and mysticism spread rapidly; a number of sects were founded, and the whole international organization of Masonry, which until then had been barely vegetating in the dark, quickly developed. At this epoch the institution assumed a clearly symbolic and fantastic cast, on the foundation of the *Chapter of Clermont* by the Chevalier de Bonneville (1748). A complex hierarchical structure, with a wealth of symbols and designations, was superimposed on the original framework of Masonry, which at the beginning of the century had been set up in England as an initiatory rite, employing the ancient terminology, degrees, and practices of the masons' and architects' guilds. In 1756 the *Chapter of Eastern Knights* was founded, in 1758 that of the *Sovereigns of the East and West*, composed of twenty-five degrees and consisting of numberless pompous rites. Gradually, throughout Europe, new, exoteric, and mysterious practices and rites sprang up. The debates of the Masons' lodges almost always centred on problems of occultism, mysticism, and at times of philosophy. The occultist trend reached a high point in Sweden with the foundation of a clearly Gnostic-Cabalistic system, consisting of nine degrees, whose foremost dignitary, named the "Vicar of Solomon," had the exclusive right to knowledge of all mysteries and rites.

In 1776 Adam Weishaupt, professor of canon law at Ingol-stadt, founded the sect of the *Most Perfectible,* which later was called the *Illuminati.* The sect spread rapidly throughout Germany and counted among its members the most famous men of that country. In all of Europe there was an almost morbid interest in all strange and occult things; a fervid fond-ness for obscure and symbolical magic practices and a vast collective suggestion swayed the most cultured, rich, and powerful classes. This was an age of continuous expectation of decisive revelations, of new and great events, and of dominant personalities. Easy credulity of even the strangest things, ac-ceptance of the most unlikely tales, and worship of everything that appeared extraordinary were prevalent.

This general trend toward occultism and mystery, toward complex and secret rites, assumed, in various countries and milieus, strange and changing forms, and offered a wide field to all who were clever enough to exploit the situation for their own profit, claiming fantastic titles and chimerical powers and exercising personal suggestion in a perfectly prepared setting. These conditions of European society of the eighteenth cen-tury account for the extraordinary popularity, with large crowds no less than in royal palaces, in aristocratic society, and in cultured groups, enjoyed by men whose adventures have a meaning that goes beyond the purely biographical do-main and which constitute a noteworthy aspect of the social life of that time.

3. CAGLIOSTRO

Among the great adventurers of the eighteenth century was Giuseppe Balsamo, self-created Count Cagliostro. He was un-doubtedly the most noteworthy, not on account of his qual-ities (he was certainly not a man of genius or of great will-power, and not even a bold charlatan), but for the reason that the story of his life fully illumines the stage on which events took place. Cagliostro was truly a wizard in the old sense of the word, and we might say that he was the last of the great wizards. He evinced no critical activity, even when a simple observation of facts might have led him to perceive the gravity of the dangers threatening him. His desires were checked by no law; no moral sense caused him to hesitate even for a moment on his path, which seems marked rather by destiny than by his will. A forger of documents and titles, an exploiter of his wife, who, on her part, was untrue to him, he was always impelled by a craving for greatness and power (more than by the greed for wealth, for which, evidently, he cared little), by his fondness for display, and by his dreams of clamorous and magnificent success.

In fact, the most interesting problem in the life of Cagliostro is, for the investigator, the ascertainment of the practical goal at which he aimed. He could have undoubtedly earned an immense amount of money by cleverly exploiting that scanty knowledge of pharmaceutical drugs which he had picked up as a boy in the convent of Caltagirone. Instead he practised medicine in his own way, and it was well known that he treated the poor with the greatest disregard for his own profit, that he often refused to treat extremely wealthy people, and that the earnings from his medical practice were very limited. Being a close friend of some of the wealthiest and most powerful men of his age (it is enough to mention among these the Cardinal de Rohan), he never exploited their friendship for the purpose of enriching himself. Although he was in touch with the individuals who took an active part in the famous affair of the Queen's necklace, he kept aloof, restrained from any meddling, and avoided even the appearance of complicity. He only requested his influential protectors to become members of his lodge or to be present at his experiments, and possibly to buy his drugs. In an age in which there were a thousand ways to pile up a fortune if one lived near a princely court, Cagliostro continued to be, throughout his life, a restless seeker after adventure.

Nor can we say that he was a mystic or a believer. Cagliostro's ideas always appeared, even in the fundamental documents attesting to his activity, disorderly, uncertain, and confused. We have the clear impression that all his speeches and writings were inspired rather by the search for bombastic words and sentences than by the need for expressing something concrete and deeply felt. He was no voluptuary like Casanova; even the fiercest of his critics could blame him for only minor faults. It is certain that he was never charged with such actions as would lead us to believe that the desire for a wealthy existence or sensual indulgence prompted his conduct.

Cagliostro was a wizard of the first water inasmuch as he was impelled only by his belief in himself and in his power of convincing and guiding, by his fondness for luxury and magnificence, for secret and wonderful things. Above all he was a wizard because of the power he possessed of exerting a profound suggestion over those surrounding him. There were numberless people of great intelligence and profound scholarship who approached him with mistrust and who, although acquainted with his shady past and the deficiencies of his education, were won over by the charm of his personality. A list of the names of the persons who came under his spell would include many of the most celebrated personalities of European history at the close of the eighteenth century. For a moment, when Cagliostro was arrested by order of the Papal Government, it seemed as if the whole of Europe lost interest in the French Revolution in order to rack its brains with the problem as to whether Giuseppe Balsamo and Count Cagliostro were one and the same person. From his earliest roaming days in London to the triumphal moment of his life—his liberation from the Bastille—when the crowd, delirious with enthusiasm, escorted his carriage to his house, while all the windows in the city were lighted in his honour, he almost constantly exerted his uncanny spell. All forms of magic found in him a passionate devotee. An alchemist of uncommon acquirements, he engaged numberless times in the preparation of the philosophers' stone, and in Warsaw persuaded Prince Adam Poninsky to finance and follow his experiments. He worked on the alchemic egg, while the members of his lodge gathered in the laboratory before the athanor; he prepared the *seconda materia* or "second matter" by distilling rain water, and with mercury and other mysterious compounds he tried to produce silver. Finally he tried to convert silver, impregnated with the "universal germ," into gold. The descriptions of his followers, who swore by all his words, enable us to perceive how Cagliostro conducted these practices and the solemnity that accompanied each of his actions. As a soothsayer endowed, he claimed, with an infallible prophetic spirit, he foresaw, according to contemporary reports, the fate of Marie Antoinette, and guessed the numbers of the London lottery of 1776. Many other times his prophecies were asserted to be right. A very renowned healer, he affected at Strassburg, Paris, and Rovereto (to mention only places in which he resided for a considerable time) marvellous cures. The Princess of Nassau, the Princess of Mont-Barey, the Prince of Soubise, the Prince of Rohan, the Duke Caylus, the Prince Archbishop of Trent, and countless other famous characters were his clients, and proclaimed his fame as the ablest diagnostician, unexcelled in recognizing the true natures of diseases and prescribing their cures. He maintained that he could evoke the shadows of the dead and compel them to answer his questions. Finally those whom he called his wards, or his "doves"—girls whom he placed behind a screen and whom he must undoubtedly have hypnotized—replied to questions concerning unknown and remote things, and were obviously cleverly selected mediums. Youth filters and the philosophers' stone, secret initiations and practices based on Cabalistic formulas, and rhythmical repetitions of names, magic cures and alchemistic experiments, prophecies, crystal-gazing, and individual and collective suggestion in all forms were the stock in trade of the vast and complex work of Cagliostro, which was accompanied by the delirious plaudits of the crowds.

In the centre of the circular hall of the mother lodge of Lyon there stood the splendid bust in which Brother Houdon, a great sculptor, immortalized the features of the prophet; and at the meetings of the Egyptian Order, founded by Cagliostro, the Great Cophta, surrounded by high dignitaries was worshipped as the Only Master, while in the Adoption lodges Lorenza Feliciani, Cagliostro's wife, a very beautiful woman, climbed the steps of the small throne around which gathered, in devout ecstasies, ladies bearing the greatest names in France.

Lorenza's betrayal and the charges she flung at her husband brought about his ruin, his arrest, his trial, and his condemnation. We cannot here examine in detail those facts which—like for instance the convulsions from which he suffered while in prison and which caused him to lose consciousness—might lead one to think that Cagliostro was an epileptic. It is never-theless certain that in the history of magic, and particularly in that of the eighteenth century, the unparalleled success ob-tained by this man of little culture and mediocre intelligence, gifted with extreme sensitivity and with all the qualities re-quired for influencing the masses, constitutes one of the most interesting phenomena. In an age in which there was a vast and deep expectation of the miraculous and a perfectly ade-quate preparation of minds through philosophical and mystical schools, Cagliostro persuaded and overwhelmed, and was in his turn persuaded and overwhelmed by events greater than he.

4. ROMANTIC MAGIC IN THE EIGHTEENTH CENTURY

If we keep in mind that the dominant and permanent fact is always the influence of suggestion, it appears evident that in accordance with the changes working upon the personality of the agent or of the subject, and with the changes imposed on them by both the sentimental and the intellectual climate in which they live, by political, religious, and social events, these currents assume a greater or lesser importance, unite or elide, complete or exclude one another, vanish or reappear. When, as toward the close of the eighteenth century, a trend toward romanticism is predominant, charlatans and adven-turers find it easy to impose on individuals and crowds by extraordinary promises, complicated hocus-pocus, boasts of great success and unbounded power. Likewise, in epochs in which, because of the impact of events on groups and indi-viduals, mystic trends are predominant, the greatest influence is exerted by persons who are adepts at cleverly exploiting theories or doctrines that fulfil the wants of mysticism.

Gradually, with the scientific explanation of unusual events, with the profound study of psychology, and with the critical examination of subconscious states and their manifestations, the causes and effects of phenomena belonging to the magic cycle are elucidated. However, since scientific explanations only partially solve the mystery surrounding those phenomena in the eyes of believers, and, above all, since science does away with the essential need for faith which is the very atmosphere in which those phenomena can take place, scientific knowl-

edge does not succeed, and perhaps never will succeed, in
banishing magic completely.

In comparison with the experimental trend of the Renaissance, the mystic occultism of the eighteenth century represents a reversion to the past, a reversion that appears logical as
an almost necessary reaction to the æsthetic and ethical revolution brought about by the Renaissance. Such reaction occurred all but simultaneously in all fields of thought. It was
one of the swings of the pendulum in the cycle of the adventures of the mind. Nor is it to be wondered at that, at the
start, the great political events of the last part of the century
made but a temporary change in this state of things. The
French Revolution, with the proclamation of the rights of man
and the abolition of privileges, with its pitiless war on religious
ideas, seemed, in its inception, a victory of rationalism, and
in truth the magic idea appeared to diminish and almost disappear. But in reality, owing precisely to the violent storm that
convulsed men and minds, to the revolutionary movements
and wars that, in the beginning of the century, destroyed hundreds of thousands of lives and upset all values, to materialism,
which emerged triumphant and ruled the democratic conception during the first half of the nineteenth century, the
Revolution did not permanently conquer magic, which is
founded essentially on the preservation instinct of the species.
This instinct, deeply wounded by the revolutions and wars,
sprang into full force again with more violent intensity. It re-
aroused all the ancient traditions of the unconscious, all the
archaic recollections of the ways of desperately defending
individual, national, or racial existence. In this, as in other historical periods, reversion to the magic idea after an age of triumphal progress of rationalism and research, is an indication
of the historical oscillation (clearly described by Goethe) between the positive and the negative poles; between the trend
toward freedom of research and return to ancient shackles.
Magic is a passionate attempt to escape and affirm independence from human laws; it is an escape into the cosmos, a reversion to the awareness of the existence of a primitive bond
between all living beings: it is an effort to rebel against the
social laws which, at a certain moment, appear to be too limit-

ing and unjust, a return to antisocial individualism. Magic may
swing between annihilation of truth and desire, in mystical
ecstasy, and revolt against religion. Such oscillations are due
to a thousand complex causes, which are hard to analyse since
they are largely unperceivable; and they occur under the influence of social, political, and economic events which determine the successive phases of the progress of mankind.

XXIV

Aspects of Modern Magic—Divination

I. THE FUNDAMENTAL MAGIC ART

DIVINATION was, in all times, the fundamental magic art. In ancient days, it was thought to derive from the particular gift, conferred on certain persons or in certain epochs, of hearing things inaudible to others, of seeing vestiges invisible to others, and prophesying future occurrences.

With the unfolding of the history of magic through the centuries, divination became systematized. It crystallized into different forms, laws, and rules, which were successively partially transformed, giving rise to an entire divinatory technique.

The traditions of all peoples attached great importance, in so far as the origins of prophecy are concerned, to the rustling of leaves, the song of birds, perfumes, and often (as among the peoples of India in the Vedic age) to intoxicating beverages. In certain sanctuaries where oracles were uttered, the prophetess fell into a trance, and the interpretation of the oracles, which had to be performed by priests or experts, presented many difficulties. We are justified in concluding that in many cases of primitive and ancient prophecy, attested by historical evidence, oracular sayings were actually hallucinations of psychopathic individuals. Among many peoples the insane were regarded as seers. When magic divination became an art practised according to fixed rules, it became necessary to establish clearly and definitely the significance of signs, such as the flight of birds, the conjunction of stars, or the manifestations of dreams, in order to avoid contradictions between different wizards and the possible erroneous interpretation of a single fact or sign by various persons or at different times.

As a consequence, divination gradually evolved into something different from the primitive type. It was no longer only the product of a psychopathological or highly emotional state of mind, nor was it interpreted according to the individual and the case, but consisted in the interpretation of events and signs according to established unchanging rules. Thus the action of the individual in a trance was almost completely dispensed with. The prophet of the ancients, the wizard of the primitives, the sibyl, the Pythian priestess, while prophesying, were under the influence of a manifestly emotional and hypersensitive mood. The magicians who in later days exercised the various divinatory arts generally conformed to established and accepted rules. By a development analogous to that which caused astrology to verge into astronomy and alchemy into chemistry, while the symbols in both cases preserved a purely mechanical value, magic divination fell into two clearly distinct categories. The first, divinatory in the old meaning of the term, included phenomena in which psychic sensations were prominent, attributable to a sensitivity that Richet termed cryptæsthesia, (i.e., telepathy, precognition, rhabdomantic phenomena, premonitory dreams). The second comprised arts which, like chiromancy, physiognomy, cartomancy, dream interpretation, and even modern astrology as practised today, can no longer be considered magical in the generally accepted sense of the word.

The first category, obviously, contains phenomena that occur in the unconscious, under the spell of a special mood, of the suggestion of a wish, or under the influence of an illusion —occurrences that later are interpreted by some agent, or meant to bring about an objectivation of desire. On the other hand, in the mechanical divinatory arts magic action is exercised by cards or other means (chiromancy consists simply in reading and interpreting clearly visible lines). The most evident expression of such technique, carried to the uttermost point, is the famous books of dreams, hundreds of thousands of copies of which are available in all languages, and which contain a lottery number corresponding to every fact or person appearing in dreams. One must add, however, that in the divinatory arts that we classified in the second category, magic action may be exercised by the person acting as interpreter; or one might say that in the arts of this category tools—such, for example, as cards—are used merely to arouse in the divinator the state of spell or of intensified sensitivity during which he is capable of sensing unknown facts of the past or future. It is clear, at any rate, that while mechanical facts have a certain importance in the divinatory arts falling within the first category, a certain significance may also be attached to psychological as well as to mechanical phenomena occurring in the practice of the divinatory arts belonging to the second category. This distinction testifies to the slow transition, the gradual transformation of magic brought about by the facts we have repeatedly examined.

2. TELEPATHY, TELÆSTHESIA, PSYCHIC HYPERSENSITIVITY

Telepathy belongs to the divinatory facts of the first category. Mind-reading was described by Brown, an American, in 1875, and later by other experimenters. A series of accurately conducted scientific experiments (described by Lehmann in the *Proceedings* of the Society for Psychical Research) apparently prove that mind-reading is only possible at a relatively short distance. Many facts seem to confirm the assumption that it is based on the involuntary vibrations of the patient. Some interesting experiments made in Copenhagen by Lehmann and Hansen show that if the patient, after having been firmly prohibited from moving his lips or breathing a sound, thinks of a number, he will make some small movement with his vocal organs. These movements may be perceived by the simple device of placing two concave mirrors, one before the mouth of the subject and the other at the ear of the observer, so that the mirrors' centres are in direct line with each other. It can therefore be assumed that the involuntary movement of the patient's lips may be easily read by a person who is closely watching the experiment near by. Everybody who has had the opportunity of witnessing some astounding examples of the ease with which deaf people, accustomed after long and patient exercise to lip-reading, recognize words and often read, at a considerable distance, the thoughts of persons who deny having said a word at that particular moment must admit this possibility.

If these explanations do not clearly and exhaustively explain this problem, they indicate the track that experiment should follow. It is apparently unnecessary to admit, as an explanation of telepathy and mind-reading, the existence of mysterious forces; but it is logical to think simply that telepathy consists of reciprocal impressions, sent out and received by persons under the influence of a special mood, and of desire.

It is evident to persons who follow this line of reasoning that divinations known as foreknowledge, premonitory dreams, and so on, may be accounted for in a like fashion. Undoubtedly, as authoritative observers have stated after serious research, a number of cases collected and described in the bibliography on the subject disclose phenomena that may be considered as founded on foreknowledge. But upon examining and attempting to evaluate the significance of such cases, we must not forget that they represent a very small fraction in comparison with many that have been proved to be untrue.

There is certainly full warrant for asserting the existence of organic phenomena that take place in the unconscious and that originate in a particular sensitivity wrought upon by forces over which it is hard to obtain mastery or control. Those impressions, when interpreted by the conscious ego under the influence of environment, suggestion, or other factors, may appear as foreknowledge or forewarning. In order to explain these feelings, it is sufficient to posit a relation between conscious and unconscious.

These phenomena bear, for various reasons, an analogy to magic inasmuch as they necessarily involve the particular mood brought about by a variety of causes. The mood may be induced by a dream, a magic wand, or any other agency that casts a spell over a particular individual, or by other close or remote factors of which we are ignorant and over which we have no control.

But why should we suppose that these phenomena occur in the unconscious? That is because the trance, as we know, is characterized by the fact that it is brought about by the action of rhythm (song, music, dance, lights repeatedly flashed, etc.)

causing past impressions to be revived or to come to the surface. Doubtless there exists an ancestral memory, a habit embedded in the remote subconscious; and there is unquestionably a remembrance, an instinctive knowledge of past and present in the organism, that retraces, by a sequence of acts that cannot be considered as purely automatic, the ways of its predecessors. Likewise insects daily perform, with a skill and precision that is bewildering to us, inasmuch as we cannot admit that it is purely a product of instinct, the actions necessary to their future life.

One may therefore think that under the influence of a spell or of a stimulus remote ancestral impressions stored in the unconscious are revived. The spell brings back the memory of the past and resurrects the experience which may determine the future. A certain perfume, music, word, chemical substance, a luminous, sonorous, or electrical factor, or an indeterminable radiation may revive in our organism a slumbering memory of the past. By means of the well-known phenomenon of the regression of personality it is possible, through hypnotic suggestion, to carry a person back into an earlier period of his existence, causing that period to revive in his mind, or making him remember facts that he apparently has forgotten altogether. Likewise nothing prevents us from believing that under the influence of a suggestion, in a state of spell or trance induced by various factors, remembrances of the past may be evoked, from which presages of the future analogically derive. This appears to be the obvious explanation of the problem, generally speaking, because we must not forget that even the concepts of the conscious and of the unconscious, of the ego and the id in the Freudian sense, do not represent absolutely determined complexes; because in every individual, period, species, and race such complexes differ in limits, contacts, and relations. According to Freud and his school, the ego controls the id, but in the opinion of Maxwell they stand side by side. Some people maintain that the id personifies the *daimon* of the ancients or the *ka* of the Egyptians. The most logical explanation, however, and the one that has been accepted most generally by man's intuition and intelligence in all ages, is that which maintains that these perceptions are due to forces over which critical reasoning has no sway and which are therefore outside of the sphere of consciousness.

All human beings, animals, and especially insects are continually brought back to a sometimes vague remembrance of the past; and the phenomena of which I am speaking were perhaps responsible for that remote belief in metempsychosis and reincarnation which was almost universal in the past. We have all experienced similar phenomena and have indistinct memories of persons whom we seem to have seen, words we seem to have heard, situations in which we seem to have lived. We are therefore justified in surmising that in the period in which our reasoning ego was still insufficiently developed or did not predominate over our unconscious, in the period that we may rightly term magic, those phenomena were normal, or at least much more frequent. The divination of the primitives appears as a normal fact of everyday life; in our times, instead, it is only a manifestation of incantational states or the expression of desire in objective form. Modern divination, through rhabdomancy, telepathy, premonitory dreams, mind-reading, and similar practices, has preserved the aims and, to a certain extent, the rites of magic, perhaps because in reality all rites in their rhythm, formulas, and words repeat or symbolize the natural agencies that in nature have incantational power, such as, for instance, songs, perfumes, music, and so forth.

3. THE TECHNIQUE OF MECHANICAL DIVINATION

Modern magic, at least that practised today, which has diverged in its essential line from divination and has become mechanical, does not belong in reality to magic, in the meaning which we have given to this word, or, at least, belongs to it in an extremely indirect fashion. The divinatory arts still widely practised—cartomancy, chiromancy, physiognomics, and even astrology in its most recent applications, and oneiromancy or the interpretation of dreams—are real systems by means of which a person, without the need of a special mood or particular sensations, can, under the guidance of a teacher or a book, reply to the problems placed before him. One might easily claim that these arts are not a part of the collective adventures of the mind, but are among the numberless attempts to fool the easy credulity of the masses. Up to a certain point this is true: neither divination nor chiromancy and similar practices or occult arts have ever affected currents of thought or of action or exerted any social or antisocial influence. They deserve mention because the flourishing of these magic arts either precedes the great antisocial adventures or accompanies them and always constitutes one of their symptoms. In themselves they do not bring about dangerous adventures of the mind, but they contribute to forming the atmosphere, to orienting and determining the mood of the masses, of which they are an extremely significant symptom. Their increased popularity in certain epochs is indicative of a particular condition of the milieu.

The divination that is practised today on a large scale in a variety of forms, by prophetesses and fortune-tellers and necromancers of every nationality and social class, from ladies of the upper aristocracy to women of the people, from Russian princesses to gypsies, at every price and for a public of every kind, may generally be considered as but a systematic and ably organized exploitation of such an individual and collective mood. It is easy to account for the fact that in some cases the observations of individual fortune-tellers may appear prophetic: it is easy to comprehend how a sensitive and intelligent person can understand, without resorting to magic arts, the thoughts and sufferings of an intelligent individual who consults her regarding his future, and can clothe these thoughts and sufferings in suitable remarks and vague elastic forecasts which often resemble those of ancient oracles, making predictions that are generally not much more keen than the fortunes told to servant girls for a few cents by a woman of the people who sometimes guesses right. Whoever has read the famous and generally accredited forecasts, such as, for example, those of Madame de Thèbes, and has compared them with actual occurrences, will admit that they correspond very little to fact even when they are interpreted with the best intentions of showing them to be prophecies.[1]

[1] The studies and experiments on precognition made by Rhine and his school at Duke University are an interesting attempt to explain the possibility of the existence of facts that may be considered as divinatory and appertain to what has been defined as parapsychology.

In conclusion, we may consider that all modern divinatory magic may be classified as telæsthesia or cryptæsthesia if we are willing to accept the vague definition of Richet, if the divination occurs during a spell or a trance, which in certain individuals may be induced also by cards, by crystal-gazing, or by some other object or substance. Such divinatory manifestations deriving from memories of the unconscious, from suggestions or self-suggestions, bear a close connection with the phenomena of magic. All other forms of modern divination, or so-called modern divination, cannot be considered, from the scientific viewpoint, other than manifestations which may be capable of acting suggestively on the individuals exposed to them. From this point of view they may be curative or in single instances beneficial, but their influence is much more often extremely dangerous.

XXV

The Metaphysic of Spiritism

I. SPIRITISM PRIOR TO THE NINETEENTH CENTURY

IF we consider that the primary origin of the magic belief lies in the instinct of life preservation and thus in the desire to prove or to ascertain that life continues in another form after physical death, we must admit that the phenomena which are grouped together under the name of spiritism, (commonly improperly called spiritualism) are dominated by these essential elements. For this reason it is evident that spiritism, or at least its essential part, is not of recent date and that the students of the spiritistic doctrine who claim that it is as old as humanity are, at least to a certain extent, right. In truth, spiritistic practices reveal facts and phenomena that, as I said, have existed since the most ancient days, and decisive analogies with the doctrines of the remotest ages are to be found in the theory and explanations of such facts.

The fundamental conception of modern spiritism differs from all older similar doctrines only because it is presented in a complete organic system in which all phenomena are explained. A series of exactly known and frequently described facts, of partially documented phenomena, of hypotheses that have assumed the form of dogmatic assertions, are collected in a closed system whose conclusions, more or less simplified, show how the fundamental idea of modern spiritism is that of the immortal soul, which continues to live after the body's death and undergoes a series of transformations or changes in surroundings beyond the world circumscribed by sense perceptions, and which can, under certain circumstances, establish contact with the living, bringing about physical or psychic phenomena which can in no way be explained by experimental science.

In addition to this fundamental concept we find the belief that spirits, or souls of the dead, in order to establish contact

[319]

with the living must employ *mediums*—that is, individuals possessing particular qualities that enable them to get in touch with the spirits and to transmit their messages.

Among ancient peoples the medium is represented by the wizard who establishes contact with the souls of the departed. The fundamental difference between an ancient evocation and those of modern spiritists consists in the fact that in older times it was not admitted that the spirits able to enter into relations with men were always the souls of the dead. However, supernatural qualities, either diabolical or angelical, were attributed to them. As beings superior to men, they possessed knowledge and powers greater by far than those which could be attributed to the souls of the dead. But if we consider that the essential requirement for establishing communications between spirits and men is the presence of a medium—namely, of an individual who is in an ecstatic condition or trance, which allegedly may be induced by different factors— and if we consider, moreover, that such an individual can exert his action only within a closed group or a circle of believers and initiates who gather around him, we shall find numerous examples of this phenomenon in ancient literature and shall meet with the same preparation of the medium, the same arrangement of the circles, and the same appearance of phenomena. Lehmann quotes a book of Abraham von Worms that teaches the practice of divine magic. The work is dated 1600 and clearly refers to spiritistic rites and practices, light-phenomena, and the materialization of spirits.

Whoever reads the accounts of the witches' trials and the numberless cases of demon-possessed individuals who repeatedly affirmed that they heard voices, saw visions, perceived fragrances, and so forth, is obliged to conclude that at least in some of these cases it was a question of the spontaneous or induced appearance of mediumistic qualities.

The growth of spiritism in the most modern sense was undoubtedly affected to a great extent by a man of genius who exerted an undeniable influence over his contemporaries and over succeeding generations. I have already referred to Emanuel Swedenborg (1688–1778), a mystic who devoted himself to the study of nature and physics with unusual application. As he himself related, he observed that he could fall into a state of self-hypnosis in which he saw an internal light. This first occurrred when he was fourteen years old and leads us to believe that he was a neuropath. He began in about 1745 to devote himself exclusively to the subject of his visions. He asserted that knowledge is only partially dependent on sense perceptions and can also derive from direct communications with the supernatural. This communication may be achieved by one who overcomes his senses and leads a life of pure asceticism. Swedenborg described a series of his visions, which he considered to be nothing less than manifestations of the grace of God. These visions present the typical characteristics of hallucinations, analogous to those described by Benvenuto Cellini and innumerable other authors. Swedenborg affirmed that he was in continuous contact with spirits until his death, and that he talked with Virgil and Luther. He also stated that he possessed the gift of telepathy.

In his interpretation of the Bible Swedenborg is a decided follower of the Cabalistic system, and he seeks for a mystical and symbolical explanation of words and letters. His fundamental work, *De cœlo et eius mirabilibus, et de inferno ex auditis et visis* (On Heaven and its Wonders and on Hell, According to Things seen and heard), (London, 1758), was widely read. He set forth in it some essential points of the spiritistic doctrine, such as that of the possibility of establishing communication with spirits, the life of the soul after death, and so on.

I shall not review all the theories originated from Swedenborg's doctrine. Some of his students regarded his statements as dogma, and founded the "Church of the New Jerusalem"; others were the founders of pneumatology (the doctrine of the spirits), whose most important propounder was Heinrich Jung-Stilling (1740–1817). The latter was the author of the the *Science of the Spirits* (Nuremberg, 1808), in which he attempted to explain man's relations with the world of spirits by animal magnetism. Jung-Stilling thought that man acquires special sight when in a state of somnambulism; he affirms that when the soul is freed from the body it may become simultaneously visible to living men located in different places, drawing matter to itself by means of its nervous power.

In Swedenborg's age many attempts were made to explain all these phenomena scientifically. Georg Konrad Horst (1767–1838) tried in his *Demonomagia* (Frankfurt, 1818) and in his *Deuteroscopia* (1830) critically to examine magical occurrences and phenomena of television and prophecy. A passing reference must be made to a medium who exerted a great influence at that time: Frederica Hauffe, the so-called prophetess of Prevorst (Württemberg), who caused the occurrence of all the phenomena later described by modern spiritism, which were written down in 1829 by the German physician and poet Justinus Kerner.

All these phenomena took place almost exclusively in Germany, and it was in Germany that this occultistic tendency found its most enthusiastic followers.

2. THE SPIRITISTIC DOCTRINE

An American, Andrew Jackson Davis, is considered the founder of modern spiritism. He was the first to describe table-tipping, and movements of objects or instruments not touched by living persons (1848), which occurred in spiritistic seances before a large public. In his *Relations with Spirits* Davis expounded his doctrine, according to which spirits are human souls that have not yet attained perfection and can do so only through a process of evolution, passing from sphere to sphere.

Spiritism spread rapidly from America to Europe. The American mystic trend became prevalent, and table-tipping was generally accepted as a means of communicating with spirits. The religious foundation of the new doctrine, according to which there is no such thing as eternal damnation, and salvation is always possible, was the principal reason for its diffusion. It quickly conquered all those who felt the need of the supernatural and were drawn to an explanation that satisfied their innate and profound desire for a life after death, disclosing new and wider horizons.

This religious tendency was more apparent in the French spiritism founded by Hyppolite Denisard Rivail, known as Allan Kardec, the name that he assumed after communication with spirits had revealed it to have been his name in a previous incarnation. In his *Book of the Spirits* (Paris, 1858) he records the communications which the medium Céline Japhet and the somnambulist Bodin held with spirits, and creates the fundamental doctrine of French spiritism.

Spiritism spread rapidly throughout Europe, the number of mediums increased, physical phenomena became more and more frequent, and communications with spirits took the most varied forms. The experiments of the famous English chemist William Crookes, the discoverer of thallium, aroused the greatest interest. He recorded, by means of extremely sensitive instruments, a series of physical results and arrived at the conclusion that physical phenomena which may be verified by instruments exactly registering their weight and measuring their vibrations may undeniably be caused by psychic action. Crookes attributed the origin of such phenomena to an unknown cause which he called a psychic force, and later identified with the force that Thury of Geneva (1857) called the *"force exteniqne"* or *agent restant*.

Manifestations of this kind were documented by photographs of spirits, which were subjected to violent criticism, and later by phenomena of materialization which occurred for the first time in New York in 1863.

In England interest in spiritism grew rapidly and prominent scientists began to study the subject. Alfred Russel Wallace, the well-known naturalist, after many experiments admitted the existence of telekinetic manifestations and communications from the beyond. A group of occultists who formulated various hypotheses to explain these phenomena scientifically was soon formed. Toward the end of the last century, during the first World War, and more rapidly after the war, experiments and studies multiplied and the number of adherents to spiritism became increasingly greater. Physical and psychical manifestations took place with greater frequency everywhere, and especially in Anglo-Saxon countries. Today a vast literature, a complete collection of documents concerning experiences of every kind, a series of hypotheses explaining such phenomena, from the ancient ones of Reichenbach (1788–1859), an outstanding German chemist who admitted the presence of a force called *Od* which determined all these phenomena, down to the most recent theories of the German philosopher Hans Driesch in his *Parapsychology* (1933), constitute a rich material of researches, criticisms, studies, and theories.

I shall now briefly summarize those data which shed light on the problem of spiritism as an adventure of the mind in its relation to magic, gathering them from a cursory examination of the facts in their general characteristics without going into detail.

3. TELEKINESIS AND MATERIALIZATIONS

Let us consider first of all the physical phenomena, and primarily the telekinetic manifestations which have been widely discussed, amply studied, and generally admitted. Table-tipping, which may occur without human contact (telekinesis), and levitation are among these. The tipping of scales, an experiment that originated with Crookes, photographs of spirits, and spirit materialization must also be included among such physical phenomena. Many materializations have been observed and described since the initial ones, which were brought about by the mediums Katie and Margaret Fox in New York (1848).

About 1850 mass-suggestion spread in the Eastern states: mediums everywhere produced luminous faces and hands, spirit music, spirit paintings, voices, and other phenomena. For two or three years the number of spiritists in the United States was estimated in the millions. The most famous of the mediums was Daniel Dunglas Home (1833–86), who was acclaimed all over the world and enjoyed enormous popularity.

In regard to these physical phenomena, it is first of all necessary to mention that while some of them are generally admitted and undoubtedly occurred numberless times under the most accurate system of control, all the more complicated manifestations are hard to check exactly, and in many cases, despite the fact that the assurances were considered perfect, evidence was later produced or confessions were made that they were fraudulent tricks.

The most discussed phenomenon is that of materializations —that is, of the formation of substances emanating from the medium and assuming the forms of persons or objects. Among the best known of such materializations are those of Martha Beraud, known in the spiritist world as Martha B., and of Eva C., which Richet and Schrenk-Notzing regarded as completely evidential, but whose authenticity was violently contested by many writers, including Dr. Gulat-Vellenburg, who produced proof that they were common tricks. In this connection the case should be mentioned of the Hungarian medium Laszlo, who, after making a series of experiments which fully convinced his audience, confessed that he had concealed strips of greased cotton in the seance room, which he placed in his mouth and ejected with his tongue. An analogous case was that of the Schneider brothers, Willy and Rudy, who performed a series of teleplastic manifestations that were carefully examined by Professor Przibram of the University of Vienna and discovered to be nothing but deceptions.

According to the spiritistic doctrine, this teleplastic substance radiates from the medium under the influence of concentrated thought, and may then assume different forms and be reabsorbed by the medium, upon whose psychical action the substance depends. It is, therefore, an ideoplastic transformation of the medium's vital energies.

Such phenomena, which are generally produced by neuropathic individuals in a nearly dark room, before persons who are almost always under the power of suggestion, in an atmosphere of credulity, are very difficult to check and judge. It is certain, however, that one cannot deny the presence of certain facts that are hard to explain on the basis of our knowledge.

As for the photographs of spirits, we may state that a scientific check has never ascertained their evidential value. Even convinced spiritists, like Hyvlov, contend that the photographs thus far been published, which were taken under conditions such as to exclude severe scientific examination, are worthless.

However, even if one reserves judgment concerning the

existence and the possibility of checking materialization phenomena and spirit photographs, it cannot be denied that there are phenomena which may be called para-physical, as Driesch suggests, and which are evidence of the physical influence exerted by psychic factors. We are familiar with many analogous instances of the effects of suggestion: inflammations, the stopping of hemorrhages, and even symptoms of pregnancy may be induced by suggestion. Levitation may be a paranormal phenomenon brought about by a psychic factor and occurring only under particular conditions and through the agency of persons possessing special qualities. The analogy to the manifestations of ancient magic appears to be evident. *too* KIND!

4. PSYCHOPHYSICAL AND PSYCHIC PHENOMENA

Psychic phenomena may be divided into two groups: physical-psychic, such as for example the spelling of names or of words by a moving table, automatic writing, etc., and purely psychic phenomena. The latter do not require any apparatus or physical facilities, and consist in communications that may be made orally or in writing, but almost always while the subject is in a particular ecstatic state or trance. This trance may vary in degree: at times it is so light that it is barely possible for an experienced physician to discern it; at other times it is very deep and is accompanied by serious suffering.

The communications of the medium which are made in the name of an absent spirit called the control, which in its turn communicates information that it receives from another being, are manifold and of varied character.

In the majority of seances employing mediums of average education the communications are very simple and rarely exceed the medium's knowledge. Lehmann, who experimented for many years with mediums of different social classes, made the interesting observation that the replies always correspond to the degree of the medium's education. The accounts and discussions concerning mediumistic communications and the possibility that in a certain number of cases these communications derive from the verifiable knowledge of the medium or of other persons present, or are instead such as to exclude this hypothesis, constitute an entire library, and it is therefore impossible to quote them in even a summary form.

Mrs. Piper's mediumistic communications around 1884–92 created tremendous interest even among scientists. The most remarkable communications concerning matters assertedly unknown to everybody present were received by this medium. William James, the famous psychologist, rightly stated that in spiritistic seances a truly dramatic exchange of ideas and suggestions occurs between the medium and the participants, who easily forget the confusions and mistakes of the medium and remember and often exaggerate the best and most exact replies. In many cases one has the distinct feeling that the medium allows herself to receive the conscious or unconscious suggestion of the thoughts or desires of some person attending the seance.

Various scientific explanations have been given of the memory powers of the medium. One such explanation is that they are due to cryptamnesia—that is, a hidden memory of apparently forgotten things. There are numerous examples of such phenomena, such as that of the hysterical Clementina mentioned by Krafft-Ebing. It may be conceded that the medium repeats things she has heard in previous seances or from other persons at other times, which she herself has apparently forgotten. This phenomenon is analogous, for that matter, to that of the remembrance of remote things which is revived, even under normal conditions, by some apparently insignificant stimulus connected with it, such as a perfume, a word, and so on (Proust).

5. THE IDEA OF SURVIVAL

Among all the hypotheses that have been advanced, none of which completely explains the phenomena satisfactorily, perhaps that of Driesch indicates the path to a likely explanation. He affirms that it is necessary to seek a non-physical solution, since even the hypothesis of radiations appears quite improbable. We must seek a biological or vitalist explanation, Driesch says, and admit, as is now the practice in biology, a superpersonal factor, something resembling an entelechy—

that is, a fundamental directive factor of psychical life. Leaving aside all the explanations that have been advanced, it is important to set down a fact that is generally admitted and has been proved by numberless verifications. In all cases of intellectual manifestations, the phenomena derive from a relationship between specified persons, and occur in specified places and under determined circumstances.

All possible categories of phenomena, all hypotheses, from those of the pure spiritists to those of the negativists, or to the most unlikely assumption of the transmission of mental images from one mind to another, or the conjecture that those phenomena are caused by waves similar to the hertzian ones that vibrate between syntonized wireless stations, or similar to waves caused by atomic dematerialization, such as the radioactive one giving rise to alpha and beta and gamma rays, are based on an essential premise: the presence of a subject under special conditions which usually determine a trance.

That the subject in a mediumistic trance can be acted upon psychically not only by the people in the audience but by other individuals as well can be admitted when we are confronted with facts that cannot have been suggested either by the medium or by the audience. Maxwell thought that the spirit is only a psychic doubling of the medium which is formed with the concurrence or under the psychic influence of the bystanders (Aksakov's and Mackenzie's polypsychism). According to Mackenzie, when several persons form a chain, each one of them gives up some of his individual psychic force in favour of a collective psychism. There is no doubt that the medium draws from the persons forming such a chain what is called the force, a psychic quality that exerts its influence over the medium. The fact that this psychic action requires the labour and effort of the medium corresponds to the analogous fact that all wizards, sibyls, and so on, accompanied the complex process of the formation of ideas (ideoplastics) with evident manifestations of physical effort.

After mention has been made of these facts, which may be considered to be generally accepted, it may be agreed that our present knowledge is insufficient to explain all the phenomena of spiritism. This ought not to surprise us if we consider that even much simpler phenomena are still unexplained. All this, however, does not render at all necessary the admission of a spiritistic hypothesis. Even if we admit a series of supernormal or paranormal phenomena—that is, phenomena which cannot be explained by our present knowledge, but on which the discovery of new manifestations of life may shed light tomorrow, just as the discovery of radiations has cleared up certain hitherto inexplicable fundamental facts—there is nothing to justify in the eyes of the calm critic the admission of survival after death, which should have been proved by manifestations of the spirits of the departed.

This idea of survival animates and dominates all spiritism; it originates, like all magical ideas, in the ancestral conviction of the primitive being, immortality, or perhaps in the unconscious and profound intuition of an immortality which is, in a certain sense, true—that is, the immortality of energy and, to a certain extent, of matter. The conception of survival is the objectivation of one of the most ancient fundamental ideas innate in the human race and necessary for its preservation. It is always the same idea, from the ancient magicians to the Indian believers in metempsychosis, from the sibyls of the early historical epoch to the fortune-tellers of today, and it finds its most complex, organic, and logically systematized form in spiritistic theory.

The idea of survival is a factor contributing also to the formation of the evidence produced by spiritists, which is formed under the influence of this suggestion. Anyone who has attended a spiritistic seance and has then read the descriptions or listened to the accounts of it given by participants can see that in these relations facts and words are always slightly altered and reveal the desire and the interpretation of the teller. We all tend to amplify and explain what we have seen and to give a subjective interpretative slant to what should be an objective relation. This means that, after the spiritist manifestation has taken place, suggestion, which continues to exert its influence over the persons who have participated in the seance, as it does over the medium and the people who give descriptions of the occurrence, is a determining factor in the construction of the bases of spiritism.

6. SPIRITISM AND MAGIC

If we carefully examine the phenomena that are known as spiritistic and perceive the analogies between the spiritism of today and the evocatory magic whose existence is immemorial, we must emphasize certain facts that stand out in clear relief.

It is evident, above all, that both ancient magic and spiritism originate in events occurring in the unconscious: events which, under normal conditions, are not noticed by normal men, or do not take place in them, but are the counterpart of phenomena occurring in dreams, in hypnoidal, delirious states, in hallucinations, or in individuals endowed with extreme and exceptional sensitivity.

A second analogy between magic and spiritism is that, in order to bring about magic phenomena, the presence of a person in a trance is necessary. Trance, "incantational state," are terms that also may be applied to persons about to attend spiritistic manifestations. Critical faculties are weakened and an atmosphere is prepared that will render the sensitivity more or even excessively acute. Darkness, a red or subdued light, silence, concentration, prayer, the suggestion of persons and environment, a sufficiently large number of spectators exercising reciprocal suggestion, and finally a state of expectation are elements preparing and eliciting the trance. Some of the most fervent supporters of spiritism call the trance a state of grace, in which people await and accept with faith and without criticism, or at least without immediate and direct criticism, occurrences that strike their senses. That this state is necessary is proved by the fact that, as believers generally admit, spiritistic phenomena fail to take place whenever incredulous persons or sceptics are present. There are, it is true, cases of originally credulous persons going to seances with the firm intention of forming an objective opinion and being convinced. This, however, does not invalidate the fact that in cases of this kind the desire to be convinced and expectation quickly overcame incredulity, because such incredulity was flaunted with the aim of concealing a profound repressed need for faith. It is absolutely indispensable that the environment and the audience be prepared. All observers generally admit that special conditions are necessary for the occurrence of spiritistic phenomena. And there is no doubt that this preparation is altogether analogous to the preparation of all magic phenomena.

A third essential similarity between magic and spiritism is the preparation of the atmosphere through actions reminiscent of symbolical and magical rites. It is characteristic that the participants form a chain by joining hands, a fact that undoubtedly points to suggestion by contact. It is well known that when the body feels itself tied by the bonds of contact, full freedom of criticism is impaired. The repetition of rhythms, invocations, formulas, the numerical scansion of the responses of the table-taps, noises, and so forth, are undoubtedly well-known features of all magical and initiatory ceremonies.

The role played by noises, sounds, and rhythmically repeated words in inducing hypnoidal, oneiric, and hallucinatory states has always struck all attentive observers and students of the history of magic and of all the ways in which suggestion is manifested in both a sleeping and a waking state. Mention may be made of the rhythmical dances, the music founded on monotonous repetition, which have accompanied mystical and religious ceremonies since the earliest periods and are the essential and indispensable premise of the preparation of the magic rite. The very word, the very concept *enchantment* is closely connected with the word *chant* —that is, with the rhythmical and musical repetition of words and phrases. Some recent French studies have shown that it is very likely that the verses of the Bible, as for that matter all ancient prayers, were originally meant to repeat the same theme insistently and musically. We shall see later which is the more important: the thing that is repeated or the fact of its repetition; it appears more likely that repetition in the same tone of voice and with the same rhythm is the more essential. It is interesting to recall the success of the monotonous repetition of optimistic formulas in Coué's therapy. The rhythms of sounds, or alternation of words, of dances, or of lights, play an important role and produce the same effect in spiritism as they do in magic, owing perhaps to the fact that rhythm is the dominant law in the harmony of the universe and therefore every manifest accentuation of rhythm exerts a profound influence on the human soul.

A fourth very interesting analogy is this: in both ancient evocative magic and in spiritism actions deriving from the automatism of motion or closely connected with it take place. For example, automatic writing which is obtained by putting a pencil in the hand of the medium and exerting suggestion to force him to write, the automatic responses of the tapping table, and other similar manifestations clearly recall analogous features of ancient magic.

The most important analogy, however, and one which almost proves that spiritistic phenomena, because of their essential characteristics, are closely akin to magic, is supplied by the fact that the presence of an intermediary, a person who receives and transmits communications with far-away or supernatural beings, is indispensable. The medium evidently has the same characteristics as the wizard: in a state of ecstasy or of possession he repeats what is suggested to him by the external or internal voice that guides him, and it is thus that the suggestion or contact occurs. The will that guides these actions, whether it be the will of the medium or the reflection of the audience's state of suggestion, or a conveyance of the thoughts of a person outside the circle, is always manifested indirectly, by degrees. Ancient religions and initiatory ceremonies of primitive peoples are characterized by the same manifestations, and this, in my opinion, is a conclusive proof of the similarity or identity of all more or less systematic and complex magic and spiritistic procedures, which encompass the same results. The highly sensitive individual is the most susceptible to magic influence. He in his turn, with his appeals to the unconscious through his words, and still more by his mood, brings about the suppression or impairment of individual self-mastery and hence of the critical faculties of the persons around him. Undoubtedly these special requirements, which are generally acknowledged as necessary for the medium, have always been known and pointed out. Mediumistic states obviously derive from abnor-

The King of England healing scrofula (Title-page of J. Brown: Adenochoiradelogia, London, 1684)

*St. Vitus exorcizing one possessed. The demon is fleeing.
Painting by Michel Wolgemut (about 1540) (Germanic
Museum, Nürnberg)*

mal phsycological conditions which are characterized by a particularly keen sensitivity, either to external phenomena or to sensations arising from the unconscious. The character of these faculties and the energies that may spring from them are still unsolved problems, but the very similarity between the mediumistic trance and ecstacy or diabolical possession is evident.

Another interesting similarity between spiritistic and magic phenomena should be taken into consideration: the presence, or the possibility of the presence, in both spiritism and magic of inimical or malicious spirits, which may impede normal actions, perform acts which are erroneously interpreted, or may disturb, in different ways, the regular course of the practices. These evil spirits, mentioned so frequently in accounts of spiritistic meetings, which make strange noises, strike or annoy the onlookers, sometimes seriously and violently disturbing them, are closely related to the inimical demons of ancient magic, whose presence was always feared and suspected even when it was not physically perceptible.

It is admissible that some slightly known vital force or nervous energy exists whose seat is in the nervous centres, such as the fluid of the theorists of animal magnetism, the od of Reichenbach, the psychic force of Crookes. The effects produced by these forces have been too little studied so far to enable us to describe their essence with any degree of exactitude. Beyond the generally known and acknowledged and, up to a certain point, easily explained psychic effects, there are physical, material effects such as the phenomenon of levitation, the movements of objects, and so on, and these are the most difficult to explain if one does not admit as a hypothesis that the central nervous system may, under certain circumstances, emit, for example, forces similar to the hertzian waves, which determine physical facts. The possible solution of the problem is extremely interesting: it is not indispensable to resort to supernatural or extranatural agents in order to explain phenomena which do not appear clear to us at the present stage of our knowledge. Certain physical phenomena may be determined by psychic facts, as is proved by stigmata, the ceasing of menstruation caused in hypnosis, the removal of warts by suggestion, and so forth. It is not evident, nor is it, perhaps, strictly necessary to admit, that these psychic forces exercise a material, mechanical influence over inanimate things. The possibility that some cases of automatic movements of persons other than the medium are caused by suggestion exerted by the medium's will cannot be absolutely excluded.

Whoever examines with total impartiality, keeping aloof, as far as is humanly possible in judgments of this kind, from the suggestion exerted by clearly emotion phenomena over the unconscious which passionately yearns for mystery; whoever refuses to be influenced by the no less notable suggestion exerted on the reasoning individual by his studies, observations, and the affirmations of those who deny all positive validity to spiritistic hypotheses, must reach a conclusion having a value that could be termed historical. Spiritism is undoubtedly a form of magic or possesses its essential characteristics. First and foremost it represents the embodiment of a desire in objective form, an embodiment that may be a complete violation of the causal nexus. All spiritistic practices without exception have their counterparts in ancient magic: they are all based on a magic spell and on the presence of an intermediary. The new element in modern spiritism is that it has fitted all these facts into a system and linked them together by a single explanation. Modern spiritism is one of the most interesting historical phenomena: an attempt at a logical reorganization of ancient ideas, a new position assumed by those who preserve faith in ancient doctrines in the face of criticism, which can no longer, as in ancient times, be disregarded. Spiritism represents, therefore, the attempt to supply an acceptable explanation of magic phenomena to sophisticated criticism. It is an effort to systematize the unconscious under the influence of the Logos, and for this reason it has not been entirely accepted either by scientists or by men of pure faith, because it is difficult to reconcile with critical reason as well as with dogma. Spiritism is an adventure of the mind which falls within the bounds of mysticism and attempts to adjust its conclusions to rational laws. It may be counted among the adventures with a constructive tendency, in which absolute faith in survival dominates.

XXVI

The Suggestion That Heals —
Magic Therapy

I. THE VALUE OF SUGGESTION

WE have seen that the origins of magic therapy are to be sought in the earliest prehistoric beliefs. Identical beliefs are still operative, to a great extent, in modern man, and for this reason magic therapy is widely used in different forms and under various names. Consisting, as it does, in suggestion and spellbinding, magic therapy is based not only on ancient traditions, which have persisted almost unchanged in all peoples in regard to certain maladies and remedies, but above all on the actual successes of such practices. Such successes have been achieved particularly in the domain of functional diseases, in respect to which suggestion or self-suggestion, whatever its origin and form, produces real and often amazing results. Besides illnesses of a purely functional character, upon which the effect of suggestion is clear and easy to explain, it has now been proved that suggestion may have a direct influence over physical facts, especially when the patient is easily influenced, and when he has absolute confidence in the "healer." The effect of psychic factors on the development of physical phenomena, such as changes in temperature, the stopping of menstruation, brought about by suggestion, the appearance of bleeding stigmata, a phenomenon that has been repeated in many cases as an experiment, and other reliable demonstrations, is well known. Such are the so-called miraculous healings, the successes achieved by Coué's method and other similar systems, of which that of the Christian Scientists is the best-known. Real cures, whose assertedly miraculous origins magnify the importance and effects, determining illusions and even hallucinations of well-being, are well known to all physicians who have had occasion to examine similar cases. In these cases the suggestion causing the abolition of criticism and often of sensitivity brings about a disproportion between the phenomena that clinical examination may objectively verify and the sensations of the patient. The temporary cessation of physical suffering, furthermore, renders possible movements that were prevented by pain; faith in success, exalting the will-power, encourages all attempts to prove that success was actually achieved.

Such successes may result from the influence of a physician who knows how to exercise the suggestive power of his personality, combining it with the real or partly suggestive power of medicaments, of instruments, or of operations (every physician can mention many such cases in his practice: the effect of substitutes for morphine, purgatives, etc., the simulated removal of extraneous bodies, tumours, etc.). A greater contribution to these successes is made by the concurrent influence of objects or actions which, because they are surrounded with the halo of supernatural power, are more apt to provoke the state of mind in which the healer's skill may be successful. This explains why a fortune-teller or a soothsayer who claims to have supernatural visions or an old peasant who enjoys the reputation of a wizard is able to obtain results that would be impossible for the most famous physician, possessing perfect scientific equipment. In the case of certain patients their state of mind is more decisive on their sensations than objective pathological facts. We all know how frequently hysterical persons, or even extremely sensitive ones, claim to suffer violent pain because of facts which examination proves to have small importance and which normally would cause no pain. It is easy to explain, therefore, that in such cases pains may be suppressed, and a partial or general anæsthesia, analogous to the anæsthesia produced by certain chemical substances, may be brought about through psychic influence and especially hypnosis.

In the field of erotic magic, some forms of absolute or relative inhibitions of the sexual act may be caused, even in persons otherwise physically sound and healthy, by mental factors determining impotence. Whoever is acquainted with these forms of inhibition can easily understand how the suggestion exerted by a miraculous or supernatural act—whose efficacy is proportionate to the degree of its strangeness and appeal to the imagination—may result in a notable increase of sexual faculties. In this connection the literature on the effect of love potions and similar practices may be cited.

The history of cures and of magic healers shows how ancient this idea is and how persistent is the people's faith in the existence of persons possessing the special supernormal powers of curing certain diseases. This faith is closely related to that in ancient wizards, witches, and saint healers. There is even today no country or city in the world which does not have some healers, some accredited specialist, whose fame spreads beyond the limits of his city, town, or village.

The influence of religious faith is well known, as is that of religious practices, which exert great influence over the patient and contribute to creating the emotional state necessary for the cure and preparing the ground for it. Many allegedly miraculous cures, from those of the temples of Æsculapius to those of the grotto of Lourdes—often confirmed and supported by objective examinations—may be explained in this way by persons who will not admit the existence of real miracles. As an example of the influence of suggestion in such cures it is sufficient to mention the successes obtained in this field by the famous wonder-rabbis of Poland and Russia, some of whom have won extraordinary fame because of their clever combining of religious and Cabalistic rites with practical suggestions founded on wide experience.

2. HISTORY OF THERAPEUTIC MAGIC

In order to clarify this interesting problem it may be useful to mention related facts, choosing a few of the most famous. To begin, let me refer to the practices of magic and collective medicine performed among ancient peoples and consisting in contacts and sanguinary rites. They are to a great extent still practised by certain tribes of Polynesia and central Africa, and are directly connected with the most modern forms of magic healing. Among the most ancient practices evincing the closest similarity to the cases which we have been discussing may be mentioned that of healing by laying hands on the diseased part of the body. This sort of healing, as is shown by recent archæological discoveries in the sanctuaries of Æsculapius, was widespread. The appearance of priests during the night in the inner sanctum of the temple, where large numbers of sufferers lay in complete darkness, and the touching of the sick part of the body with a wand or a serpent (the wand is one of the essential attributes of Æsculapius and the serpent has been the healing god and later the symbol of medical art because of its character of mysterious and infernal divinity), are extensively described in Aristophanes' *Pluto*. For more than ten centuries the sick gathered in great crowds at the temple of the healing god and the enthusiastic testimonies of the cures performed were no less numerous nor less overflowing with gratitude than those one hears today about wonderful recoveries, the only difference being that the former are recorded on marble tablets instead of in newspapers.

In these cures the suggestion was generally made during sleep, and there are many like practices in the Orient today. For example, Christians, Jews, and Mohammedans sleep in the cave of the Prophet Elijah near Haifa to have their illnesses cured.

A few years ago, when I visited the Egyptian Museum in Cairo on a Friday, a Mohammedan holiday, I was amazed to see a crowd of humbly dressed women file past an ancient statue of an Egyptian god. I expressed my surprise at the interest displayed by the natives in works of art to the director of the museum, and he explained that the reason these women came was that since ancient days the statue had been reputed to possess the supernatural power to make fecundation possible, and women of the people who wished to bear children believed that quick contact with the miraculous image would bring about the desired result. This is an example of an ancient treatment for sterility (similar treatments were very popular in Rome in the Temple of Priapus and throughout the Orient) which possesses the three essential characteristics I mentioned.

The history of the cure of scrofula by means of touch is particularly interesting from this viewpoint. Much has been written concerning this kind of therapy. It is connected with the ancient tradition that healing is a sovereign attribute. Pliny (Book VII of the *Natural History*) relates that Phyrrhus, the King of Epirus, healed diseases of the spleen by touching the diseased part with the great toe of his right foot. According to Tacitus' *History*, there was a popular belief in Rome that Vespasian healed the blind by touching their eyes, and that the Emperor Hadrian had the power to cure dropsy with the touch of his fingertips.

Mediæval chroniclers gave lengthy accounts of the healing powers of the French kings. Algaldus the monk, who lived in the eleventh century, relates that Robert the Pious, King of France, healed the sick with his hand, marking the sign of the cross on the suffering part of the body. Gilbert, the Abbot of Nogent, who lived about a century later, relates that Philip I and Louis VI of France cured scrofula by touch. Since then scrofula has generally been known as the "king's evil."

A serious dispute arose between the King of France and the King of England, each of whom claimed to be the sole possessor of the privilege of healing. Edward the Confessor, King of England (died in 1066), undoubtedly treated a large number of patients. A drawing of that period, now in the Cambridge University Library, shows the King in the act of making a cure. Gilbertus Anglicus, who studied medicine at Salerno between 1180 and 1190 and left the school to join the crusade of Richard the Lion-Hearted, in the chapter entitled *"De scrophulis et glandibus"* in his *Compendium medicinæ*, writes that scrofula is called the royal disease, because the kings heal it. The household accounts of Edward I, King of England, for the years 1277–8 record the expense for 73 persons touched by the King on April 4, for 192 treated the week after, and for 288 more treated and cured by him on Easter Day in the year 1277. Hundreds of sufferers flocked to be treated every year. According to the description in the *Life of St. Louis, King of France* by Tillemont, the treatment was as follows: "The King, after preparing himself for the ceremony by fasting and prayer, received the sick, who bowed before him. He placed his finger on the ailing part of the body, making the sign of the cross and uttering the words: '*Le Roi te touche et Dieu te guérit.*' The King then blessed the patient and ordered that he be given food from the royal kitchen and money for his trip home." The number of patients touched by the King of France was enormous; Philip de Valois (1293–1350) touched 1,500 persons at a single sitting. It is interesting to note that the physicians of that time did not hesitate to advise their patients to take the royal treatment. John of Gaddesden (1280–1371) in his *Rosa anglica,* after advising various dietetic medicinal prescriptions for the treatment of scrofula, added: *"Si hæc non sufficiant, vadat ad Regem, ut eum tangat atque benedicat: quia iste morbus est vocatus regius ad hunc valet contactus Serenissimi Regis Anglorum"* ("If these [cures] are not sufficient, he shall go to the King, that he may touch and bless him; because this disease is called royal and the touch of the Most Serene King of England is helpful for it").

This royal cure continued uninterruptedly throughout the eighteenth century, and the ceremonies accompanying the treatment are exactly described by the chroniclers of the times. A Latin tract by Tooker, Queen Elizabeth's chaplain, published in 1597, relates the controversy between the kings of France, who claimed that Clovis had possessed the power of curing scrofula as early as 496, and the kings of England, who maintained that the French kings had obtained this power as a collateral heritage from the kings of England. William Clowes, the royal physician to Her Majesty the Queen, who attended the ceremony, claimed that many of Her Majesty's subjects and numerous foreigners as well, since the patients came from all parts of the world, were cured by her touch and would have perished in misery without it. Andrew Laurens, the first physician to Henry IV of France, published a reply to Tooker's book in 1609, claiming as a positive fact that the gift of healing was the absolute property of the King of France, and that the sick came to him from Spain, Flanders, Germany, and many parts of Italy.

In 1775 Louis XVI of France, on the occasion of his coronation, touched 2,400 sufferers, and he was not the last French king to perform this cure, since when Charles X was crowned in 1824 he touched 121 patients, who were taken to him by two of the most famous physicians of the time: the great dermatologist Alibert and the famous surgeon Dupuytren. This is the interesting story, supported by an exact documentation covering centuries, of a healing practice characterized by three essential features: suggestion deriving from the personality of the healer—the power of the King could not be doubted—immediate contact, and collective suggestion.

3. MAGNETIC THERAPY: FRANZ ANTON MESMER

At the close of the eighteenth century the number of cases cured by the laying on of hands increased. In this period a trend toward imaginative mysticism predominated and consequently the practice of magic medicine based on suggestion was very successful. An Irishman, Valentine Greatrakes, was famous throughout England as the healer of rheumatic ailments by means of the laying on of hands, and the most famous men of his time lauded his powers. The whole of France was enthusiastic over the miracles accomplished by the famous François de Paris, a fanatical Jansenist (1670–1727), whose tomb, after his death, was visited by multitudes of believers.

But the most successful healer of all was Franz Anton Mesmer (1734–1815), born at Iznang near Constance, who studied in Vienna and introduced into general medicine magnetic therapy based on the laying on of hands, a method by which he claimed to effect amazing cures.

Mesmer reintroduced an ancient method of treatments, examples of which are to be found in ancient Greece, and tried to explain it scientifically, creating the theory that every living body possesses a magnetic fluid that circulates and emanates a special force animating all of creation and even the inorganic world. It is this fluid that binds living beings together. Mesmer's doctrines, and to a much greater extent the fame of his cures and the power that he possessed to heal the sick and stop their pains by inducing a state which he called somnambulism or clairvoyance, won him great fame. His healing methods were widely used. In spite of the fact that, or perhaps because, medical schools and scientific associations condemned his assertions, sick people in every country in Europe declared their enthusiasm for his treatments.

Journals and books of the time are filled with interesting

data concerning Mesmer's method and successes. When he arrived in Paris in 1768 he refused to submit the results of his observations to the Academy of Medicine; however, he aroused the enthusiasm of the Parisians and, boasting of his miraculous healing powers, earned extraordinary sums of money. He was protected by Marie Antoinette. The King begged him to remain in France, offering him an annual salary of 10,000 francs to establish a magnetic clinic, and 20,000 francs as an annuity. Lafayette and many of the most famous men of letters, statesmen, and aristocrats were among his patients. He received his patients in a magnificent suite where, in the middle of the salon, stood a large basin full of water in which sulphuric acid was dissolved. Curved bars of iron, placed in such a way as to be turned in every direction, protruded from the basin, and from the end of every bar hung an iron ring, which was applied to the body of the person being magnetized. There were also wires which were conductors of the magnetic fluid. The patients were placed in a circle around the magic basin, holding an iron bar in one hand and forming a chain every now and then by joining hands. With many devices in which perfumes and lights were important, Mesmer then drew near the patient and began the magnetization, touching various parts of the patient's body and inducing a hypnotic state, during which he suggested cures. Mesmer's success was enormous; in spite of this the Academy dared to express an unfavourable opinion of him, which created a great stir in Paris and aroused new and bitter controversies. Although people from every side attempted to defend magnetism, it was practically finished. The history of magnetism, however, will always remain one of the most interesting chapters in the annals of medicine.

Stefan Zweig in his *Healing through the Soul* has shed a new light on the figure of Mesmer, asserting that his work marks the beginning of the recognition of dynamics of the soul and of the functional law governing its life, the first clear knowledge of the inward cosmos, a psychological science perfectly accessible not only to the physician, but to the thinker, poet, and scientist. Mesmer's experiment proved that between sleep and waking, reason and instinct, will and coercion, conscious and unconscious, there is a series of suspended, uncertain, os-cillating states. All the problems of the spirit, according to Zweig, acquired a new meaning, a hundred problems like that of free will, which hitherto were assigned to dogmatic the-ology alone, assumed a psychological and physiological tinge, and a number of impulses rushed toward this suddenly opened door. Pierre Janet rightly stated that, thanks to mesmerism, people have been for the first time obliged to examine the phenomena of concentration and deconcentration, fatigue, attention, hypnoses, nervous crises, and simulations which constitute as a whole the fundamental problems of modern psychology.

Mesmer's work throws an unexpected light on the accounts of witches and miracles, on the entire history of magic and exorcisms, and draws our attention to the efficacy of manual contact, evidence of which is supplied by countless cases. The tremendous effect that the news of Mesmer's discovery pro-duced immediately in his age is easily understandable. It seemed as if the mystery of long-hoped-for miracles had sud-denly been disclosed. Mesmer's wand suddenly provided an explanation for a set of problems. Philosophers like Schelling, Hegel, Fichte, and later Schopenhauer, were deeply interested in mesmerism. Zweig rightly observes: "Whenever science opens a crack in the mysterious black wall of the universe, the fantasy of the poet rushes in at once and animates the open space with images and figures. With the renewed psychology a new psychological literature begins."

Mesmerism, the fundamental conception of magnetism, un-doubtedly contains some truth—nay, more, an initial though still vague vision of the truth of the facts. The danger was that speculators, charlatans, crackpots, and purely literary men might exploit mesmerism for their own purposes. It was thus that Mesmer's students, instead of intelligently continu-ing his work, instead of understanding mesmerism's great im-portance and following out its basic idea, engaged exclusively in magnifying its successes. They represented the universe as being a magnetic system. This exclusive emphasis on a system is the typical fault of other doctrines in previous or subsequent times. The great idea was forgotten and set aside after mesmerism was condemned for its theatricalness. Mesmer died in exile, almost forgotten, and for decades animal magnetism was relegated, according to the judgment of scholars, particularly in the epoch of materialism, to the museum of superstitions and errors.

Mesmer had among his students a great many philosophers, physicians, and mystics, and in general attracted all persons who saw in his theories an answer to their tendency toward the supernatural, occultism, and mystery. This tendency is one of the typical features of the close of the eighteenth century. It is only in terms of this atmosphere that we can account for such strange and fascinating phenomena as Casanova, Cagliostro, and other great adventurers of the period.

Scholars like Hufeland and Heim, however, seriously took up the study of these phenomena. We may say that in the last decades of the eighteenth century and the beginning of the nineteenth, simultaneously with the development of romanticism, which, if it did not originate in, at least undoubtedly received a new and powerful impulsion from the circle of the French *Encyclopédistes*, magnetic medicine and occultism dominated central Europe in particular. The attempts to localize the seat of the soul, which brought about the phrenological doctrine of Gall and his followers, gave an impulse to the anatomical and physiological studies which, through long and conclusive experiments, established the seat and functions of the nervous centres. These are new rational orientations of the adventures of the mind.

The history of hypnotism is another example of critical, experimental, and scientific explanations of an abnormal state of mind similar to an incantational one. A clue to the characteristic phenomena of hypnotism was already to be found in the cures of Valentine Greatrakes, already mentioned. He was able to immobilize an outstretched arm by passing his hand over it and ordering the patient to keep it immobile. Hypnotism may also be discerned in the suggestions of the famous Gassner, priest, exorcizer, and miraculous healer, who induced hypnoidal states, of which we have exact descriptions, in the treatments of Mesmer, and above all in those of the Marquis A. M. J. Chastenet de Puységur, who put his pa-

tients to sleep and caused mesmerism to take a decisive trend
toward hypnotic healing. Important roles in the development
of hypnotism were played by a Lyon physician, Dr. Tetetin,
who described animal electricity in one of his books; and the
Abbé Faria, a Portuguese whose treatments were investigated
by the Paris Academy of Medicine in 1837. Finally the whole
problem was accurately and objectively studied by James
Braid, who ascertained the relationship between agent and
subject, and in his book *Neurohypnology* (1843) proved himself to be one of the profoundest connoisseurs of hypnotism
and to be fully aware of its dangers. Thee school of Charcot,
and that of Nancy, directed by Bernheim, have made definite
contributions to the knowledge of hypnotic states and to their
appraisal.

4. ADVENTURES IN MEDICINE

Magic medicine in a wider sense includes other practices
which were remarkably diffused even among the most highly
educated persons. There is a widespread magic prophylaxis
that aims at averting certain illnesses, dangers, or the unpropitious and magic influence of persons who may be harmful:
such practices as tying rue or coral around children's necks,
touching wood or iron on meeting certain persons, or refrain-
ing from uttering the name of a person believed to possess
evil powers. I shall not enumerate the countless practices, gestures, words, actions, and objects which are believed to serve
this purpose, and which now constitute the popular stock in
trade of persons exposed to special danger, who are therefore
in a state of mind particularly susceptible to such suggestion,
which for many of them has become a habit. Thus, during
examinations, automobile trips, hard trials, and, as we see, during the war, people turn with greater faith to such beliefs and
to prophylactic and apotropaic devices (mascots, gremlins,
etc.). These devices, like all the practices founded on suggestion, have been widely employed in times of great calamity
and danger, recorded in the history of the centuries following
the fall of the Roman Empire, through the period of the
plague, and later; and such practices reappeared and spread
widely and rapidly during and after the first World War.

In no other period of history, perhaps, have there been so

many descriptions of healings judged to be miraculous because science was unable to explain their cause as there have been in recent times. Perhaps magic and superstitious practices have never enjoyed more widespread popularity than today, nor have people ever turned with such faith and frequency throughout Europe, and especially in Germany and France, to miracle-workers, magnetizers, card-readers, to all those who in various guises and forms, starting from various premises and employing apparently different means, promise cures. It is easy to identify the cause of this phenomenon, which is manifested periodically in history after all great wars and epidemics, in the fact that after intense sufferings the critical faculties of the group and the individual diminish and their suggestibility and emotionalism increase. Despair, wishful thinking, and hope of escape are intensely active. A group is no different from an individual in this respect. After having just recovered from a serious illness, the latter is more susceptible to all suggestions and tends almost instinctively, perhaps remembering the danger he has escaped, to resort to the supernatural and to think of the threats and assistance beyond the visible and known. The same is true of the group in which a state of easy susceptibility is created by a general lowering of physical resistance, determined by the enormous number of war disabled, by undernourishment and manifold economic worries. One very important factor today is the diffusion of magnified news and unconscious suggestion by the press. Many newspapers seize all occurrences of this kind, as they do all sensational facts that arouse the morbid interest of the public, and describe all miraculous cures at length, placing the healers in an almost heroic mysterious light which notably contributes to the spread of their fame and the increase of their power.

The attitude taken by physicians in regard to these wonder healers varies according to the times, the country in which they appear, and the importance that they assume. Healers, or so-called healers, have sprung up in every period, and physicians have often been satisfied to observe them without undue uneasiness, believing that their popularity would be short-lived. In America as in Europe there are frequent cases of healers of different denominations, societies, and sects with pseudo-scientific names which promise to heal all ailments, and the public health authorities take no notice of them unless the cases appear to be very serious and liable to injure the dignity of science and the moral and material interests of the medical profession and, what is more important, to threaten public health. In such cases energetic and even violent protests have been made without success.

The last case of this kind, which had vast repercussions far beyond the boundaries of Austria, was that of Valentine Zeileis, who founded in Gallspach, a village that was almost unknown until a few years ago, a healing institute to which thousands of patients flocked from all over the world every year. Hotels and sanitariums sprang up overnight; the place suddenly became one of the most popular cure centres of Europe, and around the miracle healer a close network of speculative, commercial, industrial, and political interests was naturally formed. Physicians attempted to discredit him and medical associations asked for the assistance of the Government, which had evaded the question and allowed matters to take their course because the entire region, which owed its quick prosperity to the then famous healer, had threatened nothing less than an uprising if he was interfered with. Professor Lazarus of Berlin began a strictly scientific campaign, analysing the systems of treatment used at Gallspach, denying their efficacy, citing a large number of cases in which patients were injured by the therapeutic applications; he stressed above all that the laboratory, institute, apparatus, and method of treatment were always kept secret and that Zeileis did not allow physicians to witness the treatments. Professor Lazarus's amply documented attacks created a great impression in medical circles, but it would be a mistake to imagine that they impaired the faith of Zeileis's followers. An assembly composed of thousands of Zeileis's former patients immediately protested violently against these attacks and proposed little less than a crusade against persons who dared to declare war on the master of Gallspach. Thus, in spite of the polemics, in spite of the attacks of physicians and the unfulfilled promise of the authorities to intervene, the wonder-worker continued his treatments and had a considerable number of patients.

And yet it may be stated that it was impossible for Zeileis to have performed diagnoses with his wands, which he claimed were impregnated with helium or with actinium. He examined hundreds of patients in two or three hours and therefore it is not even to be faintly imagined that he could make even an approximate diagnosis. It is also difficult to admit that the so-called high-frequency current may have exerted a beneficial action. All Zeileis's work was evidently based exclusively on suggestion.

The cases of the Steinmeyer healers of Hahnenklee and of the parish priest of Gudmannsbach, described at length in Liek's book, are similar. The magnetizer Tetter, who practised his art in Vienna, in a sumptuous apartment of a large palace, was one of the most interesting of modern wonder healers. He enjoyed immense popularity and attracted hundreds of patients.

One of the most famous of these men, comparable to Cagliostro, is the bricklayer Josef Weissenberg, acclaimed as a prophet and divine master. By means of hypnotic practices, contact, sexual suggestion, and therapeutic preparations, in which a sort of soft cheese played an important role, Weissenberg won more than a hundred thousand followers in Germany in a few years, published a newspaper, to which he claimed that the spirits of Luther and Bismarck contributed, and was worshipped by his supporters with boundless devotion.

It is interesting to examine the characteristics of these and similar cases and the motives and forms in which they are manifested. When this problem has been clarified it will be easier, perhaps, to draw conclusions and determine the attitude that physicians, conscious of their duty and dignity, should assume. Whenever an academy has to check the attempts of an insurgent to flout its laws, whenever an official school has to put down an innovator or a professional association is obliged to fight a quack, the official bodies are always at a disadvantage in relation to the public, which demands first of all and above all to be cured and does not care whether the healer and the method of healing are officially recognized and approved. In the opinion of the masses, the healer who claims that his power is founded on personal abilities and talents, or on secret systems, and not on science, has an overwhelming advantage over the scientist. Desire for escape, hope for a miracle, instinctive clinging to the supernatural, all favour these adventures in medicine.

5. CHARACTERISTICS OF MAGIC TREATMENTS

Let us now examine the characteristic features of the methods of Zeileis and similar healers. Without pausing to discuss the irradiations, which are utterly hypothetical, or ultraviolet rays deriving from the mixture to be found in the magic wand, which are claimed to reveal the seat of the malady, and without penetrating the secret which the healer wishes to keep inviolate and which, according to what we may reasonably believe, has no importance beyond its secrecy, let us see what facts characterize the treatment. The first and most important is the "contact" between the healer and the patient, by means of a magic wand touching the body. Such contact has all the characteristics of a magic practice, and is performed to the accompaniment of highly suggestive phenomena. The wand is connected with a high-powered current and, according to Zeileis, becomes luminous upon contact with the diseased organ. Healing is brought about by this contact, repeated three or four times at successive sittings.

The second feature is the "atmosphere," the magic aspect of the room, weirdly lighted by pieces of apparatus which throw off intermittent beams of light, with streaks of sparks which affect the skin; the thaumaturgic aspect of the healer who appears in a priestly costume and whose long white beard gives him a venerable appearance; the play of words that appear mysterious to the profane, who know little or nothing of the helium lamp, of radium-bearing alloys, and of ultraviolet rays; finally, a complicated though apparently simple set of preparations during the long wait of the patients, the suggestion exerted on them by the atmosphere, pervaded with conviction of the miraculous power of Zeileis, and, above all, the enormous prosperity that his abilities have brought to him, to his collaborators, and to the whole district.

The third and perhaps most decisive feature is the system of receiving fifty to a hundred patients at a time, all half-naked, all equally suffering and hoping, all equally ready to receive the miracle. This feature gives rise to reciprocal and collective suggestion, manifested through phenomena that have been amply studied by specialists in mass psychology. There is no need to mention the numberless examples given by history and experiments of the great importance of collective suggestion: every single patient who claims to have been cured, singing the praises and merits of the healer, immediately arouses a wave of hope, a general will to be cured, and absolute faith in the miraculous act. In the group it is the instincts of those who express their thoughts and certainty with the greatest violence and openness that always prevail, and not the critical faculties of the single individual. Ancestral memories or manifestations of what Jung calls the archaic unconscious rapidly rise to the surface; obscure memories of thousand-year-old superstitions, ancient legends, supernatural events related by others, and the overpowering instinct of self-preservation, of the desire to abolish pain and be cured at any cost, create the state of mind of the individual and the group. When the healer finally arrives, the group is in a state of what might be called grace, prepared to accept as a miracle even a slight and temporary diminution of its sufferings.

These three features—contact, atmosphere, and collective suggestion—seem to be particularly noteworthy, because they are essential characteristics of all healings of this kind—of the case of Asuero, a famous Spanish physician who claimed to heal all diseases with a treatment of the mucous membranes of the nose, as well as of the Zeileis phenomenon. One must consider the essential point of such cures, whereas the therapeutic application to which the healing power is attributed is of scant or no importance. The role of the magic wand, of the silver probe and all equipment of this kind, is identical with that of the amulet, talisman, magic formula, and perhaps also of many medicaments which were prescribed for centuries with great success and many of which are still recommended today. The value of these treatments derives from the faith with which they are recommended, the faith with which they are accepted, and the atmosphere that individual and group suggestion prepares for the direct contact.

It is easy to imagine that treatments such as those of Voronoff, which have proved to be of slight consequence, also owe their success partly to the above features. The results that may be obtained by suggestion in causing the disappearance of verifiable anatomical growths has been proved by the extraordinary success of many surgeons in the sympathetic treatment of warts. This treatment has now been adopted by scientific medicine and described by Bloch (1927). By means of resolute and energetic suggestion warts almost invariably disappear, and according to the statistics of many writers, complete cures are obtained in eighty per cent of the cases.

6. CURES AND SPELL-CASTING

Countless healers and miraculous cures of this or analogous kinds could be mentioned; but I have limited myself to but a few of the most famous in the history of all times, leaving aside all those which might be called miraculous and are attributed to divine intervention and those, on the other hand, which are obviously the tricks of charlatans, even though they have some elements in common. Collective suggestion derives from the atmosphere, from the personality of the healer, and from indirect or direct contact. In all the cases mentioned, the healer is a physician, or a person possessing the characteristics of a physician, and the treatment and cure have been witnessed and checked by a physician. The cases of Asuero and of Zeileis should be considered to belong to this group, because of their common characteristics. Their foundation is evidently a set of complex and manifold factors which determine and, as it were, systematize a suggestive practice, which undoubtedly can, in certain cases, bring about the cessation of phenomena that do not derive from serious organic lesions. Nobody can doubt that patients who suffer from hysterical ailments, or whose illnesses are aggravated by extreme sensitivity, can obtain notable benefit from such treatments. The difficult problem which still needs to be carefully studied and clarified is that of the influence which psychic factors may have upon phenomena due to organic processes. This problem is undoubtedly very difficult and obscure, although many authorities have attempted to attack it scientifically by means of critical examination and experiments. It is impossible to deny its existence.

It appears that all treatments and cures of this type belong to the field of magic, because they postulate that it is necessary for the patient to be under magic influence, which may be exerted by different factors. The attitude, figure, and leading idea of the healer may differ, but it is necessary that he be sure of success and know how to create the physical and psychic state that is the indispensable requisite for the cure. The method employed by the healer does not have excessive importance: it may be a drug chemically and essentially efficacious in its verifiable physiological effect upon the organism, but it may also be a drug that becomes such only through the faith with which the patient expects it to work a miracle. It is said in the Gospel of St. Mark (vi, 3–6) that when Jesus returned to his native town and was greeted by the diffidence of his compatriots, who saw him as "the carpenter, the son of Mary, the brother of James, and Joses, and of Juda, and Simon": "Jesus said unto them: A prophet is not without honour but in his own country and among his own kin and in his own house. And he could there do no mighty work, save that he laid his hands upon a few sick folk, and healed them. And he marvelled because of their unbelief." It is clear from this narrative of the Gospel that faith is considered an indispensable premise for healing.

Between ancient therapeutic magic and all the practices of modern magic medicine a line of continuity runs: the laying on of hands (the German word *Behandlung* indicating the treatment of the physician emphasizes this manual act), contact, suggestion of faith, creation of a spell with the abolition of objective criticism.

Undoubtedly these methods of healing may become dangerous for the individual and the group, because by removing authority from the scientist it causes the patient to resort to the healer rather than to the physician and often leads him to lose valuable time waiting vainly for a cure and allowing himself to be exploited by clever impostors. Patients suffering from diseases believed to be incurable can be easily persuaded to accept the suggestion of wonder healers, and any lessening of their pain, any possibility of hope, increases their confidence and suggestibility. That is the reason why all measures taken by authorities, and the campaign waged by physicians, are unable to limit the work of these healers, which, in fact, is becoming increasingly widespread and remunerative. In every time and place, despite the progress of civilization, there is a return to or persistence of ancient ideas, a passionate desire for miracles. The faith that heals must and can be, at least up to a certain point, controlled, systematized, and usefully guided by positive knowledge. Such evolution of ancient healing magic, thanks to the skilful psychological talent of the physician, will perhaps bring about a decisive change in the near future, without, however, succeeding in suppressing new desires and desperate attempts.

In the patient labour of the laboratory, as in accurate psychological research, modern science has listened to and verified the mysterious voice of the blood, weighed atoms, and set down figures—inconceivable to our minds—of billions and trillions of atoms contained in an invisible cell. In new, unforeseen forms, revealing some aspect of the unknown, science has wrought its spell. I do not believe that anybody who knows the history of magic iconography and can call to mind the figures of the ancient wizards, or has seen among the primitive peoples of India, Africa, and certain regions of South America—as has been my opportunity to see—the garments, costumes, and practices of persons performing magic acts, can fail to be impressed by the similarity of such forms to those created by modern life, and sometimes their identity.

The surgeon in his white gown, the chemist who, protected by a metal and glass mask, works with dangerous substances, the physician who handles quartz lamps and treats patients with red or ultra-violet rays, the radiologist with his gloves and leaden apron, the psychologist listening to his patient's account of his dreams, are modern visions which seem to have stepped out of an ancient magic picture book and would not be out of place there. How can this analogy be explained? We might say simply that it is due to the fact that in both ancient and modern cases it is a question of devices aimed at protecting the individual's life against well-known or partially known dangers. This statement is undoubtedly true. But if we admit, as we are forced to do, that the preponderant part of all that we consider and call scenic apparatus stems from the desire or the necessity for active suggestion, it is not altogether improbable that a necessary and unconscious suggestion partially contributes to the creating of the modern aspects referred to. A certain part of the success achieved by that suggestion consists in those vividly impressive devices. It is undeniable, at any rate, that they function not only as means of defence but also as incantational or magically suggestive means. Every psychologist knows that the atmosphere of an operating-room creates, from a psychological as well as from a clinical point of view, a special mood in both physicians and patients. This is undoubtedly one, and not the least important, reason why the surgeon feels perfectly safe in his operating-room and in his atmosphere, and the patient enters it prepared for a miracle. It is, in fact, the expectation of the miracle that suggests faith in success, an essential element perhaps for recovery, and I refer but briefly here to the magic cures discussed more fully elsewhere in this book. If such cures are founded exclusively, or almost exclusively, on magic action, on incantational suggestion, one might say that suggestion plays a part in every cure. In his excellent book *The Miracle in Medicine*, Liek repeatedly points out this essential feature of magic, which exerts its action in thousands of ancient and new forms.

Modern science has partially or wholly inherited the magic idea, has admitted it under new forms, justified it, directed it according to the results of experience, classified and catalogued it, and successfully substituted faith in science for superstitions and magic beliefs. The diminutive, invisible demons which, according to the ancient Egyptians, entered the human body, caused illness, and had to be expelled by magic exorcisms have been imprisoned, coloured red or blue, covered with slabs of glass, and studied under the microscope. We have thus learned that they are the true cause of sickness and have discovered how to destroy them or make them harmless, by methods more reliable than magic practices, and we can now prevent them from entering the human body better than could the ancients by their amulets and talismans. Science has, to a great extent, solved the problem; in fact, for a time it seemed as if it had been completely and definitely solved. Recent research, however, has shown that there are other factors which cannot be coloured and are not completely verifiable, which have an important place in causing sickness as they have in all life emergencies: namely, the predisposition and the resistance capacity of the individual and of the group.

The sciences of today—chemistry, physics, biology, medicine, and lastly psychoanalysis—are slowly assuming a vitalistic trend, admitting, that is, the existence of a still imperfectly known vital force. Ancient theories, which seemed magic, concerning the influence of meteorological factors on the human body, the mixture of humours or the secretions of the different glands, the results of unsuspected chemical combinations taking place in the animal organism, are reappearing under new forms and with scientific justifications.

One of the most interesting and evident examples of collective suggestive influence, exercised according to ancient methods in a modern form, is that of moving pictures, which are truly magical. Lights, colours, music, and, above all—and this point is very important—the rapid rhythmical succession of pictures which arouse passions and stress hidden desires, obviously exert over crowds the identical suggestive action that we saw to be characteristic of magic practices of the ancient Aztecs and of Malay tribes. Moving pictures often cast a magic spell over the audience: they determine an exaltation of the spectators' emotional powers and abolish their critical faculties. This probably explains why, today, movies are in greater favour with the public than the legitimate stage. The play contains arguments and provokes discussion, and the actor on the stage appears on the same psychic plane as the spectator. Moving pictures, because of their mechanical, extraordinary character—this being the most important point—arouse less rational criticism. The theatre is human because theatricalness is an innate characteristic of human nature; the cinema appears superhuman to the person who obeys the unconscious. Although we know the factors that determine it, and know more or less how it functions, all of us who are not technicians must nevertheless make an effort, however slight, to realize exactly what the cinema is and what mechanical laws it obeys. The theatre appeals to reason and criticism; the cinema speaks more directly to emotions and leads them within the bounds of imaginary, possibly constructive adventures—those of the socially acceptable escapes.[1]

In general—and this seems to be one of the characteristics of our age and civilization—images are rapidly taking the place of words. Facts speak their efficacious and sometimes violent language by means of figures rather than narratives. Images created with great speed, launched through space, reproduced by procedures that allow the complete change of expression of a face, the aspect of a monument, or the significance of a fact, fill the pages of newspapers and take the place of daily news. The myth of images is substituted for that of words; and this represents, fundamentally, to the persons who understand, a return to the ancient magic idea, to that primitive mentality which thought and spoke in images and for which images symbolized exorcisms, prayers, invocations, and the letters of the alphabet. The American comics are evident proof of the success of images. If it were contended that

[1] An interesting example of individual suggestion, followed by mass suggestion, which can probably be ascribed to the moving pictures is the case of the boy Joseph Vitolo in the Bronx (New York City). In November 1945 the boy, who had attended the picture *The Song of Bernadette*, had visions in which the Virgin appeared to him on a rock for sixteen consecutive evenings, ordering him to erect a chapel in her honour and announcing that a spring of miraculous power would gush forth in the place. The eight-year-old boy, belonging to a poor Italian family, told his story to his relatives and neighbours, and great crowds began to flow to the place, amounting sometimes to thirty or forty thousand people. Among them were a great number of sick people, especially paralytics, who prayed for the miracle. Recovery succeeded in only one or two cases and seemed to be very doubtful. Finally, as the spring did not materialize, the boy reported that the Madonna had said to him she would no longer appear; but for a long time people continued to gather at the place, digging in the mud and hoping to find the promised spring.

photography guarantees the truth of the image, an easy reply would be that exactly the opposite occurs, and that the brilliant, able, and efficiently advertised practice known as *photomontage* bears the same relation to reality as did the ancient myths to the facts. In the modern *reportage* of the great American magazines, the actress or the athlete is presented in the same light as was the ancient warrior in epic poetry: in a different manner, naturally, because the methods of exercising suggestion over the masses are different.

The popular figure of Superman, which exercises a widespread fascination on the readers of American comics through his extraordinary and unlikely adventures, has a great analogy with the magic figure of ancient times and expresses the child's desire for escape from his work and everyday life. An interesting example of collective suggestion, with all symptoms of hysterical contagious manifestations, which attracts the attention of all observers of modern American life, is given by the pathologic demonstration of passionate interest in movie stars and some popular singers.

The whole mechanism of modern life represents this evolution of incantational practices and magic. Employing perfected technical means and a wider knowledge of vast and remote connections between cause and effect, modern life, in an epoch in which the telephone and the radio have replaced telepathy, and television has taken the place of divination, has substituted the technique of suggestive and violent advertising for the influence of ancient wizards. And in fact is it not with the aim of inducing a state of suggestion analogous to that deriving from magic practices or stupefying drugs that modern life acts through a gigantic collective suggestion over the public of great cities, illuminating the walls of houses and the roofs of buildings with bursts of resplendent and alternating light, flashing flaming letters in the no longer inviolate sky, and repeating political news, musical features, and commercial advertisements to millions of listeners? Do these methods not recall the great fires lighted by ancient wizards on the summits of hills, and the thousand lighting and musical effects employed as a powerful device by the magic of all times? The aim of reducing the critical power to a minimum, exciting the emotional faculties by a series of sensations repeated in rapid suggestions, is obviously identical and leads to new, sometimes pleasant, beneficial, but, because of the limitless extension, dangerous adventures of the mind.

XXVII

The Suggestion That Kills—
the Political Myths

WE know from the history of epidemics how contagious epidemics at times occur with frequency and unexpected violence, for reasons we are as yet unable to evaluate, whereas under other conditions, when immunity has been wisely induced or acquired, the same pathogenic factors engender only sporadic cases or easily conquered foci of infection. Similar occurrences take place in social and political life for reasons that, according to time, place, and counteracting provisions, bring about different results. The great adventures deriving from creative suggestions, within the limits of ethical laws governing the possibilities of social life, fecundate and renew ancient civilization, cause the blossoming of its offshoots, and determine a new intellectual and economic springtide. Destructive suggestions arrest progressive growth for a time and destroy most of the work accomplished and the treasures acquired. In both cases suggestion exerts an influence that may become strong enough to determine decisively the development of contagious collective manifestations.

In this brief analysis of the history of recent political and social events there is no intention of considering all cases that might be easily interpreted in this sense or of attempting an exhaustive and final examination. I shall merely choose a few of the most typical instances and emphasize some characteristic factors by which their course was shaped, paying particular attention to occurrences that eventuated in far-reaching and unexpected antisocial results. Many economic, social, and political factors, to which a considerable amount of study has already been devoted, went into the making of these events.

In the development of many of them mistakes in the evaluation of facts or the impulsive action of statesmen or leaders resulted in fatal or nearly fatal consequences. My purpose is not to retrace the history of events, but to ascertain the origins of some psychological factors which determined them, although they may not have been their primary cause. In epidemics of contagious disease, to mention an analogous example, the presence of a specific microbe is doubtless the primary cause, but this does not explain why under certain conditions such epidemics spread with greater or less speed or why the powers of defence and resistance function differently. The history of epidemics shows that knowledge of the facts, the growth of resistance, the creation of means of protection, the mustering of counteractive strength by the threatened organisms, not only determine the extent of contagion, but often result in the establishment of better and safer conditions of well-being.

Undoubtedly, in all the adventures of the collective mind, suggestion played a predominant role. The group mind, in its orientation and development, was determined by it. Nothing but constantly exerted suggestive influence could guide or lead it. The orientation of the collective mind may change under different conditions, losing its destructive and antisocial character and evincing constructive or metaphysical tendencies. The contrary may also occur. It is undeniable, however, that suggestion occupies a prominent place among the factors causing the most serious and tragic consequences for the group. Facts must be studied, and their importance and character assessed from a psychological viewpoint. Careful observation of the psychology of the individual, the mass, ethnic groups, and their reactions to suggestion explains many events and indicates how they can be prevented or counteracted. Observation of the world events of the beginning of the twentieth century from this viewpoint, with due consideration of the social, economic, and moral crises through which the world has passed and which historians, sociologists, and statesmen have fully studied and documented, may give us an insight into some of the multiple factors that laid the path for these adventures.

The first World War (1914–18) had consequences we may consider similar to those of the Black Death of the fourteenth century or of the Thirty Years' War: it threw the entire economic and social life of Europe into confusion. The war was accompanied and followed by all the phenomena and characteristics of serious social catastrophes: decline in birthrate, frequency of contagious diseases, uncertainty of new arrangements provisionally created, economic upsets, outbreak of violent conflicts between various nations and social classes, fantastic pursuit of a new high degree of well-being, desire for ferocious, unreasonable revenge against the supposed originators, accomplices, or scapegoats of the world-enveloping catastrophe, rapid spread of all forms of superstition and magic, profound mistrust of social, moral, and religious laws, and finally creation of a new political mythology, a mysticism of violence and collective terror, patterned, to a large extent, on ancient examples. In different countries affairs took a different course.

A characteristic factor, in this case as in those mentioned in the history of the previous adventures of the mind, was the appearance of wizards: local, national, or even international leaders or rulers who exerted a vast and profound suggestive influence and created the myth of their supernatural power.

In the United States, after the serious economic crisis that, for a time, threatened the established order, democracy—that is, freedom of thought, criticism, and action, based on universally accepted traditions, on unshakable foundations, and on the individual conviction of the absolute necessity for the American way of life—and, to a greater extent, the material well-being of the people, firmly convinced that chances of prosperity and success were always open, were the first and most reliable defences. The conviction and, in fact, certainty of an ineradicable right to the pursuit of happiness, even under the most serious and trying economic conditions, prevailed; the future always appeared in an optimistically rosy light. As a result, the Americans were always less susceptible to collective suggestion of any kind, and especially to any antisocial suggestion tending to overthrow the principle of constitutional liberty. Tendencies of this kind succeeded in asserting themselves to a limited degree only and were rapidly extinguished by public opinion, which unanimously rose against them in defence. They have certainly never represented, at least up until now, any serious danger. The collective adventures of the Ku Klux Klan, like the witch-hunts in Salem in the seventeenth century, or Negro lynchings, were undoubtedly serious episodes, but they never affected collective mentality deeply, nor decisively influenced common thought and action beyond the sections where they occurred. The sane and reasonably critical mentality of the citizenry, conscious of its rights and duties, has always reacted, more or less quickly, against such adventures.

Examination of some of the great adventures of the mind which constitute the most serious problem of the present epoch because of their threat to world peace prompts a classification of them into different groups. Let us first examine the events that have taken place in the Orient, inasmuch as the mentality of Eastern peoples evinces certain noteworthy common characteristics. In the second place, we shall consider developments in Russia, where the development of a new political myth is from many viewpoints remarkable. We shall subsequently take up the adventures of the mind in the Mediterranean countries, where secular tradition, the ethnic psychology and race-mixture have undoubtedly exerted a decisive influence over the adventures of the collective mind. Lastly we shall study the situation in Germany, which also presents certain clearly distinct features. I think that it will be easy to find an analogy between the adventures of the mind and their characteristics in the past and in the present time.

I. INDIA AND GANDHI

From the psychologist's viewpoint, no collective group, perhaps, deserves greater attention than India. No country seems to offer a clearer picture of the close relations between present and past, or to present a more definite example of the traditional tendencies of the mentality of a people, or prove with greater evidence how such mentality leads the group mind into characteristic developments and is open to the dominating influence of suggestion.

The social system that has existed in India for centuries was established by the clans of invaders who subjugated the natives and ensured their own power. They created a perfectly organized, closed society, strictly bound by a magic conception that forbade the individual to transgress the laws of the group to which he belonged. No other law in history, with the exception of those of primitive tribes, has been so rigid, and anybody who broke or attempted to break these bonds was immediately branded as an outlaw.

The history of India presents numberless illustrations of collective suggestion exerted by persons who knew how to win the devotion and the boundless faith of the masses. The widely accepted teaching of Buddha, the Enlightened One, overlaid but did not overcome the religious structure of Hinduism, and gave to the entire Indian mind a more decided inclination to metaphysical aspirations. The doctrine of the Enlightened One was in harmony with the way of thinking and of feeling and, we might almost say, with the physical constitution of the inhabitants of a country where the luminous atmosphere and a luxurious and almost fantastic vegetation, paralleled by an art assuming a thousand grotesque and strange forms, caused the inhabitants to be readily accessible and predisposed to suggestion. Given their metaphysical tendencies, the people were constantly dominated by ancient magic, with its beliefs, rites, practices, and countless symbols. The ancient conception of metempsychosis found expression in the doctrine of Buddha, advocating the annihilation of desire for the purpose of keeping life pure in all its incarnations, and met with general acceptance. The worship of all animals, each of which represented or could be made to represent a new incarnation of the spirit, endowed the life of the Hindu people with a characteristic note. The cow, the Hindu totem, became the symbol of fecundation and fertility and was considered to be the mother of the race. This is a new form of the ancient worship of the Dea Mater, the Mother Goddess, common to all agricultural and pastoral tribes.

The magic law of taboo found a synthetic, decisive, and immutable expression in the universally accepted law establishing that a Brahman and in general a man belonging to a

superior caste may not be touched by, or even placed in contact with, the shadow of an individual belonging to another
social class. The laws prohibiting certain foods, the prescriptions of frequent baths to be taken according to set rites, the
rules for funerals and the cremation of corpses, all the fatalis-
tic attitude of the Hindu toward death, belong to the magic
world of the primitives. Infidels in India are prohibited from
access to sacred places, and there exists a widespread belief in
amulets and talismans and in the magic power of names.

If, in judging the recent situation in India, we keep these
ideas in mind, we can readily understand the suggestion exerted by Gandhi amidst such surroundings. Gandhi, like all
wizards, is the product of the earth from which he sprang and
of the people whose ancestral traditions he inherits, of environment and education. Humble and holy in his spiritual aspirations, which transcend all earthly interests, he wields a
power deriving from an exceptional personality. He has created or adopted all the symbols of the soil: the peasant's manual labour and clothing, the loom, the spade, and the hoe. He
has proclaimed the fundamentally ethical principle of *Satya-
graya*, the power of the soul, which is expressed in his longing
for a calm life and in his passive resistance to all obstacles and
threats. Like all rulers of this kind, he is fully and sincerely
convinced that he is always right. He has succeeded in stand-
ardizing the mind of his followers, abolishing every form of
freedom of action and criticism, though permitting freedom
of speech and discussion. We saw in the history of magic that
the wizard obtains power by assuming various garments and
aspects: the devil's clothing, the masks of frightening animals,
a grotesque appearance, and even, as in the case of Girolamo
Savonarola, the behaviour, the garb, and the aspect of the an-
chorite, in accordance with the individual's inward thoughts.
The masses feel the suggestion stemming from the sensation
of contact with a being who appears to be superhuman because he is capable of things that no other person can accomplish. The deep faith that animates his actions and words, his
long fastings, constant prayers, and insistence on leading a
life directed to a single ideal purpose of purity overmaster the
collective mind. Whoever has seen crowds following Gan-

F. A. Mesmer. Portrait by Jules Poireau (1849)

Rasputin and his adepts at the court of the Czar

dhi's guidance in blind, devoted, and ecstatic obedience can understand that the suggestion exerted by him is essentially in harmony with the traditions and tendencies of his people. There is perhaps no other example of such profound and intimate compliance with the word of a leader who has been capable of appealing to all the emotions and instincts of the unconscious as well as to the love of the soil and the country. Perhaps nothing impresses witnesses of the great demonstrations of perfect obedience aroused by his words more than the fact that the Hindu crowd never shouts, applauds, or makes an untoward gesture of assent.

Gandhi has created around himself an organized and closed society possessing all the characteristics, laws, and functions of the ancient secret societies. His society is more important than a political party, no matter how large and powerful. Only members of his group of faithful followers can obtain a commanding position in the political or economic life of the nation; no one can count on his support for the purpose of gaining the smallest personal advantage. The contempt that Gandhi feels and shows for all forms of violence as well as for all forms of material well-being is one of the fundamental factors of his success. The religious and mystical adventure stemming from the Indian mentality, has developed into a political adventure to which Gandhi has given direction without, however, relinquishing or changing its character. The political trend may be summed up in the essential postulate of complete political liberty for the Hindu nation: the sole weapon is passive resistance, without any attempt at economic prosperity or individual independence. In reality this postulate is but a superstructure, needed to satisfy the aspirations of the intellectuals who have absorbed some of the directing ideas of Occidental civilization. The overwhelming majority of the Hindus have no political aspirations or understanding other than those suggested by their leader. India's is, therefore, a characteristic example of a great collective adventure of the mind developing in an extremely favourable soil, thanks to the contagion of a mystical suggestion. Everything was in preparation for such an adventure; the tropical climate, the history of events, the unceasing invasions of foreigners, prepared the surroundings for this metaphysical and fantastic orientation, according to which life has no end, but changes form and seat with the forward march of time.

2. JAPAN AND SECRET SOCIETIES

The adventure of the Japanese mind is in many respects analogous to that of the Hindu. In both cases the starting-point is the same: an invading ethnic group enslaved the first inhabitants of the country. In both cases rigid stable patterns of absolute domination were established, and both peoples possess the same kind of magic and religious ideas. In both India and Japan Buddhism played a notable role; in both, the influence of Occidental civilization or of the interests of stronger and better-armed nations attempted to throw open the closed gates of intellectual, social, and economic life. Nevertheless, the results were different. In both India and Japan the foreign impositions were accepted to only a slight degree, and with reluctance: India and Japan never absorbed the culture and ideas of the Occident. But whereas Japan, with an extremely practical spirit of self-adjustment, adopted all the practical teachings of the Occident, preserving at the same time an intense hatred of foreigners, India did not even accept the practical consequences of Western economic postulates and resisted them in a passive way alone. The reason for this difference between the two countries may lie in the different development of events (in India European penetration was of long duration, aggressive, systematic, persistent, methodical, and economically helpful; in Japan it was episodic, peaceable, and frankly egoistical), and perhaps in the fact that India has always been subjected to foreign influences and continuously invaded, whereas Japan was for centuries the closed possession of a single dominating race. Events undoubtedly show how, originating from the same starting-point, the adventure of the mind unfolds, in dissimilar cases, in opposite directions. It is harder to understand why, whereas the Indian mentality always appears clearly comprehensible to European scholars and statesmen, the Japanese mind has been ill or not at all understood. This is perhaps due to the fact that India offered to foreigners a glorious, partly legendary history, a magnificent literature, a fascinating art, the suggestion of her epic poetry, her mystical legends, her original, fascinating philosophy. The path to an understanding of India's glorious past and of her mind was therefore open to everybody who possessed the necessary comprehension.

Japan, little understood and barely known until a few years ago, even to statesmen and students of psychology, appealed to the Western world in a purely literary and romantic light, just as Italy did to the average American tourist. It seemed to be a country of poor men with simple and modest tastes, pervaded with a great, naïve religious faith, endowed with a fine artistic spirit which was highly prized in the Occident and prompted the whole world to a passionate love of Japanese etchings, ceramics, and bronzes, rather than to a scrutiny of the emotional and political tendencies of the inhabitants. Japan was a country of geishas and volcanoes, of cheap counterfeit wares, but also of delicate works of art, of simple, modest wooden houses, of men obsequious in their bows and childish phrases; a picturesque and delightful country, kind, and almost fabulous according to the descriptions in the books of of the nineteenth century. The picture of Japan that Europeans and Americans formed was a result of the superficial contacts they had had with Japanese in the Far East or in Europe and America. It was a conventional picture of a conventional race, inasmuch as the Japanese deliberately and obstinately made themselves inconspicuous and naïve, passing almost unobserved without arousing suspicion, visiting European schools, factories, and markets, copying again and again machinery and plants, scientific equipment and study-methods, armies and weapons, until they were able to produce unassisted the things they needed. They studied everywhere and learned the facts, not the spirit, perfectly, with incomparable diligence and profound accuracy. Above all, they learned the system of army organization in Germany, and the principles of the industrial and economic system in America. Japan's preparation was long and laborious and, above all, silent. The Japanese knew how to remain silent and to conceal their plans with a tenacity inexplicable to our mentality. This was perhaps the most singular and decisive feature of the whole complex Japanese organization created under the cloak of maximum secrecy, like an essentially and typically "initiatory" system. All Japanese were bound to it by rites of sacrifice and blood, from methodically cold-blooded assassination, prepared with complicated passionless calculations, to individual or collective suicide constituting the honourable end of the unsuccessful individual adventure and awaited fearlessly and practically without emotion. Japan, locked within the isolation (in this case the word truly denotes the fact) due to its geographic location, adopted the Chinese language and culture in order to forge its weapons and overcome and destroy China, just as it later adopted the inventions of Western civilization with the same long-term intentions.

Some extremely important factors, which may be learned from the history of Japanese religion, fall within this tendency of the collective mind. Toward the end of the sixth century B.C., in the epoch of the earliest man-Emperor, Buddhism was introduced to Japan, which had already felt the influence of Chinese civilization. But Japan accepted Buddhism in its ritual alone, not in its ethical concept. The Japanese gods of Shintoism became Buddhist saints or reincarnations of Buddha; the two rites were intermingled in what might be called a compromise, and Buddha and the national gods were worshipped in common temples. When, in 1809, the Shoguns, or feudal lords, grasped power, the concept of Japanese racial superiority began openly to assert itself, and Shintoism was proclaimed the religion of the Imperial house and of the State; Buddhism was ostracized. The deification of the Emperor, the symbol of the Empire, assumed a definite religious and political character. Thus, while in an earlier period the imitation of a superior civilization dominated the country, and its literature and religion were accepted, Japan slowly returned to her ancient beliefs and to faith in her racial superiority. The episode of Buddhism bore a similarity to that of the apparent absorption of Occidental civilization in the nineteenth century; neither the one nor the other left any essential traces in the Japanese mind. In the victorious religious and political myth the Emperor became, and remained, the eternal symbol; and the Empire grew to be considered the beginning and end of national life, destined to conquer and master the entire world. The Japanese people were proclaimed the most ancient and glorious race, being the only dynasty to reign uninterruptedly for thousands of years as a direct descendant of the Sun, and hence the only one directly to inherit and perpetuate its power without outside authority.

With the first appearance of American ships in Japanese waters in 1853, when Western civilization by armed force broke Japanese isolation, which was unique in history, systematic preparation for revenge began and was continued without interruption. Revolutions took place in Japan, but they always had the same purpose: the defence of the past against the future, the maintenance and strengthening of the basic system, the ancestral law of ancestor-worship, respect for sacred and inviolable national traditions, and fanatical devotion to the Emperor.

The rebellion of 1868, with the abolition of the shogunate and the apparent stabilization of a new political order, according to which the Emperor is the centre and life itself of the nation, was in reality but the new guise under which the ancient belief assumed the dignity of a final and absolute religion. Such religion was, according to the believers' program, universal and set up the justification of violence as a principle. The acceptance of a constitution and of a semblance of a parliamentary regime were new steps toward political adjustment; in reality, however, nothing but the façade of the political structure was changed. The decision that representatives of military power in the Cabinet must be preponderant in all deliberations made the Government the pawn of a military group. Government officials were forced to bend to the will of the representatives of the Army leaders, especially in matters of foreign policy.

The preparation and development of the Japanese mind, from Emperor to soldier, from banker to peasant, for the totalitarian adventure was founded on unshakable and absolute faith in the superiority of the Japanese race, religion, Army, and State over all like institutions in other countries and times. The dogmatic dominant principle is identical to that proclaimed by Ymmu Tenno, the first "man-Emperor," the classic type of national hero. Schools, popular literature, legends, and the theatre extol sacrifice to the Emperor as the absolute duty of every citizen. In the atmosphere created by this totalitarian doctrine, over which no foreign influence had any power, the conviction naturally was formed that Japan should dominate first Asia and then the world, and this has been the central idea of Japanese policy for almost a century. Statesmen and philosophers made individual attempts to defend the ideas of peace, justice, and political liberty, but they failed. Many of them were assassinated, and their murderers were exalted as national heroes and escaped unpunished.

Japan's foreign policy developed simultaneously with that of the Germany of Bismarck. In 1894 Japan conquered Formosa; in 1904 she invaded Korea, the intended springboard for the conquest of Asia. The Japanese Government had, originally, requested only the right of passage for Japanese troops across Korea, and guaranteed Korean independence in a solemn treaty. This treaty was broken in 1910 with the annexation of the entire peninsula, followed by the suppression of its language, culture, agriculture, and commerce. The rule of the Japanese super-race was openly proclaimed and thousands of Koreans were imprisoned or shot. After the victorious war against Manchuria, parts of that country were annexed, and in 1918, after the first World War, Japan occupied the Pacific islands which had belonged to Germany and which, according to the Japanese plan, were cleverly considered as outposts of a final conquest in a new World War. In 1931 Manchuria was entirely occupied and a fictitious state was created with a puppet emperor intended to exemplify the enticing promise of Asiatic states independently governed, though in reality tightly bound to the Empire.

The war of conquest against China, announced as a program of Pan-Asiatic solidarity and prosperity, was the inevitable consequence. With an exact plan, perfect awareness of her aims, and complete conviction of success, Japan proceeded from victory to victory.

It is evident that Japan followed the German master, outdoing him in intensity of work and absolute silence. This is attested by the complete absence of criticism and, with few

exceptions, of every independent individual expression of
opinion, by the destruction, through swift and decisive assassination organized on a vast scale, of all opposition, and finally by the necessary conclusion of the program, the great
adventure of war, the logical and necessary consequence of a
consuming, century-old suggestion, the aim pursued throughout a systematic evolution along the same lines. The adventure became the expression of a well-established mentality.
Suggestion having reached its maximum development thanks
to exceptionally favourable conditions, was now directed toward a single purpose; domination by the super-race. The
group-leaders, especially the military leaders, who were
through centuries the greatest promoters of the system,
brought their aim to fulfilment, creating absolute totalitarian
obedience beyond life and death. The will to power was transferred from the individual to the State or to the Emperor, who
personifies the State, and traces back to the forebears, symbolizing in a perpetual continuity the glorious destiny of Japan.
Joy of life, desire for pleasure, the pursuit of happiness are
suppressed, and nothing remains but attachment to the fate
of family and nation. Woman in Japan is nothing but the
servant of her husband, and the mother, whose sole function,
as in primitive clans, is that of procreating soldiers who will
fight for the ruling and omnipotent Empire.

The atmosphere, a prime factor in the development of collective suggestion, was exceptionally propitious; the Oriental
mentality is traditionally respectful of ancestors and paternalism. The entire nation, locked in a group of islands where
no foreign influence has ever been able to get a foothold and
where no immigration and no mixture of races has ever occurred, has kept and developed its collective mind along lines
conforming to traditions. The Greek islands, open to all the
influences and currents of trade and thought of the entire
Mediterranean, created a universal civilization in the Ægean, a
matrix of all the major creative actions and achievements in
all fields of intellect. The Japanese islands, hermetically
sealed, have been the scene of a hothouse blossoming, of a
fantastic, gigantic, and malevolent efflorescence culminating
in a destructive adventure. Japan is perhaps the sole example

in history of thought-processes that have developed in a tightly closed atmosphere impervious to other nations. The characteristics of insular mentality to be found in the primitive groups of the Pacific islands and, through the course of history, in barely accessible islands such as Australia and Sardinia and, to a much lesser degree, in islands along the great lines of trade, like Sicily, have undergone their maximum development in Japan.

The origins and history of the Japanese adventure evince all the typical traits of the antisocial adventures that tended to create political structures contrary to the rules of law sanctioned by the religions, ethics, and philosophies of the Occident. In the insular environment all the instinctive primordial tendencies of the unconscious have developed unchecked, a condition that appears to us as a collective psychosis. The myth of the divine and eternal rule of the Son of the Sun, patterned after the solar myths common to all racial groups of prehistorical times, has crystallized into a totemistic dogma. The power of the leader of the tribe, clan, and nation was integrated into the permanent suggestion of religious and political leaders; secret societies in which fanatics constantly rekindled the flame of their faith were formed. To mention only the most famous of the many secret societies of Japan, the Black Dragon Society was inspired by Mitsui Tojama, whose influence is revealed in a series of premeditated assassinations performed according to an inflexible program. Mitsui Tojama, a Councillor of the Emperor, is still surrounded by the admiration of the people. Every day he devotedly worships his ancestors before his domestic altar. The ancient mythical belief in survival after death, which, as we saw, is common to all racial groups, has created ancestor-worship and sanctioned the law of revenge against all ancient and contemporary enemies of the Emperor and the State. This law is kept intact with unquestionable loyalty and is firmly rooted in the minds of the people. The myth of the universal destiny of Japan and of its historical mission to dominate all other peoples stems from this principle.

Mythical symbolism, another characteristic of ancient magic, survives in Japan as it does in no other country in our time; the Emperor God is a man and the accepted symbol of political and religious faith. In the name of this symbolism, human sacrifice, practised in ancient primitive religions as the most welcome sacrifice to the supreme deity, is revived. Death becomes a symbol of faith and suicide; the *harakiri* is the climax of honourably performed duty, of the voluntary sacrifice of the individual who has been unsuccessful in definitely demonstrating his loyalty. Finally, the Japanese language itself is still symbolical; symbolism determines not only its ideograms (attempts to introduce the Latin alphabet were consistently repulsed), but the construction of the language. Accent or intonation are sufficient to change the meaning of a word completely, so that even the language itself is closed to foreigners in its secret significance.

The Japanese world, like the world of the ancients locked within the magic circle, is completely dominated by the belief that the supernatural has a part in everyday life. The supernatural is accepted without discussion by scientist and philosopher, statesman, soldier, and peasant. The ancestors live on and every Japanese is convinced that his own life continues in his sons for endless centuries by a magic and fantastic plan. The Japanese societies prove the truth of the statement that the activities of the mind of past generations influence the manifestations of the collective mind of today, and that every society is composed of both the dead and the living. They show the active prestige of the dead predominating over the living, or, in psychoanalytical terms, the domination of the unconscious over the conscious ego.

It still remains to be discovered what role the suggester, the leader, or wizard plays in this gigantic collective suggestion. His presence in Japanese history is undoubtedly as important as it was in the past and present adventures we have studied. It is much harder to identify the suggester in this case, however, inasmuch as in the complex Japanese system the suggester is constantly masked, like the actors on the Japanese stage. The personality of the wizard is hidden, and the work that he accomplishes is attributed to the symbol, the Emperor or the ancestors; the mind, educated in closed groups and according to secret rules, tends to shun open and clearly intelligible actions and to make identification difficult or impossible. The suggestion actually originates in a group of suggestive factors, symbols or persons, groups or castes. Only a knowledge of the intimate history of secret societies can reveal the identity of the greatest suggesters, as those already generally known are doubtless among the least important. This loss of responsible individuality in the mystical twilight of political religion, which, in all its particulars, constitutes the best-organized magic structure, is typically Oriental. The totalitarian response of the Japanese people to such a continuous suggestion may be attributed to its being exercised over a perfectly organized mass. It was mainly due to the Army, which was created by this suggestion and has lived by it. In Germany the Army was firmly organized first by Prussia and later by Nazism. Conflicts occurred between the mentality of the Army and that of the Führer; the echoes of these conflicts have not yet died away and may be observed in many events of the last decade. In Japan, on the other hand, the Army definitely adopted the myth without open reluctance; and from the Army, thanks to the secret societies organized with the same stern discipline, it spread bit by bit, so that every citizen, from the time of his birth on, belonged to the Army and was firmly bound to it.

In Japan the episodes of violent individual and group rebellions, like the famous officers' revolt, were expressions of the will, or of the need, for the complete domination of the Army, of a more immediately violent action. The trials of the plotters, which were given the greatest publicity, the accused being allowed to express their ideas in long and impassioned speeches, aroused a new wave of popular emotion which led to a greater collective suggestion. Thousands upon thousands of persons manifested their solidarity with the accused by violent demonstrations and suicide, thereby making their condemnation impossible. Constant reciprocal suggestion succeeded in maintaining a close solidarity and uninterrupted continuity in the trends of the collective mind. Under these conditions the success of Nazism—another political myth whose immediate development appeared in agreement with this trend—was the opportunely chosen starting-point for the decisive issuing of the popular movement into war.

The conventional manners and the obsequious smile with which the conquerors and their decisions are accepted today belong to the habitual and well-known picture of the Japanese and their external and superficial relations with people whose superiority is necessarily acknowledged. But this apparently quick and easy adjustment to the new situation certainly does not give any assurance for the future.

3. STALIN'S RUSSIA

Collective adventures of the same type, at least in their origins, are to be found in contemporary history; it is therefore logical to think that conditions of unrest and of economic and spiritual conflict have affected the whole world at different times and to different degrees. If the vast triumphant suggestion of Russian Communism resembles some of the great tragic adventures in its origin, it also, in its more recent development, has the characteristics of a reconstructive and creative adventure which, through serious mistakes and sufferings, and after the destruction of great values of the past, is creating a new order of things and a new mental orientation. Russian Communism stems from the atmosphere of depression and misery created by Czarist autocracy. It was animated by the spirit of revolt against the efforts of the ruling classes to bind people with the chains of absolute monarchy. Before its outbreak into social revolution Russian political and social life bore all the hallmarks of tragic absolutism, creating, as in other cases, "nihilism"—that is, a trend toward destruction. Cruel repressions, exile to Siberia, large-scale pogroms prepared and carried out by the Government or its followers, vast suggestion of revolutionary groups conspiring in silence, upheavals like that of 1904, which was smothered in blood and the futile attempts of the Government to create a purportedly parliamentary regime, and finally, during the first World War, the avalanche of superstitions and clearly magical phenomena such as the episode of Rasputin were the consequences. The need of a spiritual escape had found expression in the asceticism of Tolstoy and the pessimism of the great nineteenth-century writers. The social revolution of 1918 exploded with unheard-of violence and was the result of another cast of thought which upset the life of a vast country after a terrible war, in which the gulf between the classes became more manifest.

A severe dictatorship was established, with absolute control over the entire life of Russia, and with complete suppression of any independent thinking contrary to the leaders' will. The leaders set up a powerful machine and organized the GPU, which later changed name several times in succession but never lost its powerful hold over the country.

Slowly and with intelligent preparation, Russia developed with strong means a systematic reconstruction of economic and social life, keeping its political structure intact, but accepting certain programmatic institutions of the social order that had been destroyed. A new trend of thought and action was created under the influence of a powerful leader, and when it became evident that it would be necessary to defend this system, which had proved acceptable in spite of the difficulties of its establishment, against the hidden machinations of its enemy and the slow and difficult adjustments of agriculture and industry, every effort was directed toward a wise reorganization, systematically planned and rigorously carried to a finish, in the fields of industry, economics, and science. Then a decisive evolution took place: Russia witnessed the creation of a new and perfectly organized Army, the rearrangement of the administrative system, the swift and efficient development of industry, the gradual and vast increase of scientific production, especially in the domain of experimental research, the rapid spread of popular culture, accompanied by a revival of individualism and an extraordinary efflorescence of science, literature, and art. There was an efficient appeal and a gradual return to the deepest, never eradicated emotional tendencies of the Russian mind: love of the soil, passionate attachment to the home, mystic traditional belief. The external threat of Nazism was apparently aimed at the social system, viewed as a serious menace to the hoped-for future of Nazism. German armies invaded the country, attempting to destroy the established order and to annihilate the recent conquests, threatening the soil of ancient Russia, and thus arousing all the emotional passions of the Russian people in an outburst of defence. It was then that a unanimous and heroic effort united all the forces of the people in a supreme will to defeat the invaders. This is undoubtedly the psychological explanation for the behaviour of the Russian nation—Army, labourers, peasants, women, and children—during the war. The world was astounded by this phenomenon, which came as a surprise, especially to those who did not believe that a wise and far-seeing political and industrial organization, both strengthening and arousing a great outburst of heroism, could produce such results and lead to such an outstanding success.

In the basic directives of Russian policy such striking changes have occurred that it seems difficult to identify the principles that rule the Russia of today with those of 1919. A new and deliberate effort to foster national consciousness is evident, and the consequences of this effort are clear. We find in all official manifestations a stress on the importance of patriotism and on the duty and privilege of all Soviet citizens to fight for their fatherland. The new Soviet Constitution of 1936 was a decisive step toward national union, and five years of war have emphasized a progression toward nationalism and patriotic duty. We may therefore assume that the tendency of the collective mind in Russia, under the mighty, suggestive leadership of Stalin and under the influence of political circumstances, has been to renounce or at least postpone international propaganda of communistic doctrines. The fundamental principles of Communism have not been abandoned in organizing the whole power, both political and economic, under the State; power remains in the hands of the rulers, but the emphasis is no longer placed on the worker, but on the citizen, no longer exclusively on the defence of the rights of the people, but on the defence of the soil and of the power of the country. That is one of the most fascinating examples of collective suggestion, which, starting from a destructive revolution, ended in the acceptance of a constructive and creative idea on a large and original basis.

Thus two great adventures, born, both of them, in an already prepared atmosphere, under the rule of the collective suggestion of a new order, developed in opposite directions. In Germany the Prussian spirit of militarism, blind worship of authority, faith in the fantastic predominance of the State over every form of life, prevailed, and the war was the necessary consequence. In Russia it was the critical spirit, born and strengthened through centuries of suffering, whose seeds germinated everywhere, that carried everything before it. The Russian experience shows that there is always, in the collective mind, a living element which, in spite of the heaviest destructions of ancient values, helps to re-establish a social order. The history of the Russian adventure emphasizes the constant influence exercised through a vast collective suggestion by revolutionary leaders and their ideologies.

The Russian adventure is not yet closed. The same facts that originated and guided its progress, and first the vast and deep suggestion by a mighty leader, are still playing a decisive role in the evolution of Russia and of its domestic and international politics. What part the Soviets, the prestige of which had a tremendous increase, will play in the organization of the peace and in the possibility of a new order is still a problem. Its solution is closely connected with the collective suggestion which is still permanent and with the reaction that it will create among other peoples. The impossibility of being well informed about the changes in the mind and in the decisions of those who are the leaders of this adventure, the scant knowledge of the factors that guide them, are the origin of the great uncertainty of the present political moment.

4. THE MEDITERRANEAN COUNTRIES

Let us now examine the trends that have developed in the Mediterranean countries and see what field for development the collective antisocial adventures found there. We know from history that the basic characteristic of the Mediterranean mind is a tendency toward the construction of philosophical, religious, social, and scientific systems. Three of the great religions of mankind were born on the banks of the Mediterranean; great philosophical systems were created by Mediter-

ranean men; for twenty centuries centres of scientific research
have flourished on the shores of the sea where all the great
battles of ideas, all the wars for trade and political forms, have
been fought. Races and tendencies were fused in the Mediterranean countries; the Mediterranean was the crucible of commerce and of ideas. Consequently all the adventures of the
mind have developed chiefly under the influence of a critical,
æsthetic, individualistic, and social spirit. I may also point out
another trait that seems to be important. Peoples endowed
with a sense of humour—that is, viewing events and persons
with the intuitive ability to perceive at once the incongruous
and comical, and exercising with full grasp this critical sense
without regard for authority or for the importance of the
things they are judging—have never been fertile ground for
destructive adventures. The critical mind has always expressed
its independence in a sense of humour, which is an escape in
the most serious situations. In France the excessive development of critical individualism, the widespread discontent engendered by a perhaps exaggerated love of physical comfort,
led the perplexed population into a state of permanent doubt,
of contagiously defeatist pessimism. But it is chiefly the economic struggle and the will of the politicians to gain and retain power that explains the lack of stable directives in French
policy, the succession of weak and wavering governments,
and the constant conflicts of individualistic passions and ambitions. The Gallic spirit, however, brought up in the ancient
traditions of the Revolution, critical and sceptical, represents
a safeguard against destructive adventures.

In Spain there was an extraordinary wave of organized
violence rather than of efficient collective suggestion. The
revolt against republican government, which was none too
firmly established, owing to the intellectual and political
temper of the country, ground down by centuries of absolute
monarchic, ecclesiastical, and aristocratic rule, was a *coup de
main* engineered by a dissatisfied military clique.

Spanish fascism was imposed by armed violence and with
foreign assistance on a disarmed people, disheartened by long
suffering. But nobody can ever feel justified in affirming that

the bloody events in Spain, which were the harbingers of the second World War, were the collective adventure of the mind of the Spanish people.

5. MUSSOLINI'S ITALY

In Italy the trend of events and the manner in which they developed came as a surprise to all persons familiar with Italian public life. The Italian people, like the Spanish, are susceptible to the theatrical, and inclined to accept emotionally the suggestions and extraordinary adventures which gain the upper hand because they are imposed by boldness of determination and carry with them a glamour of grandeur. This suggestibility, perhaps, originates in an inferiority complex which is partially the result of the conviction, strongly emphasized by Fascist suggestion, that Italy was never successful in encompassing her rights in the economic and political field or in obtaining her deserved place among European states. This is the heritage of centuries of suffering and poverty, persecutions, wars, and foreign rule; centuries during which Italians saw themselves regarded as a nation of barrel-organ players and tattered rag-pickers. Fascism appeared, in its early days, as a defence against the threat of bolshevism, as a protest against the injustices assertedly committed by the Versailles Treaty, and had the approval of all those who feared a new social revolution. Fascism was favoured by the supernationalism created by d'Annunzio and a flourishing nationalistic literature, and was welcomed by noisy more than by sincere manifestations of assent. But the temperate, sceptical, critical spirit of the Italians, a result of their climatic and cultural environment, of thousands of years of historical development, of the mental habit of viewing facts dispassionately, of correcting impulsive judgments and moderating emotionalism by criticism, created, soon after the first Fascist misdeeds, a full understanding of the threatening danger and gave rise to a widespread feeling of deep discontent. The theatrical and violent suggestion exerted by the Duce and his chiefs, the evocation of past splendours and the promise of unfailing future greatness, conquered the masses in the beginning. In Italy, however, people have never been susceptible to suggestions of national or racial hatred, and Fascism's clamorous suggestions of grandeur were received with great scepticism, with ironical smiles at the symbolical masquerades. In the beginning people were, perhaps, partly Fascist out of sentimentalism and an error in judgment; they accepted Fascism as a temporary phenomenon, a violent but efficient treatment of the crisis through which the country was labouring in an attempt to solve its serious problems. They thought that Fascism would quickly disappear or be compelled to remain within the bounds of the established order, obedient to ancient and opportunely revised laws. When people realized Fascism's real nature and fatal evolution it was too late. A rapidly established system of organized violence, backed by the support of all profiteers, the silence of all agnostics, and the deliberate suppression of all opponents, spawned terror as a system of government and accepted, perhaps going beyond the original program, the suggestions of Nazism, which Fascism had helped to create, undoubtedly without knowing that Nazism would overpower and dominate its early assistants.

Mussolini was no paranoiac, nor a great wizard; he was perfectly aware of his actions, often uncertain in his choice of allies, or vacillating in his decisions; his moves were performed with exact but erroneous calculation and dictated by an elastic and opportunistic judgment. Being an Italian and a lover of the theatric, he was extremely accessible to the suggestion of the crowd. He would have been equally willing to stage the so-called Fascist revolution in alliance with God or with the Devil, the Church or Masonry, Socialism or Conservatism, and undoubtedly would have preferred to be on the side of France and England rather than on that of Germany. He sought and found followers everywhere for his system of organization of the corporative type, reminiscent of the guilds of the Middle Ages. He spoke of heroic greatness and of necessary dictatorship. Fascism was supported by the dissatisfied, the dubious, and the wavering; it was these who were, or believed they were, the promoters of great economic and industrial achievements, and they were joined by a motley crowd of individuals longing for adventure and contemptuous of the laws, by the violent and the exceedingly weak. Bourgeoisie and labour were subjected to the imposition of Fascist directives through threats and promises. A vast suggestion was exerted over all social classes, and the new doctrine was imposed on the schools, where the ultimate triumph of power and the mysticism of violence were taught, creating, after the pattern of the often falsified teachings of Nietzsche, Sorel, and Pareto, the new theory of the ruling Fascist State and of the super-nation transfigured by the myth of ancient and new greatness. Italy, the majority of whose citizens are intelligently critical, submitted to the fascist laws without an open rebellion (which appeared impossible), but with the greatest mental reservations and with a continuous, often heroic opposition. Fascism, because of the circumstances under which it was born and the extreme violence with which it was imposed, was sometimes accepted by the crowds unwillingly as a symbol and a banner, but it was never an adventure of the Italian spirit. Fascism was undoubtedly an incident of collective suggestion, but it was episodic and temporary and never led the people to deeds of cruel violence or bloody revenge, which were due only to the fanatical supporters of Mussolini. It was a noisy and grotesque theatrical performance, full of spectacular promises of a future political glory and economic prosperity. The Italians, having experienced but fifty years of liberty, waited, applauding meanwhile the great scenes, the apparent successes of re-established order, which, for that matter, won the unconditional applause of expert foreign statesmen as well. These facts originated or strengthened a fascist current in France, England, and America and elicited open statements of sympathy for Fascism or enlisted the practical support of these governments, manifested by a tacit and often by a decisive approval.

In Italy, however, the reaction of the people was always marked by profound scepticism, and the many individuals who asserted their anti-Fascist faith and their open opposition to the regime were persecuted, threatened, beaten to death, or locked up in concentration camps or jails. They were the courageous exponents of the sanest and most active public opinion of the country. Fascism's political adversaries, particularly teachers who were excluded from schools, and writers who, like Croce, remained firm in their critical attitude, won the too often silent but sometimes unqualified and open approval of intellectuals and thinkers. Only those—and there was quite a number of them—who owed or believed they owed their economic security and the satisfaction of their political ambitions to Fascism, and who hoped for greater personal advantages from the regime, were its out-and-out supporters. Soon they were joined by a part of the Italian youth who had grown up and received their education in the Fascist environment, to the constant sound of a suggestive propaganda and with the almost daily spectacle of party meetings and rallies of supporters, indoctrinated with the metaphysical theories preached by the Fascist "school of political mysticism." The difference between the reactions of a homogeneous and a non-homogeneous crowd is that the latter is less open to suggestion because in it individualism is not suppressed, whereas in a homogeneous crowd response to suggestion is easier, quicker, and more violent on account of the emotional or artificial bond that ties the single units of the crowd.

The Italian masses have never been tightly organized because in them criticism could never be suppressed, just as the individualism of the Mediterranean man could never be quelled. Full awareness of individual dignity was never abolished, though it may have been disguised under a black shirt. For this reason the masses were sensitive to collective suggestion only as long as Fascism appeared a creative and co-ordinating force. It was passively accepted by the Italian people. The only enthusiastic supporters it had among the people were the youngsters who had been poisoned by Fascist teaching and by military rallies. When the course of events became openly violent and constricting and the most harmless criticism was severely suppressed and historical teachings falsified, Fascism no longer enjoyed the consent of the intelligent public. It was this same, essentially critical and æsthetic temper that, even when its manifestations were theatrical, brought about the two great historical events of Italian national life, the Renaissance and the Risorgimento, which caused them to unfold without iconoclastic violence and destruction, and respectfully to preserve the monuments of the past and Italy's historical traditions. Witch trials were rare in Italy; psychic epidemics were slight local phenomena of short duration. The Renaissance's great fight for freedom of thought and for a new political order was won by scientists, critics, and historians, but to a much greater extent by the collective mind of the Italian people, unfalteringly drawn toward the new creative adventure.

The Risorgimento—that is, the nation's great contest for political, economic, and social freedom—was won primarily by an intellectual and emotional preparation of long standing, guided by men of great faith rather than by heroic struggles on the battlefield. The leaders at that time were so assured in their guidance of the collective mind and the ardent passions of this rational people that they neither drew their co-nationals nor allowed themselves to be drawn into manifestations of factional hatred.

The criminal leaders who destroyed Italy's moral and economic power and were guided by boundless desire of might may have inspired terror, but never acceptance of their doctrines. They were definitely condemned by public opinion long before the military defeat of Fascism. The heroic silent struggle of the underground culminated in the brave fight of the partisan, and the successful uprising of the people against all the enemies of liberty.

6. HITLER'S GERMANY

The development of Nazism in Germany is closely connected with the history of the past. The Reformation, bringing in its wake the frightful Thirty Years' War, with its explosions of violent hatreds and cruel persecutions, destroyed not only hundreds of thousands of human lives but inestimable treasures of the past as well. The reconstruction, in a Germany impregnated with feudalism, progressed slowly and chiefly under the influence of the Latin nations. Neither Occidental philosophical currents nor poetic and literary influences left any deep traces in the German mind. The adventure of Nazism marked a decidedly fatal turning-point. It is hardly necessary to repeat the well-known observations concerning the social conditions of a Germany oppressed by Prussian

Junkerism, the intellectual crisis of pessimism undergone by German philosophy, and the emergence of a new metaphysics of violence, subsequent to the postwar economic conditions. The German Republic was too weak to maintain democratic liberty in the face of the oppposition put up by the mentality of the German people themselves, accustomed to military discipline, collective obedience, and to blind faith in an unbending system. The suggestion created by the enormous number of discontented and disillusioned individuals after the war, and by the misery that prevailed, found vent in the new political and social system of Nazism. Since then the structure of Germany and the collective mind of her people have undoubtedly been a threat to peace and civilization. The part that literature, the theatre, clubs of every description and particularly student and athletic clubs, and school teaching have played in the creation of the typical mentality of the dominant race is a matter of record. Richard M. Brickner in his book *Is Germany Incurable?* has illustrated the factors co-operating in the formation of what he calls the paranoidal state of Germany. With many clinical and historical examples he tried to point out the presence of characteristic symptoms of paranoia such as megalomania, persecution mania, systematic mendacity, in the great majority of Germans, asserting that these paranoidal tendencies developed independently of, and long before, Hitler's coming to power. All historians and intelligent observers of recent events agree, however, that such tendencies originated partly in the events and suggestions mentioned, which have been thoroughly analysed by various writers. But, before Hitler this tendency, or aggregate of tendencies, was limited to single groups: the Army, Prussian aristocracy, Pan-German associations, anti-Semitic groups, and so on; and such groups were opposed by others which arose to combat them successfully. The definitely new note of Nazism was the unitary political trend, the compulsory organization of a society solidly massed around the Leader, and the programmatic, efficient systematization of propaganda and action. The rights of the State over the individual were categorically affirmed: the State, identified with the super-race,

assumed the almost deified functions of a superhuman individuality, and the entire political myth of the super-state
crystallized into dogma.

This orientation of the German mind was perhaps never
understood and expressed with greater clarity than in the
prophetic words of the exile Heinrich Heine, who had such a
profound knowledge of the German people's mind. He wrote
in 1843:

> "Christianity has—and that is its fairest merit—somewhat miti-
> gated the brutal German lust for battle. But it could not destroy
> it: and once the taming talisman, the Cross, is broken, the savagery
> of the old warriors, the insane berserk rage sung by Nordic bards,
> will flare up again. That talisman is brittle. The day will come
> when it will pitiably collapse. Then the old stone gods shall rise
> from the forgotten rubble and rub from their eyes the dust of a
> thousand years; Thor will leap up and his giant hammer start
> smashing Gothic cathedrals. . . . And when you hear a crash
> the like of which was never heard in world history, you'll know
> that the German thunder has finally hit the mark. . . .
>
> "A show will be performed in Germany that will make the
> French Revolution seem like a harmless idyll in comparison. . . .
> You have more to fear from a liberated Germany than from the
> whole Holy Alliance with all its Croats and Cossacks."

Whoever is familiar with the history of Nazism and recalls
the typical traits of the great tragic collective adventures of
the mind will acknowledge the truth of Heine's words. Never
in the history of these adventures has collective suggestion
conquered and overmastered, directly or indirectly, a whole
people; it is therefore clear that when we speak of the adventure of Nazism we do not mean or fancy that it was longed for
by the whole German people or even by an overwhelming
majority of them. But, as is usually the case in all contagious
diseases, there are various degrees of infection and the compass
of spread of the disease varies. In a great epidemic, even if
every single person is not stricken by manifest symptoms of
the disease, all individuals feel its direct or indirect consequences; there undoubtedly are disease-carriers who spread it
without sharing any symptoms, but mark that all contagion
occurs more easily, quickly, and on a vaster scale today than

in the past, since contacts are more immediate and easier and, in fact, inevitable. The natural protection of city walls and distance and a sufficient allotment of time necessary to overcome the danger no longer exist.

But just as in great epidemics a part of the population is not attacked by disease, thus, undoubtedly, liberal, democratic, republican, or socialist prewar Germany, and, above all, reasonable and honest Germany, still lives in the thoughts, faith, and hopes of a great number of its inhabitants who sternly judge and condemn the evils of Nazism. The domineering arrogance and violence due to triumphant technical progress, supplying new weapons and means of propaganda, and the organization of the police, which were all perfected in Germany as is every institution subject to a severe and disciplined surveillance, have overthrown all obstacles and killed, jailed, exiled, or crippled all its enemies. The progressive phases cleverly arranged for the great adventure explain the origin and success of the enormous collective suggestion of Nazism, but likewise predetermined its necessary failure.

The environment was prepared by the diffusion of the new racial myth, the military organization of compact groups bound by initiatory formulas and the secret, and by the employment of the brown shirt, which became symbolical. The tune was set by lavish and constant use of all known suggestive devices, mummeries and military music, flamboyant proclamations, incendiary words, generous promises of a glorious future. The mystic and Aryan symbol of the swastika dominated everything: the mirage of *Lebensraum* and the prestige of all the classic slogans: *Unser Führer, Ein Volk Ein Führer, Kraft durch Freude, Juda Verrecke,* and many others; the acceptance of the book *Mein Kampf* as a gospel; the exaltation of martyrs or alleged martyrs, a title given to roughneck criminals who perpetrated Nazi violence; the ferocious propaganda of hatred and destruction, the systematic murder and sadistic torture of hundreds of thousands of Jews, directed by a clever insight into the exploitation of the hatred of the masses for rich people and intellectuals, of their thirst for pillage and craving for a chance (which they were quick to seize) of looting the property of private citizens, bank deposits, and the holdings of great firms which were said to be controlled by the enemy or by persons who were so represented. All this was insisted upon day after day by an intelligently, perfectly organized propaganda of words and of facts, at times apparently restrained, but always springing up with new intensity under one pretext or another. The entire Nazi system represents the perfection of violent, systematic propaganda and of organized discipline and blind obedience. The historical novelty consists in the fact that all the modern benefits of science and of organizational technique were systematically applied for the first time with inflexible methodicalness and maximum energy. This system had already been tried out experimentally and had ensured the success of German industry and the national commercial life, scientific research, and teaching. Directed toward an irrational and destructive purpose, it enabled Nazism to achieve its greatest triumphs and guaranteed that the Führer's will would be put into effect down to the most minute details. Thus the deeds of violence that episodically punctuated the history of the past were accepted as the foundations of a system of government, and the principles of dictatorship were tricked out in the taboo garb of intangibility. The adventure born in surroundings of depression and of postwar economic and moral crisis developed under the systematic and violent suggestion of a paranoiac and his criminal followers, and established a new State law, with the manifest tendency to rule as a universal sanction dictated by a dominating will brooking no restraint.

The Christian religion was openly opposed and was forced to make room for the new deification of the Führer; moral laws had to yield to State law; criticism was no longer permitted, even in science. The fundamental difference between the Nazi adventure and all previous ones is that Nazism was able to carry out the results of a vast practical experience, of unsurpassed technical progress, and of a cleverly mechanized preparation which placed the most nearly perfect and dangerous of all weapons in the hands of a hallucinated leader. Great crowds marshalled in compact organization stalked on the stage with Nazism; the suggestion of the Führer was exerted amid these surroundings, which differ from others not in their fundamental make-up but in the perfection of the Nazi system, the tremendous resources at its command, the weapons supporting it, and the masterly fashion in which it functioned.

Let us examine the personality and influence of the Leader, who may, without question, be considered as a type of wizard. He was convinced that he was always right, like all paranoiacs and megalomaniacs. He was a man of mediocre intelligence, and therefore perfectly sure of himself because no doubts or criticisms of his own actions troubled him. Animated by the desire for revenge, in order to compensate for the frustration of his impoverished childhood and mediocre youth, as well as for the lack of recognition of the merits he fancied he possessed, an impassioned, repetitious orator, doing to death his repertoire of aggressive phases, for ever dischanting on his program of Germanic superiority, world conquest, hatred, and destruction; a liar on principle, he claimed in his book, the gospel of the Germanic people, that people have to be deceived, and stated that the bigger the lie, the more easily it is believed. The evoker of legends, stories, and slogans, of a remote past, of the Holy Roman Empire, and of the heroic deeds of the Teutons, the Führer constantly belittled and calumniated all the achievements of his predecessors in government, poured contempt on the culture of all other nations, on the accomplishments of all epochs in literature and science which were used for purposes foreign to his aims. The architect of a fantastic structure of hatred, the man who planned the burning of the Reichstag, Röhm's killing, the pogroms against the Jews carried out as a sadistic, ferocious, pitiless plan, the Führer expressed his program of homicidal elimination, of systematic annihilation of all the enemies of Nazism wherever they may exist, in the destruction of Poland, the slayings in Russia, Italy, and France, and the suppression of all opposition—nay, of any form of independent life—in occupied countries. By these methods and the terror deriving from them and from threats he created a collective intoxication with violence to which only men who despised their own lives or dared to continue the struggle in silence were immune. The perfect systematization of its methods of domination created the Gestapo's machine, which obeyed the directive will of the Führer alone, and in which all laws of humanity were suppressed.

An entire system of formulas and symbols disciplined the Nazi concept and fixed it definitely within its limits. Slogans were raised to the dignity and importance of social laws, the swastika was substituted for the cross, and the German god attempted to supplant Christianity.

As always happens, a reciprocal suggestion took place between the masses awaiting the words of the Führer and the wizard who led them. But in Germany the wizard was decidedly the stronger; he conquered the militarism and Junkerism which thought they could make use of him, as he did the reactionaries who thought they had found in Nazism protection against the proletarian revolution. Hitler, unlike Mussolini, was always perfectly sure of himself and never yielded a single point of his program; he believed, above all, in his personal mission, in his genius as a general and as a statesman.

The early military successes were the consequence of a preparation cleverly begun even prior to Nazism and carried on with unbending will and tremendous energy down to the last detail; they were the results of a program that never swerved even when it seemed about to give way to the influence of other factors.

Were one to believe that in cases like that of Nazi Germany one may speak of a real psychic epidemic, and state that often the actions of a crowd present the symptomatic characteristics of paranoia, one should be asked this question: under the influence of the suggestion of a paranoiac or of an hallucinated individual, may not the same symptoms develop in the group even when such a group is not organically diseased? We know of numberless cases of epidemics of collective suicide or hysteria, or of criminal actions committed by individuals predisposed to suggestion, who found themselves in conditions in which reasoning was practically annihilated. The fact, therefore, that the symptoms manifested by the crowd are apparently the same does not prove that the psychic conditions of all those affected by suggestion are identical. We know from experience that crowds have repeatedly accepted the suggestion of visions, of fantastic apparitions, and so on, with the greatest readiness, although it could never be said that the crowd was composed of individuals suffering from hallucinations.

Megalomania originates in a suppressed desire for power, a sense of frustration, of inferiority, which also gives rise to persecution mania. It is therefore obvious that an organized group or a closed society in which this feeling of economic, racial, and political inferiority is predominant reacts with a fantastic craving for grandeur, which may assume a religious-transcendental form, like the Messianic idea of world-salvation, or an antisocial and supernational one, like the German idea of Nazism. The most important and characteristic feature of this phenomenon lies in the decisive effect of collective suggestion over individuals predisposed to receive it.

7. THE END OF THE MAGIC ADVENTURES

All the destructive psychic epidemics of history end in tragedy and are sooner or later succeeded by a renaissance. Violence can only temporarily suppress the living germ of criticism and the forces of reason, constantly in pursuit of a new stable order (sanitary protection, religious and ethical laws, new political orders). Have such tendencies undergone suppression by Nazism by reason of this new explosion of terror, this unprecedented suggestion? The impartial observer will find it difficult to answer. Manifestly in all Nazi-occupied countries, and even in Italy, all mass suggestion failed. But it is true that in Germany the systematic sadistic killing of hundreds of thousands of people, of hostages and children, women and old people, and espionage perfectly organized in every detail, with an intimate knowledge of the psychology of the German people, have created an unbreathable atmosphere and suffocated every attempt at criticism and rebellion. Terror in Germany, in the occupied countries, and in countries unoccupied but bound to the German war-chariot, terror applied with absolute lack of moral conscience turned Europe into a charnel-house over which the Führer and his followers apparently triumphed. Perhaps the most serious aspect of the situation is that, to a greater extent than in other cases and times, the young people have been deliberately conditioned by the Nazi indoctrination; this infection was transmitted to them by their parents or their schools, their friends, the newspapers, and the radio. A whole new generation was born and grew up in this atmosphere of mental contagion, without sufficient strength to free itself; perhaps it did not possess the very elements of defence. The reasoning and critical power of this generation was suffocated at birth; the absolute and total lack of criticism, the impossibility of reading, hearing, or saying a word indicating anything but complete approval of the official system, the prohibition even of silence, because silence was considered hostile, are new facts compared with which even the most severe measures of the Inquisition seem light. Psychic contagion had temporarily enchained the mind, silenced the living forces of the intellect, and made any opposition impossible. Many hundreds of thousands were jailed or killed; others were starving in concentration camps or lived in exile.

Wherein lies the fundamental difference between the two great destructive mind-adventures—the Asiatic and the European—which we must perceive in order not only to understand the essence but also to foresee the methods and form of the final dénouement? In Germany, because of the mentality of her people, the rationalization of violence and its reduction to a logically constructed system of apparent respectability appeared, from the beginning, to be necessary. Such a rationalization was compounded of elements drawn from the philosophy of Hegel, Nietzsche, and Sorel, from the propaganda of Jahn, Schönerer, Wagner, and their followers. These elements were gathered up and adapted to a fanatical mentality in the book of the Führer, *Mein Kampf*, which became a classic. The Darwinian view of the struggle for life and the doctrine of natural selection, which awards victory to the strongest and fittest, was developed in the doctrine of the superman and super-race, in the selection of the strongest racial group, the fittest ethnic collectivity. Such a doctrine was partially accepted by biologists like Huxley, who claimed that man, having inherited the characteristics of the tiger and the monkey, owes his success—to a large extent—to these qualities, and that it was only later that he acquired the intellectual and social qualities in which ethical laws originated. The Ger-

manic rationalization and idealization of violence thrust to the
fore the doctrine that violence is a determinant of all racial
manifestations and that individual responsibility is cancelled
by this necessity. Prompted by a spirit of imitation and not of
conviction, Fascism, following the German example, founded
a school of Fascist *mystique* along similar lines, with the purpose of establishing the laws of the new ideology.

Japan, instead, never attempted to rationalize violence or to
give it a logical explanation, deeming it sufficient to accept and
impose myth as a final reality. In Germany, for the reasons
mentioned, the diffusion of collective suggestion was enormous; but in Japan it was absolutely complete. Belief and religious feeling were the dominant factors in preparing events
in Japan; cool logic and perfect technique were victorious in
Germany.

The end of the adventure in Germany was brought about
by the victorious Allied armies. The framework of the Nazi
system has finally collapsed, and a new order will be based on
the spiritual currents and traditions of German civilization.
These forces may be a pledge and a safeguard of the future,
after revolutionary conflicts, and will exert a directive influence in the stabilization of a lasting peace.

But the consequences of this adventure are not at all still
to be evaluated. Perhaps the upset of the collective mind has
originated a condition that cannot be healed. The economic
situation in Germany in the next few years will be decisive
in the evolution of the events—just as nutrition and the physical restoration of the physical organism have a decisive part
in the recovery after an ailment. Revolutions or revival and
renewed activity of hidden germs—famine and misery and
attempts at a mistaken treatment—may make the situation
worse and delay or exclude the possibility of recovery.

The solution of the Japanese problem is hard to visualize.
The Occident recognized too little and understood too late
the threat represented by the aggressive mentality of Japan.
The problem that the world will have to face in the postwar
epoch is unexampled in history. The conquerors of antiquity,
the invaders of India, Egypt, Greece, and the Mediterranean,
and, in a more recent period, the triumphant, fanatical Arabs

or the adventurers who became the masters of pre-Columbian America could, with their weapons, impose their will and establish a new order, often inferior to that previously existing, by destroying the ancient civilization, decimating and enslaving the population; but can we envisage a reconstruction of Japan along these lines today? We can imagine the destruction of her cities, but this does not mean that, when the aggressors are punished, the governmental system wrecked, and the forces of the dominating Army dispersed, the Japanese mentality, permeated by myth, will also be demolished.

It is possible that, up to a certain point, China will be considerably more useful in the reconstruction than either Europe or America. No matter how serious the conflicts and disagreements between the Chinese and Japanese peoples, the Chinese mind is undeniably imbued with the ideas and traditions of the Orient, which both China and Japan share at their place of origin. Perhaps China will again be able to dominate Japan and enforce her intellectual rule as she did once before, imposing her language, philosophy, and ethical religion. China, because of the mentality of her inhabitants, which created, in the most remote epoch, a noble ethical code, has always been, above all, a country in which teachers, writers, philosophers, and founders of religions had tremendous authority. The collective mind had a craving for the spiritual and abhorred violence. Individualism was never suppressed, and criticism, though respectful and couched in the most courteous terms, was always permitted. In China the adventure of the mind had, from the outset, a decidedly metaphysical trend, which later led to a vast reconstructive movement. We may thus hope for China's help in the establishment of a new order, whose outlines can barely be guessed at now. It is too early for us to be in a position to judge whether our attempts at reconstruction will find efficient support in those currents of Japanese thought which propaganda and terror, violent suggestion, and the conviction of the futility of every resistance reduced to silence.

The solution of the Japanese problem is therefore infinitely more remote, complex, and difficult than that of the countless other problems that, with the end of the war, face not only the conquering powers but the whole world. Reciprocal lack of understanding exists between East and West. It is evidently impossible for the Japanese to accept the social orders and moral laws of the Occident and the critical functions of the Occidental, Anglo-Saxon, or Græco-Roman mind. Nor will the examples of the past clear the horizon; other great destructive clashes have taken place in history, although on a minor scale, but they were brought about by the impact of brute force and its weapons—that is, by the victory of the unconscious over the reasoning personality. In Japan's case, instead, the collective adventure was founded on violence systematized and carried out not only by weapons but by all means dictated by a highly conscious suggestion which cleverly exploited, thanks to a perfect knowledge of the environment, the situation that it had itself created. Never, perhaps, have individual criticism and the freedom of discussing coercive measures been more ruthlessly quelled. Suppression of the power of the Army necessarily means, at least until such time as a governmental system is definitely established, suspension of all manifestations of the social life of an ethnic collectivity. It will be necessary, if we do not wish to thrust an entire people back into their ancient self-created traditional isolation, to make them more susceptible to the influence of an ethical conception and to give assistance in creating conditions for the free expression of a heretofore suppressed individualism.

In the near future only the universal conviction of a necessary, supreme ethical law, the certain acceptance of a principle of justice and equality, valid in all countries and under all conditions, should develop and afford reliable protection. All ramparts would then be watched and defended by all organized forces of civilized mankind. If this is not possible, the tragic failure of the social and moral order will have to be expected. It might culminate in the disappearance of the collective ego in the face of a violent reversion to the unconscious, assuming power under the disguise of a new doctrine, and exploiting all the discoveries of modern science.

The functions that will have to be discharged by the lawmakers of the postwar world were pointed out in their fundamental outline in a saying of Thomas Jefferson: "Ills may be corrected only by reason or by a free search into their causes." Doubtless the most severe and decisive punishment will be meted out to the contrivers or leaders of this adventure, but can the German people as a whole be punished as has been suggested? This problem, envisaged from the medico-historical viewpoint, cannot be solved, but it should be possible to assess what organized forces of defence and what remedies the German people possess to ensure their salvation and the peace of the world. However, the system applied for centuries in the cure of persons subject to hallucinations, such as exorcizing the demons by whom they were believed to be possessed, burning them at the stake, putting them in the stocks or in chains, and so forth, definitely proved a failure. A strait-jacket is no cure either for individuals or for society.

In all epidemics and what I have called the great tragic adventures, healing was begun and brought about by pre-existing factors which formed in the organism itself. Defence originates automatically as a product of the poisoning. It will be admitted that in the case in question defence likewise originates in the existing elements and that protective barriers are built, which are strengthened and made more efficient by the intelligent will of the convalescent. It is equally obvious that an important task will devolve on those who, from the outside, will direct and actively supervise the process of reconstruction.

The essential problem has been examined from various viewpoints and in various forms as to whether the innate or acquired inclination of the Germans to military discipline and their craving for power will be strong enough to set at nought all defences and to create, in a more or less remote future, new tragic adventures for the German nation and for mankind.

There is no question of the necessity for the construction of lasting defences which must give the greatest possible guarantee of success. However, until now discussions of the manner in which defensive measures should be applied and of their essential character have been a constant source of controversy. We can hope that the re-education of the German people, or rather the reorientation of their social trends, will make them return to what might reasonably be called the normalcy of social life and to rational, critical functioning of the collective mind. The suggestion of triumphant violence and terror through Nazi successes has ceased. We may expect that the elimination of the poison that has been cleverly administered for years will begin. The German people will rediscover their creative energies and resume the path indicated by the restored harmony of the national organism. Regeneration will be the necessary consequence of the slow but sure return to activity of the individual energies. We must nevertheless expect that after the elimination of the elements responsible, many people will prove past recovery. For these people critical activity will be impossible, and every ethical and social law, every order not founded on violence and the myth of the super-race, will be unacceptable to them. Such people must be compared with the dead, necrotized part of the social organism; they will be the victims of the inevitable postwar social revolution, of the ungovernable revenges, of the reaction consequent upon the disappointment caused by the failure of the great wizards. But the healthy national elements will begin to function again and reliable elements of defence will be formed on the conviction of the necessity for eliminating the past and creating a new life. Such a conviction will be generated not only, or not primarily, by the success of the victorious idea and the conditions imposed by the victors, but predominately by the evidence that the sufferings of individuals and groups have been a menace to the wellsprings of individual and social welfare and have in part destroyed them.

Undoubtedly the collective experience has been more tragic than ever before in history, but it behoves us not to forget that the destructive tendencies and the cruel measures were suggested to the German masses and imposed on them by a suggestion of unprecedented violence. Apparent success was achieved by favouring the cravings for adventure, the emotions of the unconscious, and by astutely playing on the people's propensity for paternalism, dependence, faith in leadership, and metaphysical pursuit of fantastic solutions of the life problem. But the sane and reasoning part of the German nation, obeying their great thinkers, scientists, and philosophers, will again exercise its critical, creative faculties. They will be prompted by the will to effect a radical destruction of the past and its creators; they will uproot the doctrines and wipe out the very memory of the Nazi adventure. They will then turn toward a normal, stable order; toward a social, ethical, religious, and constitutional regime of law. It is to be feared that, as a result of the collective poisoning, the generation born and bred in the Nazi atmosphere will be lost or that the task of saving it will be exceedingly difficult. But it is a characteristic and a normal function of youth to be open to creative suggestions after the destructive ones have failed; to be accessible to the wish for a harmonious and peaceful solution of the severest conflicts; for the natural need of creating a new solidarity in an atmosphere of peace is a biological law. Youth is always endowed with unsuspected vitality and an extraordinary power of recuperation and regeneration.

A safe remedy against the repetition of phenomena such as those which have devastated the world will perhaps be afforded by collective measures of defence, and by what we may call acquired collective psychic immunity against contagion caused by mind-adventures transgressing the bounds of human laws. I believe that the experience of the past, the fear of a possible repetition of similar disastrously antisocial events, will hold a dominant sway—at least in some future time—over the collective mind of humanity.

CONCLUSION:

Adventures of the Mind

I. ORIGINS OF MAGIC AND INCANTATIONAL SUGGESTION

IN the fervour of modern research the materialistic orientation in the field of science has been replaced by a biological, vitalistic, and historical unitary and cosmic trend, and the time is long past when one could consider magic events as isolated pathological processes. If we examine magic facts and ideas and the concepts deriving therefrom, not as stiff images lifted, as Bergson writes, from a mutable aggregate, but as essential parts of a living whole, as manifestations of life, as appurtenances of an individual, they appear in a very different light from that in which they stand forth when looked upon as isolated phenomena appearing in persons, space, or time. From that viewpoint they can no longer be termed mental aberrations, inexplicable pathological occurrences, or be used as the source of metaphysical conclusions and transcendental teachings.

Magic derives from a behaviour pattern of nature tuned to the objectivation of desire of life and escape, which constitutes its leitmotiv. Incantation is, to use a modern term, cosmic sex-appeal or libido expressed in the music of the universe, in the rhythm of its laws, in the entrancing beauty of flowers, the stupefying effect of thousands of intoxicating fragrances and glittering lights, in the perfect elegance of animals and in the sparkle of their colours. Every manifestations of the beauty of nature is a note in the eternal symphony. Through all forms of fecund, germinating existence nature exerts its fascination, which is evidently the premise of life itself, presides over its essential aspects, and asserts its laws.

There is no denying that certain rhythmic manifestations of life, and perhaps all of them (although they may not always be apparent to our senses), evince nature's predominant intention to direct living organisms toward procreation and to ensure the stability of their species. It is interesting to note that the means to which nature resorts in order to achieve this result are increasingly complex, elastic, adaptable, and the more varied in their effects and gradations the more highly developed are the beings for which they are destined. This magnificent, universal suggestion created the essence and the conception of beauty, peace, and goodness, and man's sexual instinct was sublimated, in the course of his evolution, to the superior end of creative spiritual activity.

Other manifestations, which the ancients viewed as disturbances of harmony and which might more rightly be called dissonances, evince a destructive aim. Where nature rules alone and all-powerful, all manifestations of destruction are terrible and violent. Such are the spell of the jungle at night, where ferocious roars of beasts of prey attracting their victims ring forth, and deadly fragrances announce and spread destruction; fights of animals which destroy one another in maddening and inexplicable wars, such as those waged by certain species of ants; or voracious insects, which quickly destroy entire forests, so that a picture of complete annihilation is revealed on the return of victorious light. All work of rapid destruction, such as that of the often described tornadoes of the South Sea Islands, constitutes the spell of death and expresses the suggestion of the annihilation of being; and the universal anguish that gripped primitive man, and still exists in the unconscious of all beings, derives therefrom. The fascination of speed, which leads to automobile accidents totalling hundreds of thousands of victims, is perhaps a form of this destructive tendency (recent figures in the United States disclose that there is a higher percentage of mortality from automobile accidents than from all contagious diseases taken together). Is it at all unlikely that an unknown law of destruction exists which, through the suggestion of growing speed, mows down human life in the same proportions as science cuts down the mortality rate from the most serious illnesses and increases the length of life? Are not the aspects of the world during and after a war analogous to those of great telluric catastrophes or devastating plagues?

The mysterious phenomenon of the migration of animals

marching across the face of the earth in countless millions toward a definite goal belongs to the fascinating evidences of
the magic spell of nature. We may refer, among many instances, to the Atlantic eels, suddenly leaving their homes and
heading out into the Atlantic for the purpose of breeding and
the continuation of the species; and, on the other hand, to the
astonishing behaviour and the mass suicides of the lemmings,
which pour down from the uplands in Canada and Norway
and plunge into the sea and disappear; or the herds of spring-
bok, little antelopes, suddenly appearing on the coasts of South
Africa and plunging to their destruction. What kind of collective suggestion drives them to their death, and what impels
the Atlantic tern to travel a distance of twenty-four thousand
miles for breeding-purposes? It is quite admissible to suppose,
as Ivan T. Sanderson has suggested, that changes in nourishment, depending on the surroundings or on the climate, may
cause the fatal migrations; or, according to a hypothesis of
A. L. Wegener, the "continental drift" may drive the eels to
the ancestral grounds, where their eggs are laid. It is well
known that in all forms of magic the influence of the surroundings and the action of the "archaic unconscious" play
an important part. But it seems evident that the spell of life
and of death finds some astonishing examples in these collective phenomena.

Bewitchment or suggestion in nature open the path for
human magic. This may be defined as a desperate defence attempt inspired by anguish under conditions in which man
does not know how to help or cannot. Schopenhauer defined
magic as the objectivation of desire outside the causal nexus,
and perhaps this formula is more evident and comprehensible
than all others. To be more exact one should say: outside the
causal nexus of which we have certain and verified experience.

2. THE SPELL OF LIFE AND DEATH

Human magic arises from the tremendous universal anguish
whenever causes of events are invisible or inexplicable and
man is constantly threatened by danger. It originates in fear
and the need for defence, and in the instinct of revolt and destruction, in sexual desire, in the desire for life, and in the need

for killing in order to live. It develops and varies in its trends in accordance with the conditions of the atmosphere, existence, and environment. Certain zones of the Andes, certain lofty plateaus, where blinding lights illuminate distant mountain-tops, create the kind of magic concentrating its beliefs in the great birds of prey which seem to rule over space, and bring forth the ferocious magic rites of the Aztecs, Incas, and other primitive peoples. The terrifying mystery of impenetrable forests gives birth to the magic fascination of reptiles slither-ing in the weird silence. In this way, according to time and place, the magic ideas connected with animals, plants, and stones are formed. Magic undergoes transformations analo-gous to the aspects of nature from which it issues. Sorcery varies in tune with the double bewitchment of life and of death, which oppose and integrate, combat and complete, and alternate with each other.

Does not the most recent scientific discovery of the fission of the atom prove that antagonistic forces existing in the atom in an apparently stable equilibrium are revealing, when the structure is destroyed, an unexpected, and for our common judgment supernatural, destructive violence? Is it not almost instinctive to think that, in an analogous way, the perturbation of the equilibrium in the human mind is unleashing the violent action of opposing hidden forces?

In the face of nature, and in the violent bustle of an agitated life, primitive man slowly formed his personality through centuries and millenniums. In the beginning, the instincts over which nature fully exerted her influence predominated, and actually ruled alone. The reasoning ego, which the Greeks called *Logos* was slowly formed through experience, the in-crease of knowledge, greater security in life, and the con-viction of the need of security. Too violent instincts needed to be suppressed or rationally overcome; every instinct that could not be mastered by, and was not compatible with, the new conditions of social life had to be repressed. These in-stincts seemed fettered for ever, buried, as Freud asserted, in the unconscious; but they become violently active when en-vironmental conditions similar to those of primitive life un-expectedly recur—violent destruction of life, terrible anguish, fear of inexplicable events—or when law and order are inefficiently administered or the elements entrusted with enforcing them are too weak—conditions of legislative anarchy and suppression of justice due to economic, political, or social events. Or when factors of collective suggestion arouse recollections of the past (psychic collective epidemics of the Middle Ages); and, finally, in individual or collective cases, when a poisonous substance exerts a dissociative power over the personality (poisoning caused by opium, alcohol, and other drugs).

The human mind, according to Vico, after passing through various progressive stages, rising as it does from sensation to imagination and thence to conceptual thought—from violence to the practice of equitable interpretation of law—is bound, in accordance with its eternal nature, to relapse into violence and sensation. Civilization comes to an end in the "barbarism of reflection," a scientific brutishness, which is worse than the primitive "barbarism of sensation." The latter was not devoid of a certain generous nobleness; the former, instead, is contemptible, untrustworthy, and treacherous.

The contrast—and this is particularly worthy of note—between the imaginative and the rational reason of Vico, *Logos*, and the unconscious, which may be designated by *Eros* (the word employed by the ancients in this sense) or by the *Id* of Freud (in contrast to the *Ego*), when studied in its different forms and multiple manifestations, reveals and explains the universal and permanent phenomenon of magic. It is this contrast that is meant by the battle of spirit with flesh, according to Christian belief, and by the struggle of Brahma, the spirit of the reasoning ego, against Atman, the instinct and spirit of the universe, according to Hindu belief. The unconscious, in the generally accepted term of Freud, is the unknown and dangerous element which must be thoroughly known and conquered: it represents the unloosed and threatening instincts. In Indian Yoga, which was discussed at length in a previous chapter, the unconscious is subjugated before its awakening. The individual must concentrate all his powers on a state of absolute repose, practising rhythmical breathing-exercises, and it is only after a long period of preparation that he may concentrate his thoughts on the knowledge of the deepest and most secret matters of personality, attaining self-knowledge. He may liberate the serpent Kundalini only when he knows him, in conformity with the extremely significant law of ancient magic stating that to recognize the invisible demon and call it by name is sufficient to cause it to obey. Language, born in the poetic imagination, becomes the efficient expression of *Logos*.

Similarly, the spiritual exercises prescribed by Ignatius of Loyola lead to concentration of will, abolition of desire, and communion of the spirit with God. All practices of modern magic medicine that I have discussed, from mesmerism to Christian Science, from Couéism to the recent contributions of Schulze, the outstanding Berlin neurologist, to what he calls "autogenous training" (that is, exercise in disregarding certain ideas and concentrating on knowledge), are steps in the same direction.

All suggestive factors are accompanied by an emotional influence on the unconscious, inasmuch as they employ the same means and reach the same conclusions as ancient magic. Who can fail to perceive the analogy between the serpent of the Bible, a symbol of the phallus and of the instincts that seduce man into performing prohibited acts, and the serpent of Hindu philosophy; between the "demons of the senses" of Christian theologians and the id of the Vienna school? The possible twofold result of the contrast between Logos and Eros, and the different paths to which magic may lead, are likewise clear. Knowledge of the unconscious and its function within the limits of personality points to an influence similar to that of Yoga, of the princess of the legend, of white magic, beneficial or social; whereas the violent awakening of the unconscious, which, when it comes to the surface, is not known and therefore is repulsed with insufficient means, signifies a trend to destruction and may lead the individual to suicide and impel the masses to collective annihilation.

In the cosmic contrast between the law of preservation and the tendency to destruction, as in the conflict between the reasoning ego and the id—the unconscious—incantational suggestion is always one of the most constant, strong, and efficient weapons.

3. CHARACTERISTIC FACTORS OF INCANTATION

If we attempt to sum up the facts that characterize magic throughout the centuries in its fundamental traits, which are unchanged and perhaps unchangeable, we may say that the indispensable premise of magic is a state of individual or collective spell, created by environmental conditions, by individual predisposition, and by toxic, mechanical, rhythmical, or otherwise suggestive elements. In this incantational state, exemplified in its original form by the suggestion exercised over animals by nature with colours, forms, fragrances, and music, attention is weakened and at times abolished in animals, and in man the functions of the reasoning and critical ego are impaired or destroyed. Primitive ideas which in modern man are normally dormant or silent and forgotten arise; emotions are unleashed, emotiveness is intensified, the distinction between real and unreal disappears. As a result, every visual or auditory image induced by any kind of suggestion assumes the value of an actual fact, and leads to illusion or hallucination.

This state of incantation may be brought about by factors that are unsuspected and hard to identify. The bewitchment exercised by the magicians of primitive peoples is similar to that exerted by nature herself. Stoll, who has exhaustively studied the suggestive methods favoured by the Malayans, notes their use of perfumes, their singing of monotonous music, and their repetition of rhythmical sounds such as the beating of a drum or the ringing of bells—all factors that are essential to primitive cosmic suggestion. Rhythmical, slow, and monotonous repetition of musical sounds brings about the immobilization of the individual, a fixation of his attention, thus inducing a state similar to that of self-hypnosis. On the other hand, in the suggestion exerted by nature as well as in that of primitive peoples, agents that provoke excitation, such as bitter and irritating substances, sharp and discordant sounds, grotesque dances, are likewise employed, and these agents are also used by wizards. This state of bewitchment may be determined by many means: passionate, emotional suggestion which induces ecstasy (static mood) or hallucinations and delirium (states of excitation), the spell of poetry (the belief that Virgil and Dante, who evoked spirits and visited the Kingdom of the Dead, were wizards was not groundless), the enchantment of art (the incantational factor *par excellence*), and so on. Physical and chemical practices, such as the so-called magnetic steps, and substances like stupefying drugs, may cause a similar bewitchment, whose degree and persistence may be calculated approximately; thus a very slight amount of cocaine, opium, ether, etc., may produce intoxication—that is, impairment of the critical faculties and excitation of the emotional. Undoubtedly, many incantational states which have not been accurately analysed (and cannot be, because their causes and their symptoms are difficult to recognize) are caused by unsuspected physical or chemical factors. Since modern science has proved that small amounts of substances such as vaccines, when introduced into the organism, may determine a biological reaction typical of such an organism for long periods or for an entire lifetime, it is reasonable to suppose that there are agents or substances that induce a sensitivity or psychic reactivity which is latent but lasting, becoming manifest under certain given circumstances.

Admitting that the incantational state—the spell—is the foremost characteristic fact, it is evident that the presence of an intermediary—a man, animal, or object (which can be the agent or the instrument employed by the agent)—may be considered constant in all magic phenomena. In interhuman relations the intermediary, agent, and subject may be conscious or unconscious, may be in turn bewitcher and bewitched, and may, as sometimes occurs, exert suggestion in turn; they may be psychopaths of different degrees and types. However, one must undoubtedly admit that they are all endowed at least with particularly active sensitivity.

Finally both agent and subject may be united in the same physical person; that is, the suggestive action may come from without, but also, under certain conditions, be exerted by the ego. The dialogues of men with dead heroes and supernatural beings, or with ancestors or spirits, which constituted a most important portion of the magic of all centuries, are probably but dialogues between the ego, the unconscious, and the superego, dialogues between the present and the past, between the reasoning wilful individual and the personality or the vestiges of the personality of which he is the inheritor. They are statements by the individual spirit in the face of tradition, family, law, and instinct: all laws, from those of the clan and of society, of life and death, and all instincts, from the primordial instincts slumbering in modern man to those which are eternal. The poet who, in that state of ecstatic spell which is called inspiration, evokes the dead and repeats the words of heroes gives voice, in reality, to that part of his personality which he views as his precursor or worships as a hero; the medium who utters the words of Charlemagne or of Napoleon almost always repeats words and ideas that, coalescing, come to the surface of consciousness under the effect of suggestion to form the complex "Charlemagne" or "Napoleon." This is why the words of the great spirits which are evoked are almost always more in conformity with the mentality of the medium or of near-by persons than with the mentality of the historical personage by whom they are supposedly uttered. The witch who, in the fearful trials of the Inquisition, overcome with the anguished terror of torture and the threats of the stake, confessed that she saw the Devil and had carnal dealings with him, under the suggestion of her environment, her period, its known and witnessed events, and the danger threatening her, acted thus because she objectified her thirst for power and her strange sexual lust in a picture that appeared to her as real as if it had truly occurred. The mystic who describes his spiritual visions has actually lived through them by objectifying his desires into an incantational mood of his soul.

4. MAGIC ACTION

In the normal physiological life of man there are states and facts which are partially identical with spell-moods, and these are manifested in dreams. In sleep the reasoning personality and the critical faculty slumber or are suspended, and in rapid and disordered succession, or rather in successions whose order is not clearly visible and whose lines of development are not apparent, rejected ideas and visions arise—repressed desires and wishes which reasoning man is wont to conceal from himself because of his practice of thrusting them back into his unconscious (Freud). The violent and primitive wishes that live in the unconscious, created by the anguish of life and the desire to live, the wish to kill, the most violent manifestations of sexual desire, all man's repressed desires, are disclosed by his dreams. They are often translated into other images, and perhaps the short life of dreams is sufficient to give a needed outlet to man's instincts. From dreams those images may influence reality, may continue to appear real when the abolition of criticism persists during the waking state. This always occurs with primitive man, who considers things of the imagination as true and real (the entire primitive world being the world of imaginings). It occurs with modern man when instinctive wishes become violent enough to overstep the limits imposed on them.

This explains the importance of dreams in all times and among all peoples, as well as the attempts that were made, by different methods and with varying degrees of success, to classify or arrange them as prophecies or recollections, warnings or communications from remote or supernatural beings, into the life of individuals. In reality, as Freud's doctrine has brilliantly shown, a dream is partly what the ancients believed it to be: a memory of facts that occurred in an epoch forgotten by the individual and his forebears, a dormant desire, a remote voice which has left vestiges in the unconscious, an instinct for rebellion, a prophecy in so far as every memory and every evocation of the past may have prophetic significance, since the history of the individual as well as that of the species represents or contains a modified reversion to the past.

In a state of psychic dissociation, caused by a permanent change in emotional tone (manic-depressive frenzy) or due to a temporary mental ailment (forms of dementia) in which the powerlessness of the reasoning faculty derives from pathological phenomena, the unconscious signally predominates and manifests itself in deliriums, hallucinations, perversity, homicidal impulses, destructive anguish, and self-mutilation.

In a transitory state which might be called accidental, determined by acute intoxication brought about by cocaine and some other drugs, the same condition occurs to a greater or lesser degree. Finally, a dissociation of the psyche, either temporary or permanent, occurs during states of hypnosis, suggestion, and spell, when the ego is under the influence of another and stronger will which dominates or immobilizes it, or when it is acted upon by rhythms, lights, etc., impairing or suppressing criticism or the exercise of reason.

In reality some minute alterations of the human brain, stupefying drugs, suggestions of all kinds and epochs, magic bewitchments, evince, on the whole, analogous phenomena and consequences. They partially or wholly suppress the reasoning personality, its control, and criticism. This action, naturally, greatly varies in degree, since organisms react very differently according to their constitution, their disposition, surroundings, time, and so on. We all know that the fascination exerted by music over various persons and at different times may run the gamut from a light feeling of well-being to a true and profound ecstasy, and may at other times engender a feeling of unrest, of acute and violent irritation. Analogous, profound differences mark the influence that the same factor and person exert over the same individual and over groups at different times or under changed conditions.

5. EVOLUTION OF MAGIC AND COLLECTIVE SUGGESTION

Now that the phenomena and essential characteristics of magic and incantation have been established, let us quickly sum up its history in order to follow its transformations through the ages. [1]

[1] In *The Psychological Frontiers of Society* (New York, 1945) A. Kardiner, with the collaboration of Ralph Linton, Cora du Bois, and James West, has made an exhaustive study of the formation of personality at different times and in different countries. The study is based on anthropological observations guided by examination of psychological factors. Kardiner calls his study an "adventure in psychodynamic technique." The relations between personality and culture in three different and contrasting societies (American Comanche, the Alorese of Dutch East India, and a Midwestern American rural community) form the object of this study, which contains an impressive amount of objective observation, clever analysis, and original conclusions. It shows the importance of child care and

In the era when man felt himself to be a part of the earth and intimately close to it, he was afraid of all threats and dangers, heeded all the suggestions of life, and was aware of the fact that existence comes to an end or undergoes a transformation. This was the era which G. B. Vico called "poetical." He lived within a magic circle and, rather than being bound by it, he formed an essential part of it. His instincts led him to seek and to follow the suggestion exercised by nature herself in her thousand open and concealed voices. He defended himself against the threats of the living and the dead. The first magic actions, dictated by anguish, were acts of defence and solidarity. In the beginning every man was a medicine-man, a magician in his own right; then stronger, more intelligent, sensible, and expert men were quickly selected, and these were the first interpreters and alleged intermediaries of the forces of nature; they had knowledge of the virtues of plants, of animal poisons, of the laws regulating the movement of the stars, of the order of nature. Their first task was to help and protect man. Because of their greater, more keenly developed sensitivity, their power of seeing farther, hearing and smelling better, their possession of more alert instincts, they believed that they knew, or perhaps they really did know, things that appear remote, secret, or incomprehensible to us. They undoubtedly possessed an intuitive knowledge of the possibility of creating a special state of mind in men who entrusted themselves to them and whom they wished to lead or dominate. The earliest wizards, operating with colours, feathers, perfumes, music, terror, or promises, were bewitchers who followed the example of nature step by step.

The wizard of primitive times interpreted sounds coming from the outside as voices, undoubtedly perceiving also voices that we no longer perceive. The sensitivity necessary for perceiving them is atrophied in us, just as our senses no longer feel certain kinds of stimuli—for instance, odours to which animals are sensitive and against which they violently react.

---

of education and their results in religion, folklore, and social behaviour. *The Psychological Frontiers of Society* represents an epoch-making development in the psychology of society and should be of great interest and benefit to all persons interested in these problems.

Music, rhythms, colours are sufficient to arouse in primitive man, as in invalids or persons recuperating from serious illnesses, an incantational mood. In primitive man, as in children, this occurs because the critical faculties are not yet formed, his individuality is still undefined, and he has not detached himself from his circle and its objects; in ailing persons it occurs because their critical faculties have been suppressed by sickness.

In the period that we call historical, sorcery springs from the relations between the conscious and the unconscious, between individual will, on the one hand, and ancestral tendencies and primitive instincts, on the other, with the formation of the critical ego and of the clearly determined will, with the defining of the limits of individuality on the shadowy basis of self-awareness, and with the establishment of the family, the clan, the tribe, and the laws. Slowly, with the growth of knowledge, with greater depth of criticism and the enlargement of research-facilities, the clarification of facts that theretofore seemed utterly mysterious, matters that in the past were held to be supernatural forces, were explained on the basis of the causal nexus. More nearly perfect knowledge armed the individual and the collective ego, illuminated events, and made the appearance of phenomena of the unconscious more difficult or repressed them altogether. The history of magic is the history of all anguish and all hope.

When the wizards' power became too dangerous to warriors and political leaders, the first decline of magic occurred with the establishment of states and of civil powers. The leader, the ruler, the prince, became the great wizard or the first in importance of wizards who were given the rank of State functionaries. The very fact, however, of the allegedly divine or legal stability of their power undermined it. No legitimate ruler or prince, no great statesman, ever enjoyed the large popularity of a famous wizard—just as no illustrious scientist ever conquered the confidence and the enthusiastic belief of the crowds, in the measure in which that occurred to a wonder healer. But when thunder, lightning, the movement of stars, facts of sexual life, of sickness, and of death appeared free from the veil of mystery, it was no longer necessary to resort to the intervention of unknown and un-mastered forces to explain them. They were disclosed, in a wider and better-ordered conception of life, as the expression of superior wills; wizards were replaced by or merged with priests.

With the formation of the religious idea, which rightly considered magic as a dangerous enemy, the magic current—that is, the power of performing magic practices as an art—once more became weakened. Moral and ethical laws began to take definite form, and all wishes were subjected to the framework of daring legislative structures in the sphere of divine laws. Religion destroyed, or rather intended to destroy, the foundation of magic belief by a simple and definite general explanation which would eliminate it. Every natural or supernatural fact, whether explicable or not, derives directly from God, who acts consciously and voluntarily, with a predetermined aim, and whose assistance or forgiveness can only be obtained by invoking His pity through good works and prayer. The Bible expresses for the first time in an imperative form the ban against wizards and magic practices, even though it does not deny their power.

In classical antiquity, with the flowering of philosophy, all the enchantment of nature and of its harmony, all the suggestive power of nature's beauty, appeared in a new ideological aspect of cosmic harmony, which found expression in the philosophical concepts contained in the writings of Pythagoras and his pupils. I have tried to indicate briefly, in the rapid sketch given in the first part of this book, the transformations through which this concept passed in antiquity and later times. The most interesting period in the history of magic, the age in which for a time it seemed as if sorcery were definitely condemned in fact as in writing, was the epoch when, with the spread of triumphant Christianity, the passionate faith of the masses turned solely to the great mystical ideal of suffering and piety. In the depths of the collective unconscious as in that of the individual soul, the ancient idea of revolt was revived in the thousand manifestations of diabolical magic, of Satanism, while the part of mankind that felt the enchantment of beauty and piety took refuge in faith, rose upon the wings of mystical ecstasy, and overcame or tempered its mutinous instincts by the abolition of desire.

With the progressive renewal of the critical faculties, and with the freeing of reason from the bonds of laws, which had become too rigid, and from systems that shackled its growth, science supplied explanations for an increasing number of facts, identified unknown forces, and discovered laws not imagined before. Sorcery became clarified, was metamorphosed, made use of other methods, in tune with the changed conditions of individual and social life; magic practices paid homage to reason rather than to imagination, to poetry rather than to myths. As a result of the instinct of the unconscious and the recall to a primitive life, magic assumed new guises and new expressions through which ancient expressions showed only under special conditions. Magic belief became mystical, speculative, attempted the path of occult science in astrology, which later gave way to astronomy, and in alchemy, which, with the widening of knowledge and the perfecting of technical instruments, sought for other aims than the philosophers' stone and became an exact science, chemistry.

The magic of the eighteenth century was romantic on account of its interest in the adventures of the metaphysicians and in the metaphysics of the adventurers. Partaking of the vast spiritistic movement of the nineteenth century, magic turned once more to the objectivation of man's desire for immortality, for the continuity of life, for contact with the beyond. Such is the drama of Faust, the profound thinker, who was driven to magic by overmastering instincts of his unconscious, by his passionate longing for life. In the human and divine drama of Goethe, magic is finally victorious, as it reaches the possession of knowledge, or at least inasmuch as it ardently longs to achieve it.

At the same time the revival of individualism, culminating in the French Revolution, was thrown out of balance by the modern mechanical civilization in which industry and mass production seriously interfered with the role of the individual. The diffusion of the press and, above all, of newspapers, spreading immediate snap judgments on persons and events, diminished or suppressed the necessity for personal critical judgment, offering an easy way out of judgment by the acceptance of previously prepared opinions. Apparently authoritative, they constituted a collective suggestion accepted by the masses.

This presents briefly the essential features of the great adventures of the mind which have occurred in recent times. These adventures disclose two great antithetical tendencies: constructive and destructive. The French Revolution and the political and intellectual trends that followed it brought about a new orientation of thought and a definite affirmation of the power of critical reasoning and of scientific experiment. Mysticism and metaphysics were opposed instinctively by criticism, scientific experimentalism, and ruling materialism. It was rightly said that the nineteenth century was overtly controlled by intellectuals and scientists, but was ruled by capitalism in the economic field.

The intellectual vicissitudes of the nineteenth century led, on one side, to ideological romanticism, to spiritism, and to analogous trends professing an indestructible faith in survival after death. But these trends soon fell under the dominance of exact research in suggestibility, hypnotism, and the activities of the unconscious, and thus assumed a new orientation. It was in sporadic cases only that the new orientation led single groups, such as those of the followers of Christian Science, into collective adventures. Economic depression and the other factors I have mentioned gave rise to the tragic adventures of the spirit which occurred and are now occurring in various countries and led to world conflagration.[1]

---

[1] One of the most interesting examples of the power of collective suggestion was the so-called rebellion in the backlands, described in masterly fashion by Euclydes da Cunha, a classic Brazilian writer in *Rebellion in the Backlands* (Chicago, 1944). A strange character known as Antonio the Counsellor, a *sertanejo*-backlander-saint, was the leader of this movement. Antonio preached and prophesied, built a great number of chapels, lived on alms, and always slept on the ground. In 1896-7 several expeditions were sent by the Government to conquer Antonio. The first two were driven off by Antonio's followers, while a third expedition which succeeded in reaching his village was defeated and its line of retreat decorated with the severed heads of the slain soldiers, which mummified in the dry air. A fourth expedition was successful, but only after attacking the city for four months.

Magic has existed at all times, among all peoples, and in all forms: imitative and contagious, fantastic and speculative magic; state magic and religious magic, white and black, mystic and diabolic, alchemistic and natural, medical, spiritistic, and scientific.

Magic has existed in all epochs and will always exist because there has always been and there always will be the possibility of, and perhaps the necessity for, creating an incantational mood—that is, abolishing criticism. Yet if we think of a continuous progress of humanity toward knowledge, of a successive enlargement and diffusion of criticism, of a greater familiarity with the methods of objective research, we may reasonably believe that magic incantations will be successively transformed by analysis, by exact science, and by ethical conceptions. This has already occurred in history. Such an idea is not invalidated by the fact that in single epochs of advanced civilization and great scientific progress, like our own, one often unexpectedly notices an impetuous flood of magic beliefs in their primitive forms. These are phenomena of collective, pathological suggestion which strike society after great wars or famines, during periods of terrific misery. When humanity is physically and economically impoverished, the critical faculties of the group-ego are impaired and the instincts of the collective unconscious rise to the surface. In a weak and impoverished society, a prey to anguish, suggestion finds fertile soil, because of the predominance of emotionalism, just as in a man endowed with a highly developed critical intelligence, who is ill or convalescing from a serious ailment, the way is open for an uprush of primitive ideas and a reversion to the search for the supernatural and for magic. A scholar recently published a report on the spread of magic beliefs in Germany in December 1932; the writer noted that at that time Berlin had eighteen newspapers (with a circulation of over 50,000) devoted to astrology, astrological predictions, and horoscopes on the outcome of political and economic

The city, however, never surrendered but was wiped out. The suggestive power of Antonio was so extraordinary that the backlanders fought with him to their death without knowing whom or what they were fighting. This battle, one of the most fanatical on record, was led by the will of an obscure man whose power derived from his personality alone.

events. Simultaneously an unusually large number of palmists, fortune-tellers, and card-readers sprang up and enlisted a tremendous following among all classes of society.

Such periodical reversions to magic beliefs in periods of serious distress may be likened to the excessive use of stupefying drugs by patients suffering from excruciating pain, who seek to experience the sensation termed "artificial paradise." It is interesting to observe that Italy, and the Mediterranean countries in general, have preserved their normal balance and resisted the vast contagious revival of superstitions and magic beliefs.

Economic and political crises of destruction and reconstruction are but manifestations of the rhythmic law of the cosmos, of the law of periodic cycle. We may say the degree of the spread of magic and its characteristics constitutes an index of the state of mind of a group, of the suggestibility of a nation or epoch. It can guide us in examining and judging the influence that, in this sense, exterior factors exert over both the group and the individual. For example, it is evident that a man or a group of men immediately after an earthquake, a shipwreck, a storm, or an epidemic, after witnessing death at close range, and the debasing of values which in normal life seem the most safely established, is liable, when not sustained by a strong, clear, firmly conscious will, to seek salvation elsewhere. When man reverts to an anguish similar to that of the primitive threatened by thousands of unknown and unforeseen dangers, there arise in him memories of childhood, beliefs inherited from the remote past, and defences suggested by fear. Emotions predominate and reasoning is impaired. The group repeats the history of the individual and of the species in its origins and evolution, transformations, and entire history. That is the "barbarism of reflection," prognosticated by G. B. Vico.

An essential factor determining the fate of magic and of the adventurous vicissitudes deriving from it is freedom of thought. The free critical spirit, in the regular rhythm of life, is not easily attracted by dangerous adventures. The magic of nature and of her rules, the sorcery of creative beauty and harmonious life, exerts, of necessity, a constructive and social influence. All the magic of nature is intended, primarily, to ensure fecundation: the continuance of life in future generations. All its fascination is directed toward this purpose.

Societies whose life-rhythm is fast and hectic have trouble in creating a means of protection. Those societies, on the other hand, whose rhythm of life is slow, such as the ethnic groups of the Orient, have a tendency to mystical and fantastic ideas which are engendered by the environment. Perhaps in a civilization whose life-rhythm is extremely rapid, such as the United States of America, collective mentality is absorbed in the effort to secure economic and social welfare, but in all countries and at all times when this is not easily achieved, or the determination to face the dangers of the struggle flags, the group is drawn, by the same violent rhythm, into fanatical and destructive adventures.

What has been called the "cultural lag" is in reality the lag between the rapid progress of science, and particularly of technical appliances, and the impossibility of adjusting human mentality with equal speed to the measures necessary to obviate the dangers stemming from this unexpected development. Evidently the human mind has been incapable of keeping up with the pace of rapid evolution of the civilization it has itself created, which has, tragically, become greater than the mind's power of grasping and controlling it. The ramparts that the human mind was capable of constructing, the checks successively dictated by a normal development of civilization, became insufficient, just as a poorly armed crowd is unable to defend itself against an enemy armed with weapons of whose importance the crowd is ignorant, although capable of learning their power by experience.

Thus all facts which have been called magic since the beginning of history, all conceptions falling within the domain of magic, fit into a framework that is found, on successive observations, to undergo continuous modifications and readjustments. In keeping with the normal evolutionary progress of the critical personality effected by the increase of knowledge, with the perfecting of perceptions, thanks to instruments that prolong or amplify the range of our senses (such as the microscope or the telescope), our volitional faculties are readjusted.

The ego acquires increasingly greater ability to explain facts that formerly appeared mysterious, to exercise increasingly independent criticism in respect to the phenomena of life, and to understand the necessity of keeping instincts in order, of controlling or suppressing them, of defending the individual against the group or the group against the individual. The defence of the ego and of its changed needs assumes a different form and resorts to other means.

Victory over the instincts and the unconscious may be accomplished, or rather attempted, in two ways. In the first place by a means that I shall call the systematic, decisive, and inflexible method of religion and asceticism, which compels, condemns, or suppresses instincts without stopping to examine them. At certain times religion even forbade the individual to notice his instincts; it taught him to regard them as demoniacal phenomena—that is, as external or accidental.

Mastery over the instincts may be achieved, on the other hand, by the method of modern psychology, which examines, studies, with scientific and biological methods, attempting to know and understand instincts and the unconscious, demonstrating their antagonism to and incompatibility with (or, under specified conditions, adaptability to) individual and social life. By strengthening criticism, will, and reasoning habits, modern science succeeds in placing instincts in order. Neither of the two methods definitely solves the problem; human life, with its continuous metamorphoses, the eternal oscillations of relationships between the factors determining it, seems to prevent a definite, precise solution of its complex problems. Between the man educated in a religious faith, living psychologically in a universe created by this faith, adjusted to this faith, and explaining by it all life-manifestations (thus creating another form of closed magic circle in which mental figments have the same value as reality), and the man who discovers in the voices arising from the innermost depths of his being an authentic authority that must be examined, studied, and may become a determining factor in his life, a thousand transitional forms exist, are shaped, repeated, and renewed. The picture changes for every epoch and every individual; and if an objective and impartial observer could trace this transition with full knowledge, it would appear different even in the same individual at different moments and under the influence of changed stimuli. That is why the judgment of persons differs according to their point of view. Don Quixote, who is a magician inasmuch as he attempts to objectify the desires of his unconscious in utter disregard of the causal nexus, by strange and impossible ways, may be considered, according to the time and the judge, either as a hero or as a madman. Madmen were frequently considered to be heroes or divinely inspired beings, and were surrounded with the admiration of the people.[1]

One aspect of our times encourages us to think that the necessity to renounce verbal suggestions and its futile rhetoric is accepted especially in America. The artificial and pretentious in all manifestations of life has lost its appeal. In architecture, interior decoration, clothes, and the theatre there is a trend toward simplicity. This is one of the means of defence against a dangerous form of suggestion. It is remarkable, especially for those acquainted with the usual phraseology of Europeans, to observe how the speeches, editorials, and declarations of the Allied leaders and conquerors are an evident reaction to the slogans of glory, ancestral tradition, and national superiority of Nazism and Fascism; they are inspired by a sound realistic self-respect and an adequate consideration of existing facts. Rereading the memorable speeches of the political leaders and chiefs of the victorious armies, we find again and again a sober judgment concerning the difficulties to be encountered, evaluating the forces of the enemy, and avoiding complacency of any kind. The future is always envisaged with a serious appreciation of never minimized dangers. This

---

[1] Professor A. G. Keller, in his recent book *Net Impression* (Yale University Press, 1945), analyses the crises of modern civilization. He stresses the history of the basic institution within society, and observes that the strength of religion derives from the element of hazard with which man is always threatened. Science, in its triumphant progress, is reducing the margins of the hazardous. Professor Keller, who believes that a rational attitude alone deserves to be accepted, is sceptical, however, about the possibility that science will be completely successful in putting an end to all mystery. Rational agnosticism is, therefore, to be considered only as an adjustment which may never succeed in working out a substitute for religion among the masses.

trend toward rational and objective thinking, which may form the basis of intelligently suggestive propaganda, is pointing out the way to the currents of thought that will direct the new democracy.

The adventures of the mind divide and re-divide into great currents. Those concerning magic practices, everyday superstitions, exorcisms, the evil eye, diabolical rites, magnetic cures, and so forth, constantly evince a tendency similar to that of primitive magic; they originate and exist in incantational states determined by new and old factors, by the varied and multiple suggestion of words, ideas, poisonous substances, stupefying drugs, and fantastic music. The entire basis of ancient and modern occultism, in compliance with the great and profound desire for the preservation of the species and of life, has found or will undoubtedly find, however slowly, its place in science.

Microbes and poisons can never be eliminated, but the individual's physical and moral endurance must be strengthened. The serum drawn from the blood of persons who have recovered from a serious contagious disease contains the elements that defend and protect a child against infection; the poison of a snake contains the elements that compose a curing serum. All the tragic adventures of the mind produce, as they have always produced, elements that can and must prepare the defence of the individual and of the group against a new infection.

Humanity is today facing one of the most serious of problems, also, if we will admit that the use of the atomic bomb shall never become actual. The general feeling of distress and uncertainty that is dominant today because of the economic and political situation can easily originate, in many countries of the world, a collective anguish. The impending menace of total destruction suggested by the new weapons is surely no less terrible than the widespread terror of the end of the world about the year 1000, which assumed the character of a collective psychosis. Only the conviction of the stability of a just peace can avert this danger.

If we consider the measures which may be taken to defend

society from tragic adventures, we shall see that they may be founded on these principles:

1. The full comprehension of the fact that psychological factors, and first among them collective suggestion, play a decisive role in the development of events. Only an international accord can create a universal system of defence, which may be called the sanitary protection of the collective mind. Only a supreme ethical law, voluntarily accepted by all nations of the world, can offer, also in face of new and unexpected dangers, the assurance of a peaceful individual and social life — limiting the need of escape, controlling it, and suppressing the contagious spread of tragic collective suggestions.

2. Liberty, with the limitations that are imposed by the different conditions of different people, is much more than a political necessity, as it is generally presented, the essential biological condition of life. To deprive man of liberty of thought and action is equivalent to denying the organisms the freedom to breathe or to take nourishment. Individuals and peoples die from lack of nourishment and suffocate from lack of oxygen or liberty.

3. The reconstruction of the consciousness and of self-respect can be achieved only through a system of education, which has to take into consideration the different surroundings and conditions of various people. This reconstruction cannot be forcibly accomplished by the conquerors.

4. The education of the individual and public mind has to stress the need of prophylaxis as a sanitary measure against psychic epidemics as well as against mass poisoning and contagious diseases. The most dangerous of all weapons that have menaced and will menace any form of a sound social life is the technically and psychologically powerful propaganda of racial superiority, of nationalism, of hatred and violence. This is the most modern and most dangerous form of collective suggestion. Guidance, control, and strong limitation of it is a no less necessary sanitary measure than international defence against contagious diseases or against military aggression. The suppression of any kind of propaganda fostering fear, tension, and hate is an essential condition for a lasting peace.

5. Only from the mutual comprehension of the mentality, of the tradition, and of the needs of different ethnical groups can arise the establishment of reciprocal relations that may lay the foundation for a new order and create a security not to be undermined by frustration or by aggression.[1]

It is evidently as impossible to check the desire for adventure as it is impossible to suppress the curiosity of a child and the everlasting instinctive struggle for life of any living creature. It would therefore be a mistake to envisage a solution of psychological problems established on identical foundations for different people living under different conditions of climate, education, surroundings, and traditions. The mind of the European nations that have suffered slavery and misery is in a state of deep depression, which will last for many years. They are longing for economic security and for freedom and still more for the certainty that their dignity and their social life will be restored. They long for an escape from the past and from the present. Only by assuring the freedom of every ethnical group to decide its own fate and simultaneously guiding the masses by means of an international accord toward their economic and cultural development based on a well-grounded comprehension of their mentality will it be possible to point out the way in which the goal of a life materially and morally acceptable to the individual and the group may be possible of achievement.

[1] I want to call the attention of the reader to an exhaustive and authoritative discussion of this problem in the "Round Table Conference: Germany after the War" (*American Journal for Orthopsychiatry*, 15:2, July 1945), in which a great number of prominent American psychiatrists and psychologists took part. In this study the necessity of a psychocultural approach to the solution of postwar problems is convincingly emphasized.

❀ BIBLIOGRAPHY ❀

THE bibliography of magic and its development is so vast that even to indicate the fundamental works dealing with the subjects in this book would require so much space that it would be out of all proportion to the benefit to be derived by a reader who did not wish to delve deeply into special subjects. The history of magic through the centuries, its various aspects, its evolution, and the influence of scientific research have been dealt with in masterly fashion by Lynn Thorndike in his work: *A History of Magic and Experimental Science* (New York: The Macmillan Co.; 1923–45), the most complete and best-documented work on this subject and from all points of view the most reliable source of information. Its bibliography is complete. There is also a very accurate bibliography in A. Lehmann's excellent book: *Aberglaube und Zauberei* (German translation from the Danish, 3rd ed., Stuttgart, 1925). Montague Summers's *The History of Magic and Demonology* (New York: Alfred A. Knopf; 1926) contains a large number of valuable references.

In the bibliographical list that follows I have chosen the works that I have had most frequent occasion to consult and that seem to me especially worthy of study. It is not intended to be complete from any viewpoint, but should serve to guide the reader to a comprehension of the problems to which this book is dedicated.

ABELSON, A.: *Misticismo ebraico (La Cabala)*. Turin, 1929.
AGRIPPA, CORNELIUS: *De occulta philosophia*. Colonia, 1651.
AKSAKOW, A.: *Animismus und Spiritismus*. Leipzig, 1890.
ALBERTUS MAGNUS: *Opera omnia*. Lyon, 1651.
ALLENDY, R. F.: *L'Alchimie et la médecine*. Paris, 1912.
ALLIER, T.: *Le Non Civilisé et nous*. Paris, 1927.
AQUINAS, THOMAS: *Opera omnia*. Paris, 1871–80.
ARAM, K.: *Magie und Mystik in Vergangenheit und Gegenwart*. Berlin, n.d.

BACON, ROGER: *De secretis operibus magiæ*. Paris, 1542.
BEAUNIS, H.: *Le Somnambulisme provoqué*. Paris, 1887.

BERTHELOT, M. P. E.: *Les Origines de l'alchimie.* Paris, 1885.

BETH, K.: *Religion und Magie.* 2nd ed., Berlin, 1927.

BISSON, J. A.: *Les Phénomènes dits de matérialisation.* Paris, 1921.

BLACKMORE, S. J.: *Spiritism, Facts and Frauds.* London, 1925.

BLEULER, E.: *Naturgeschichte der Seele und ihres Bewusst-werdens.* Berlin, 1932.

BODINUS, J.: *De magorum dæmonomania,* 4 vols. Basel, 1581.

BOIS, J.: *Le Satanisme et la magie.* Paris, n.d.

BOODIN, J. E.: *The Social Mind.* New York, 1939.

BONCOMPAGNI, B.: *Della vita e delle opere di Guido Bonatti, astrologo.* Rome, 1851.

BOZZANO, E.: *Le prime manifestazioni della voce diretta in Italia.* Rome, 1927.

BREASTED, J. H.: *Development of Religion and Thought in Ancient Egypt.* New York, 1912.

BRECHER, A.: *Die transzendentale Magie und die magische Heil-arten im Talmud.* Jena, 1850.

BUDGE, E. A. W.: *Egyptian Magic.* London, 1899.

BURKITT, F. G.: *The Religion of the Manichees.* Cambridge, 1925.

BURR, G. L.: *Narratives of the Witchcraft Cases.* New York, 1914.

CAILLET, A.: *Manual bibliographique des sciences physiques ou occultes, etc.,* 3 vols. Paris, 1913.

CANTÚ, C.: *Gli eretici d'Italia.* Turin, 1865.

CASSIRER, E.: *Sprache und· Mythos.* Leipzig, 1935.

CASTELLI, G.: *La vita e le opere di Cecco d'Ascoli.* Turin, 1892.

CASTRO, C. DE: *Il mondo segreto.* 9 vols. Milan, 1863.

CAUFEYNON and JAF: *Les Messes noires.* Paris, 1905.

CAUZONS, T.: *La Magie et la sorcellerie en France.* 4 vols. Paris, 1900.

CHEVREUL, A.: *De la baguette divinatoire.* Paris, 1854.

CLEMENTIS, ALEXANDRINI: *Opera.* 2 vols. Venice, 1757.

CONSTANT, A. L.: *Transcendental Magic,* trans. by E. A. Waite. revised ed., Philadelphia, 1923.

CROISSART, J.: *Aristote et le mysticisme.* Paris, 1932.

DANZEL, T. W.: *Handbuch der präkolumbische Kultur in Latin America.* Hamburg, 1932.

——: *Kultur und· Religion der primitiven Menschen.* Stuttgart, 1925.

——: *Magie und Geheimwissenschaft.* Stuttgart, 1926.

DAVIES, D. W.: *Magic, Divination and Demonology*. London, 1896.

DAWSON, R. WARREN: *Magician and Leech*. London, 1929.

DEBAY, A.: *Histoire des sciences occultes*. Paris, 1860.

DORÉ, H. S. J.: *Recherches sur les superstitions en Chine*. 15 vols. Shanghai, 1911–25.

DORNSEIFF, F.: *Das Alphabet in Mystik und Magie*. Leipzig, 1925.

DRIESCH, H.: *Parapsychologie, die Wissenschaft von den okkulten Erscheinungen*. Munich, 1933.

ELLIOT, R. H.: *The Myth of the Mystic East*. Edinburgh, 1934.

ENNEMOSER, J.: *The History of Magic*. 2 vols. London, 1854.

EVANS-PRITCHARD, E. E.: *Witchcraft, Oracles and Magic among the Azanda*. Oxford, 1937.

FISCHER, H.: *Magie und Mystic in Vergangenheit und Gegenwart*. Berlin, 1929.

FLIESS, W.: *Zur Periodenlehre*. Jena, 1924.

FORKE, A.: *The World Conception of the Chinese*. London, 1925.

FOSSEY, C.: *La Magie assyrienne*. Paris, 1902.

FRAZER, J. G.: *Folk-lore in the Old Testament*. London, 1919.

——: *The Golden Bough*. 3 vols. London, 1936.

FREUD, S.: *Psychology and the Anaylsis of the Ego*. New York, 1922.

——: *Totem and Taboo, Resemblances between the Psychic Life of Savages and Neurotics*. London, 1929.

FROMM, E.: *Die Entwicklung des Christus Dogmas*. Vienna, 1931.

GINZBERG: "Cabala," in *The Jewish Encyclopedia*. Vol. III. 1902.

GRILLOT DE GIVRY: *Le Musée des sorciers*. Paris, 1929.

GRUENWEDEL, I.: *Tuska*. Leipzig, 1932.

GUAZZO, F. M.: *Compendium maleficorum*. Milan, 1608.

HALLOWELL, A.: *The Child, the Savage and Human Experience*. Langham, 1895.

HANSEN, J.: *Quellen und Untersuchungen zur Geschichte des Hexenwahns*. Bonn, 1901.

HASCHEK and HERZFELD: "Physikalische Erkärung des Wünschelruten Problems," in *Wochenschrifte für die Fortschritte der Naturwissenschaft*, 1921, No. 51.

HEHN, E.: *Siebenzahl und Sabbath*, etc. Leipzig, 1907.

HENRY, V.: *La Magie dans l'Inde antique*. Paris, 1904.

JAIDA, W.: "Zum Verständnis der primitiven Zauberei," in *Arch. für Psychologie*, 1938, No. 102.

KAPLAN, L.: *Das Problem der Magie*. Heidelberg, 1927.
KEYSERLING, H.: *Südamerikanische Meditationen*. Stuttgart, 1932.
KING, J.: *Babylonian Magic and Sorcery*. London, 1896.
KUNZ, G. F.: *The Curious Lore of Precious Stones*. Philadelphia, 1913.

LEA, H. C.: *A History of the Inquisition of the Middle Ages*. 3 vols. New York, 1887.
——: *Material towards a History of Witchcraft*. Philadelphia, 1939.
LE BON, GUSTAVE: *Psychologie des foules*. Paris, 1895.
LENORMANT, F.: *Die Magie und Wahrsagekunst der Chaldäer*. Berlin, 1920.
LEROY, OLIVIER: *La Raison primitive*. Paris, 1927.
LEVI, ELIPHAS: *Histoire de la magie*. Paris, 1922.
LÉVY-BRUHL, L.: *L'Âme primitive*. Paris, 1927.
LEXA, F.: *La Magie dans l'Égypte antique*. 3 vols. Paris, 1925.
LIEK, E. W.: *Dans Wunder in der Heilkunde*. Munich, 1936.
LILLIE, A.: *Modern Mystics and Modern Magic*. London, 1894.

MADDOX, J. L.: *The Medicine Man, a Study in the Character and Evolution of Shamanism*. New York, 1923.
MARIE, A.: *La Psychanalyse et les nouvelles méthodes d'investigation de l'inconscient*. Paris, 1928.
MAUCHAMP, E.: *La Sorcellerie au Maroc*. Paris, n.d.
MAURY, A.: *La Magie et l'astrologie dans l'antiquité et au moyen âge*. Paris, 1877.
MAXWELL, J.: *La Divination*. Paris, 1927.
——: *La Magie*. Paris, 1925.
McDOUGALL, W.: *The Group Mind, a Sketch of the Principles of Collective Psychology*. New York, 1920.
MICHELET, J.: *La Sorcière*. Paris, 1922.
MOLITOR, U.: *De lamiis et phitonicis mulieribus*. Costanza, 1489.
MONTMASSON, J. M.: *Le Rôle de l'inconscient dans l'invention scientifique*. Paris, 1928.

NEVINS, W. S.: *Witchcraft in Salem Village*. Boston, 1892.

OGBURN, W.: *Man and His Machines*. Washington, 1942.
OLLIVER, C. W.: *An Analysis of Magic and Witchcraft*. London, 1928.

PAREDES, M. R.: *Mitos, superstructuras y survivencias populares in Bolivia.* La Paz, 1914.

PARSON, R. P.: *History of Haitian Medicine.* New York, 1930.

PAYNE, J. F.: *English Medicine in the Anglo-Saxon Time.* Oxford, 1904.

PERINI, O.: *Storia delle società segrete.* 2 vols. Milan, 1863.

PERRY, W. D.: *The Origin of Magic and Religion.* New York, 1923.

PONZINIBIO, F.: *De lamiis.* Venice, 1584.

PREUSS, K. T.: *Arte monumental préhistorico* (trans.). Bogotá, 1931.

RELE, VASANT GANGARAM: *The Mysterious Kundalini.* Bombay, 1927.

RIBET, M. J.: *La Mystique divine.* 4 vols. Paris, 1895.

RICHET, CHARLES: *Traité de metapsychique.* Paris, 1923.

RIDGEWAY, W.: *The Drama and Dramatic Dances of Non-European Races.* Cambridge University Press, 1915.

ROCHAS, DE: *La scienza psichica.* Rome, 1924.

SCHURÉ, E.: *Les Grandes Légendes de France.* Paris, 1922.

SELIGMANN, S.: *Die magischen Heil und Schutzmittel aus der unbelebten Natur.* Stuttgart, 1927.

SIGHELE, S.: *L'intelligenza della folla.* 2nd ed. Turin, 1922.

SINGER, CHARLES: "Early English Magic and Medicine," in *Proceedings of the British Academy,* vol. IX. 1920.

———: *From Magic to Science.* London, 1928.

SINISTRARI, L. M.: *Opera Omnia.* 3 vols. 1753–4.

SMITH, W. ROBERTSON: *The Religion of the Semites.* London, 1907.

SPRENGER, O. P. J.: *Malleus maleficorum.* Nürnberg, 1494.

STEINER, R.: *Les Mystères antiques et les mystères chrétiens.* Paris, 1920.

STERN, B.: *Medizin, Aberglaube und Geschlechtsleben in der Türkei.* Berlin, 1903.

STRUNZ, F.: *Albertus Magnus.* Vienna, 1925.

SWOBODA, H.: *Das Siebenjahr.* Vienna and Leipzig, 1917.

TARTAROTTI, G.: *Del congresso notturno delle lamie.* Rovereto, 1749.

TONNINI, A.: *Psicologia della civiltà egizia.* Turin, 1906.

TRACHTENBERG, J.: *Jewish Magic and Superstition.* New York, 1939.

UPHAM, C. E.: *Salem Witches.* 3rd ed., Salem, 1891.

VALDIZAN, H.: *Dicionario de medicina peruana.* Lima, 1923.
VAYRA, P.: *Le streghe nel Canavese.* Turin, 1874.
VIVEKANANDA, SWAMI: *Carma Yoga.* New York, 1901.

WAKE, C. S.: *Serpent Worship.* London, 1888.
WEBSTER, HUTTON: *Società segrete primitive.* Bologna, 1922.
WIER, I.: *Histoire, disputes et discours.* 2 vols. Paris, 1885.
WUNDT, W.: *Völkerpsychologie.* Leipzig, 1910–15.

YVE-PLESSIS, R.: *Bibliographie française de la sorcellerie.* Paris, 1900.

❃ INDEX ❃

A NOTE ON THE TYPE IN WHICH
THIS BOOK IS SET

This book was set on the Linotype in Janson, a recutting made direct from the type cast from matrices made by Anton Janson some time between 1660 and 1687.

Of Janson's origin nothing is known. He may have been a relative of Justus Janson, a printer of Danish birth who practised in Leipzig from 1614 to 1635. Some time between 1657 and 1668 Anton Janson, a punch-cutter and type-founder, bought from the Leipzig printer Johann Erich Hahn the type-foundry which had formerly been a part of the printing house of M. Friedrich Lankisch. Janson's types were first shown in a specimen sheet issued at Leipzig about 1675. Janson's successor, and perhaps his son-in-law, Johann Karl Edling, issued a specimen sheet of Janson types in 1689. His heirs sold the Janson matrices in Holland to Wolffgang Dietrich Erhardt, of Leipzig.

The book was composed, printed, and bound by the Kingsport Press, Kingsport, Tennessee. The typography is by James Hendrickson.